Cincinnati Art Museum

Chinese Art in the Cincinnati Art Museum

Ellen B. Avril

with Contributions from Nora Ling-yün Shih

Cover illustration: Gu An (circa 1295–circa 1370), *Bamboo*,
Yuan dynasty, 14th century, detail (entry 31)
Frontispiece: *Wenshu, Bodhisattva of Wisdom, at a Writing Table*,
Yuan dynasty, 1354, detail (entry 32)

This publication was funded in part by grants from the
National Endowment for the Arts, a Federal agency,
the Andrew W. Mellon Foundation, and the Fleischmann Foundation.

Additional support was provided by:
Ferdinand and Carol Avril
Joseph Biancalana
Sylvan and Faith Golder
Alan B. and Marsha Lindner
Sydney L. Moss, Ltd.
Edward and Nancy Rosenthal
Stanley M. and Louise Rowe
Jacob and Polly Stein

Distributed by University of Washington Press

Design and typography by Noel Martin
Map by Reid Martin
Photography by Peter John Gates, Ron Forth,
Tony Walsh, Thomas Condon
Set in Adobe Minion by Kelby and Teresa Bowers
Printed by The Merten Company, Cincinnati, Ohio

Library of Congress Cataloging-in-Publication Data

Avril, Ellen B.
Chinese art in the Cincinnati Art Museum/
Ellen B. Avril with contributions from Nora Ling-yün Shih.
p. cm.
Includes bibliographical references and index.
ISBN 0-295-97663-2
1. Art, Chinese — Catalogs. 2. Art — Ohio — Cincinnati — Catalogs.
3. Cincinnati Art Museum — Catalogs. I. Shih, Nora Ling-yün.
II. Cincinnati Art Museum. III. Title.
N7340.A93 1997   97-38647
709'.51'07477178 — dc21   CIP

The Cincinnati Art Museum gratefully acknowledges the
generous operating support provided annually by the
Greater Cincinnati Fine Arts Fund, the Ohio Arts Council
and the City of Cincinnati.

Contents

Foreword

The broad reach of the Cincinnati Art Museum collection embraces works of art from every continent and from every period of human history, a scope that offers visitors opportunities to experience the beloved and familiar as well as to be rewarded with new discoveries. The reputation of the Museum's fine Asian art collections have for many years attracted scholars and others "in the know." But the quality and breadth of the Asian collections speak eloquently to first-time visitors, as well.

For the expert and the amateur alike, the experience of looking at a work of art prompts thoughts — and often questions — about its origins, its purpose, its meaning, how it was made, and its qualifications for inclusion in a museum's collection. For this reason, museums not only collect, preserve and display, but also research and interpret their collections, using vehicles such as catalogs to provide current scholarly opinion to those questions in an accessible manner.

This publication joins a distinguished group of catalogs produced by the Museum on its temporary exhibitions and permanent collections and follows *Pride of the Princes: Indian Art of the Mughal Era in the Cincinnati Art Museum*, published in 1986, as the second devoted to a portion of the Museum's Asian collections. It presents a survey of the Chinese collection and is the culmination of years of research by associate curator for Far Eastern Art, Ellen Avril, the first specialist in Chinese art to serve on the Museum's staff in its more than 110-year history. Joining her in this endeavor, Nora Ling-yün Shih, independent art historian, artist and calligrapher, provided expertise in inscriptions, colophons and seals, the important historical documentation that accompanies many Chinese paintings. The reader will find much new information about the Chinese collection here, including re-interpretations of some well-known works and introductions to many recent acquisitions. All of these enrich the story of Chinese art and culture that can be told by the Museum's outstanding collection.

Our sincere thanks go to the underwriters whose support made realization of this publication possible. Initial research, documentation and photography of the collections was funded by a generous grant from the Andrew W. Mellon Foundation. The National Endowment for the Arts awarded a substantial grant to partially cover costs of publication. The generosity of the Fleischmann Foundation and of individuals listed in the front of this book ensured the completion of a high quality publication.

The Cincinnati Art Museum is indebted, above all, to the donors of works of art, to the benefactors whose financial support provided funds for acquisitions, and to the public and private underwriters whose general operating support assures that the Museum's collections remain available for the enjoyment of all.

Barbara K. Gibbs
Director

Introduction

The Cincinnati Art Museum's collection of Chinese art spans nearly 5,000 years, from the Neolithic period to the present. Illustrated and discussed in this catalogue are the arts of imperial China — the period from the earliest times to the end of the Qing dynasty (1644–1911). The comprehensive nature of this portion of the collection reflects a cultural continuum whose length is unsurpassed in world history. The Museum's most important works represent Chinese art at its best: imbued with a sense of tradition, but balancing the strong respect for artistic heritage with a high regard for individual creativity, technical ingenuity, and occasionally a fascination with the foreign.

The Museum's holdings include ancient bronze ritual items, sacred sculpture and painting, painting and calligraphy by literati and professionals, ceramics, lacquer, cloisonné, and glass. The core of the collection was formed from 1946 to 1952, largely through purchase. Before that time, the art of China was represented primarily by a few Han ceramics (entry 50), late Qing-dynasty ceramics (entries 89, 95–97), and decorative arts (entry 100); the collection was rather uneven in quality and scope. Through the efforts of Philip Rhys Adams (Director 1946–1974) and John J. Emery (President and Chairman of the Board of Trustees, 1945–1976), the Museum began to collect Chinese systematically. Despite relatively limited funds, a fine survey collection was made. Other areas of Asian art, such as ancient Near Eastern, Islamic, Indian, and Japanese, were similarly pursued during the tenure of Adams and Emery. Today these works form the heart of the Museum's Asian collections.

Adams and Emery resolved to provide Museum visitors with magnificent treasures from Asia's great civilizations. When a colleague from another museum once asked, somewhat condescendingly, what interest in Chinese painting there was in Cincinnati, Adams replied, "There isn't any at all. Cincinnati has never seen any Chinese painting, so it is the duty of the Museum to show it."[1] Such conviction about a museum's role in broadening its audience's aesthetic experience set the scope of acquisition policy during those years. With regard to the Chinese collections, the approach was to acquire choice examples of the highest achievements of painters, sculptors, potters, and artisans of the dynastic periods.

In pursuit of this goal, the Museum looked to prominent Chinese art dealer Cheng Tsai Loo (1879–1957), who started his business in Paris around the turn of the century and had unprecedented access to sources of early Chinese art in China.[2] Loo's connoisseurship and willingness to educate collectors and curators had a tremendous impact on the development of public and private collections of Chinese art in the United States and Europe. Loo also encouraged rigorous scholarship and regularly donated items to his public clients.[3] The Museum was fortunate to receive his gift of the Guangsheng temple mural depicting the bodhisattva Wenshu (entry 32), one of the collection's great treasures.

Loo's involvement influenced the high standards of quality set for the growth of the Museum's collection. In 1946 the Museum purchased its first major Chinese work of art from him — the large Northern Wei Buddhist/Daoist stele (entry 15). Many more purchases followed in only six years. Superb Shang- and Zhou-dynasty bronzes were purchased in 1948 with funds provided by the Charles Williams family (entries 1, 3–7, 10). Endowments established by John J. Emery and by Fanny Bryce Lehmer made possible the acquisition of scroll paintings in 1948, including works by Jin- and Yuan-dynasty masters Liu Yuan, Qian Xuan, and Gu An (entries 28–31, 35–36). In 1950, handscrolls by Ma Yuan and Bada Shanren were purchased with funds provided by an anonymous benefactor (entries 27 and 38), along with thirty ceramics dating from the Neolithic period to the Yuan dynasty (entries 44, 46–47, 49, 53–54, 57–58, 60–61, 63–64, 66–71, 73–76, 78–79, 81, 93). Important sculpture entered the collection in 1950 and 1952 (entries 12, 19–21, 23).

This commitment to Chinese art encouraged significant gifts from private Cincinnati collections during Adams's tenure as director. The New Year's painting by the Qing-dynasty master Leng Mei (entry 41) was donated by Mrs. James L. Magrish in 1953. Fine Buddhist sculpture and tomb ceramics from the William T. and Louise Taft Semple collection (entries 13, 16–18, 55–56) entered the Museum in 1962. Yuan- and Ming-dynasty paintings and lacquer from the private collection of Mr. and Mrs. John J. Emery (entries 33–34, 99) were given in 1964. Donations or bequests from Mr. and Mrs. Philip R. Adams (entry 14), Katharine J. Appleton (entry 94), Mrs. Robert McKay (entries 72, 86), Mrs. Alfred Anson (entry 90), Mrs. Benjamin Moore (entry 98), Mrs. Louis Ransohoff (entries 8, 52) and Edward Greeno, Jr. (entries 91–92) added further depth to the collection.

The Museum's Chinese art collection entered another period of growth with the establishment of the Department of Ancient, Near Eastern, and Far Eastern Art in 1975. After a hiatus of more than thirty years, purchases of Chinese art resumed with the creation of a curatorial position devoted to Far Eastern art, the first in the Museum's history. Through the encouragement and support of directors Millard F. Rogers Jr. and Barbara K. Gibbs, in concert with the Collections and Acquisitions Committee, the Museum acquired significant metalwork, paintings, and ceramics (entries 11, 26, 37, 39–40, 45, 48, 51, 59, 62, 83–84). A special grant from the Oliver Charitable Lead Trust made possible the most recent of these purchases, a stunning pair of Longshan blackware goblets (entry 45).

Over the last twenty years the Museum has benefited from important gifts, notably fine Chinese glass and porcelain from the collection of Drs. Martin and Carol Macht (entries 22, 87, 102–109), a bronze gu with a rare Fu Hao inscription from Miss Z. E. Marguerite Pick (entry 2), and ceramics from Dr. Robert A. Kemper (entries 77, 80). Many gaps in the collection were filled by donations from Dr. and Mrs. B. Kemper Westfall (entry 9), the estate of John J. Emery (entry 24), C. D. Lindhjem (entry 25), Rosemarie E. Megrue (entry 42), Olga Dobrogorski-Platz (entry 65), Dorothy Christian Pipkin (entry 82), Paul Ashbrook Barker (entry 85), Mary and Edward O'Connell (entry 88), Clifford Thies (entry 101), and Faith and Sylvan Golder (entry 110).

This catalogue, like others published by the Museum, is intended to draw attention to one of the strengths of its permanent collection and to reach a wider audience of collectors, scholars, and Chinese art enthusiasts with updated information and interpretations of the more famous works of art. It also publishes, for the first time, many works not widely known outside the Museum. The catalogue is organized by medium: Each work is illustrated and discussed so as to serve interested general readers and specialists alike.

Throughout the research and writing phases of this project, numerous individuals offered incalculable assistance. To Nora Ling-yün Shih, who carefully studied all inscriptions, colophons, and seals, provided many translations and a line drawing for entry 15, wrote the entries on selected colophons (entries 27a–d and 29a–c), and the landscape painting attributed to Wen Zhengming (entry 35), I affectionately and respectfully offer my thanks. I am grateful to Robert L. Thorp for his careful review and cogent suggestions regarding the entries on the ritual bronzes, and to GE Aircraft Engines' Quality Technology Center for providing the means for scientific analysis of these bronzes. My heartfelt thanks go to Richard Barnhart for his insightful critique of the painting entries. Colleagues from around the world shared their knowledge and expertise on individual works of art; I am grateful to the late Kamer Aga-Oglu, Terese Tse Bartholomew, Roger Bluett, Robert J. Brill, Susan Bush, W. Thomas Chase, Julia B. Curtis, Shen Fu, Fu Qingyuan, John C. Huntington, David Torbet Johnson, Ellen Johnston Laing, the late Clarence W. Kelley, Thomas Lawton, Chu-tsing Li, Stephen Little, Paul Moss, Glenn Mullin, Elinor Pearlstein, Jim Robinson, Rosemary Scott, Doreen Stoneham, Pamela Vandiver, James C. Y. Watt, Ann Barrott Wicks, Robert Wicks, Donald Wood, Marshall Wu, and Zhou Baozhong. Jenni Rodda of the C. T. Loo archives at the Institute of Fine Arts, New York University, and Kathryn Phillips of the Freer and Sackler Galleries research library, provided invaluable assistance during my research.

Grateful thanks go to all those involved in editing and production. Karen Feinberg, the copy editor, masterfully and unobtrusively brought clarity and consistency to the text. The stunning photography of Peter John Gates, Tony Walsh, Thomas Condon, and Ron Forth captures the beauty and subtlety of each work of art. Noel Martin overcame the many challenges of format and layout to produce a graceful, integrated design. To realize the finished product, he worked closely with a dedicated production team consisting of typesetter Kelby Bowers, and the fine professionals at The Merten Company. I would also like to thank Pat Soden and his staff at the University of Washington Press for their work in distributing the book.

Many Cincinnati Art Museum staff members, past and present, provided unstinting support. Former curator of Ancient, Near Eastern, and Far Eastern Art Daniel Walker and director emeritus Millard F. Rogers Jr. encouraged the project from its inception. Dr. Carol Macht, senior curator emerita, was a mentor and friend in every sense; she and her husband (Dr. Martin B. —"Bud") encouraged research, provided financial underwriting of travel to collections and of book purchases, and introduced me to Chinese glass through their wonderful collection. I am deeply grateful to the Museum's current administrative staff, especially Director Barbara K. Gibbs, Chief Curator Anita Ellis, and Head of Finance and Operations Debbie Bowman for their commitment to the completion of this publication despite institutional financial constraints. Glenn Markoe, Curator of Classical and Near Eastern Art, has provided unflagging support, encouragement, and advice. Chief Conservator Stephen Bonadies collaborated on the analysis of the bronzes. Along with Cecile Mear, Assistant Conservator for Paper, and Fred Wallace, Assistant Conservator, he provided consultation on the physical condition of the collection. Former Publications Coordinators Ann Cotter, Catherine Brohaugh, Dena Braun, and past and present Photographic Services staff members Joy Payton Roe, Terrie Gabis, and Liv Henson, coordinated aspects of editing, photography, and production. Development Director Pat Murdock and former grant coordinator Leslie Klahn were instrumental in securing and managing the contributions and grants that supported the project. Librarian Môna Chapin, former Assistant Librarian Cathy Shaffer and Assistant Librarian-Cataloguer Peggy Runge all provided crucial support in locating research materials near and far. Curatorial Secretary Linda Pieper performed many tedious word-processing and clerical tasks with professionalism, efficiency, and good cheer. Departmental volunteer Pat Osbourne diligently compiled the index with utmost care and attention to detail.

Finally, I wish to dedicate this catalogue to my parents, to my sisters and their families, and to the many dear friends who have encouraged and supported my work over the years.

Ellen B. Avril
Associate Curator for Far Eastern Art

Notes:
1. Louise Brunner, unpublished transcript of interview with Philip Rhys Adams, 1976.
2. See La Farge, "Mr. Loo and the China Trade."
3. Many of Loo's clients acknowledged their indebtedness to his knowledge and connoisseurship in the formation of their collections. See Cohen, *East Asian Art and American Culture*, pp. 109–11.

Map of China

- Cities
▲ Mountains
▪ Kiln Sites

Silk Road

Silk Road

Turfa

Kashgar

XINJIANG

Taklamakan Desert

Khotan

TIBET

Lha

1. *Jia*
Shang dynasty, 13th century B.C.

1. *Jia*

Shang dynasty, Anyang period, late Yinxu I, 13th century B.C. Cast bronze. H.28 cm.
Given in honor of Mr. and Mrs. Charles F. Williams by their children, 1948.74

The body of the vessel is S-curved in profile and is supported by three legs, triangular in cross-section, that curve outward from the rounded bottom. Attached to the vessel is a plain strap handle. Two square posts with roof-shaped caps project from the rim. Surface decoration, organized in horizontal registers, consists of the following, from rim to base: spiral-filled triangles; confronted dragons in profile with bulging eyes and upturned curled tails that form small taotie *(animal masks) where their heads meet; and large* taotie *composed of spiraled ribbons delineating the S-curved horns, downturned curled tails, and C-shaped fangs, all against a spiral-patterned* (leiwen) *background. Decoration on the caps echoes that of the vessel, with spiral-filled triangles on the triangular surfaces and inverted* taotie *on the rectangular surfaces. The outward-facing planes of the legs have spiral-filled blade designs. A single-character graph is inscribed on the interior.*

In royal Shang cult practice, political power and the natural order were maintained through lavish rituals designed to assuage the royal ancestors, the nature spirits, and Shang Di, the High God. In the late Shang dynasty a great ceremonial center flourished at Anyang, in Henan province, where rites involving divination and offerings of food and alcoholic spirits were performed near the royal necropolis. Opulent and sophisticated ritual accoutrements made of bronze have been unearthed there in large quantities, testifying to early Chinese royal perceptions of power and the seriousness of ritual obligations.

Current knowledge of late Shang civilization owes much to the efforts of archaeologists working at Anyang; the discovery of this site was prompted by the appearance at local shops of inscribed bones dug up by local farmers. These so-called oracle bones, used in Shang times as instruments of divination, led to scientific excavations by the Academia Sinica in 1928. Since then, more than 600 bronze ritual vessels have been unearthed from Anyang sites under controlled conditions. Almost three-quarters of those have been found by the Anyang Work Team of the Institute of Archaeology, Beijing, since the late 1950s. The Anyang Work team has unearthed vessels that parallel those for which archaeological records do not exist and has proposed a chronology of sites correlated with the reigns of Shang kings.[1]

Shang dynasty bronze vessels apparently were used primarily for storing, preparing, or serving foods and liquids made from grains.[2] The tripod vessel types *jia* and *jue* (see entry 3) functioned as warmers for an alcoholic beverage made from fermented millet grain, an important liquid offering used in the rituals.[3]

Chinese foundries produced magnificent vessels through a unique bronze-casting technique that employed complex ceramic section molds. With abundant natural resources of copper, tin, and lead (the primary ingredients for bronze alloy) at their disposal, the Chinese foundries did not need to conserve metal; they were able to experiment liberally and to develop a casting method best suited to meet their patrons' demands for lavish vessels.[4]

Chinese bronze production relied heavily on ceramic technology. The rich surface decoration of vessels was produced in the molds themselves, which were made of loess. These windblown deposits of feldspar, mica, and quartz soil originated in the Gobi desert and were scattered across northern China over millennia, accumulating to hundreds of meters in depth. Loess is characterized by a loosely packed texture and a low percentage of clay. These qualities enabled mold sections to absorb the trapped gases that developed in molten metal, thus contributing to the success of the section-mold casting technique. In addition, shrinkage after drying and firing was very low. Thus individual parts could be made to close tolerances, an important factor in the reassembly of complex molds.[5]

Surface decoration on Shang bronzes consists of various animal-derived motifs. The most prevalent of these is the *taotie*, a fantastic masklike creature composed of two bulging eyes and a body that looks as if it were skinned and splayed across the surface. Several *taotie* dominate the surface decoration of the Museum's *jia*; each is composed of finely drawn spirals to delineate the horns, snout, and body. All of these elements are confined to the surface contours of the vessel, and only the projecting pupils of the eyes break through the largely two-dimensional decoration.

The single-character pictograph, in the form of two figures standing back-to-back, is related to the modern word *fei*, "not."[6] The Museum's *jia* is nearly identical (varying only in the design of caps and legs) to the *Mu Ya jia* excavated in 1959 at Anyang.[7] Other, similar jia have been unearthed from the Anyang area;[8] several were dated by the Anyang Team to the late Yinxu I period.[9] An Yinxu II *jia*, from m539, is also related to this type.[10]

Technical remarks: Industrial computed tomography (ICT), utilized to examine the *jia*, disclosed techniques of casting as well as past repairs to legs, handle, and rim (Technical Appendix fig. 1).[11] A cross-section through the legs shows that they are not formed of solid metal but were cast around clay cores (TA, fig. 2). The digital radiograph (TA, fig. 1) reveals that one of the legs, whose repaired break is clearly visible on the surface, was reassembled with a modern screw, perhaps shortly before the vessel was purchased by the Museum in 1948. The same radiograph exposed an older repair in another leg which was mended with a metal (most likely bronze) pin. That repair may have been performed in antiquity because no evidence of a break is visible on the surface; it is completely concealed by patination accumulated during millennia of burial. The CT cross-section of the legs (TA, fig. 3) illustrates these repairs with relation to the leg walls. A lead-tin solder, which appears as bright white on the radiograph and the CT, also apparently was employed for repairs.

Provenance:
    C.T. Loo
Published:
    Avril and Bonadies, "Non-Destructive Analysis," pp. 52, 56, 59–60.

Bonadies and Avril, "Technical Examination," pp. 104–105, 107.

Chen, *Yin Zhou qingtongqi fenlei tulu,* no. A299.

Sculpture Collection of the Cincinnati Art Museum, p. 108.

Exhibited:

"Chinese Ritual Bronzes: Modern Technology Encounters Ancient Art," Cincinnati Art Museum, September 12–November 26, 1989

Notes:

1. The chronology developed by the Anyang Work Team is applied here only when close excavated parallels to the museum's bronzes exist. For a discussion of the chronology, see Thorp, "Archaeology of Style at Anyang," pp. 47–49.

2. Meat or vegetable dishes were prepared and served in vessels of pottery, wood, lacquer, or basketry. See Chang, *Food in Chinese Culture,* pp. 34–47.

3. Chang, *Food,* p. 30.

4. Section-mold casting was also employed in the ancient Near East, but exclusively for casting weapons and implements in simple bivalve molds. Archaeological evidence of lost-wax casting in China does not appear until the sixth century B.C., although it had been used in the Near East as early as the fourth millennium B.C. for casting small figural objects. In the production of vessels, Near Eastern metalworkers relied on hammering to conserve metal, which was in scarce supply, and did not employ casting at all. China therefore was unique in developing complex section-mold methods for casting vessels. See Bagley, *Shang Ritual Bronzes,* pp. 15–17.

5. Wood, "Recent Researches," pp. 143–44.

6. In Chen, *Yin Zhou qingtongqi,* no. A299, the inscription is misread as *bei,* "north." The same single-character inscription, *fei,* is also found on a *jue* in the Sackler Gallery; see Bagley, *Shang Ritual Bronzes,* no. 12, pp. 180–83. Bagley notes another *jue* with the same inscription, published by Yu, *Shang Zhou jinwen luyi,* 389.

7. *The Chinese Exhibition,* no. 84.

8. Bagley, *Shang Ritual Bronzes,* p. 160, lists four similar vessels unearthed at Anyang: the *Mu Ya jia,* a *jia* excavated from Xibeigang M1400, one from tomb 77AXTM18 at Xiaotun, and one unearthed from Tomb 1, Wuguancun, similar in shape but varying in decoration (illus. fig. 91).

9. See Table 1 in Thorp, "Archaeology of Style at Anyang," p. 48. Another comparable *jia* is in the Arthur M. Sackler Collection at the Sackler Gallery, Washington, D.C.; see Bagley, *Shang Ritual Bronzes,* no. 5, pp. 158–60.

10. *Yinxu qingtongqi,* pl. 61.

11. Avril and Bonadies, "Non-Destructive Analysis." Also, see Bonadies and Avril, "Technical Examination."

2. *Gu*

Henan province, Shang dynasty, Anyang period, Yinxu II, late reign of Wu Ding, circa 1200 B.C. Cast bronze. H. 25.5 cm.
Centennial gift of Miss Z. E. Marguerite Pick, 1981.412

The slender cylindrical beaker has a trumpet-shaped mouth, a narrow neck and a flaring foot. The intaglio decoration is confined to three registers. The lower register consists of compartments divided by flanges, each containing spiral patterns in low relief and openwork designs surrounding a bulging eye. Three smooth bands delineated by simple raised threads are pierced by two openwork crosses. The central section is composed of low-relief spiral designs surrounding bulging eyes, and separated into quadrants by flanges. The design of the flaring upper section is horizontal bands of spirals above which rise vertical blades filled with spirals, all in low relief. The two-character graph is located inside the foot.

Before Wu Ding's reign, Anyang was little more than the site of some small tombs and pit dwellings, but by about 1200 B.C. it had emerged as the most important Shang cult center and the location of royal burials. In the latter part of Wu Ding's reign and the reigns of his successors, Zu Geng and Zu Jia (which together encompass the period known as Yinxu II), the Anyang necropolis expanded greatly through the construction of separate areas for royal tombs, a palatial divination complex, and lineage cemeteries for aristocrats and commoners.[1]

The royal tombs included those of kings as well as high-ranking consorts. In 1976 excavators discovered an undisturbed tomb that yielded not only a spectacular cache of jade and bone objects, stone sculpture, and ivory carvings, but also approximately 460 bronze vessels and weapons, the largest, most complete set yet recovered from an Anyang tomb. This burial, located near Xiaotun village and known simply as Tomb 5, is generally accepted as that of Fu Hao, a consort of Wu Ding, on the basis of numerous bronzes bearing inscriptions with that name.[2]

The Museum's *gu* is inscribed with Fu Hao's name and is one of a distinct group of about forty examples with openwork decoration in the foot. These recently have been assigned to a single workshop or master.[3] Of the sixteen *gu* from the group unearthed from Tomb 5, six were inscribed "Fu Hao" and ten were inscribed "*ya qi.*" The foremost distinguishing characteristic of these *gu* is a *taotie* whose outlines are defined in openwork. The *taotie* designs are divided into quadrants separated by flanges; each quadrant contains a one-eyed motif. Two variations of the openwork design have been identified. In the first, the one-eyed motifs face the same direction, in a serial sequence; the other consists of bilateral constructions formed by the pairing of one motif with its mirrored opposite to form a complete frontal mask. In the group from Tomb 5, those *gu* with the Fu Hao inscription follow the serial mode of decoration; those inscribed "*ya qi*" display the bilateral pairings.[4] The Museum's *gu,* which is of the bilateral type but bears a Fu Hao mark on the interior of its foot, represents a departure from the Tomb 5 pattern. It is also the only known openwork *gu* found outside Tomb 5 to bear a Fu Hao inscription.

Technical remarks: Industrial Computed Tomography (ICT) examination revealed no breaks or repairs. A CT slice disclosed slight misalignment of core and outer mold sections in the upper part of the vessel, resulting in uneven wall thickness (TA, fig. 4). Microscopic examination of the inscription, prompted by the question of whether it was incised or cast, showed no signs of scratching.[5] Patination surrounding and inside the graph was found to be continuous and identical to that on the rest of the vessel. Thus the inscription was produced while the vessel was cast.

Provenance:

C. T. Loo; Baron Cassell van Doorn; Z. E. Marguerite Pick

Published:

Archives of Asian Art, 36 (1983), p. 94.

Avril, "Highlights of Chinese Art," pp. 66 and 68.

Avril and Bonadies, "Non-Destructive Analysis," pp. 51–53.

Bonadies and Avril, "Technical Examination," pp. 104–05, 107.

Chen, *Yin Zhou qingtongqi fenlei tulu,* no. A488.

Loo, *An Exhibition of Ancient Chinese Ritual Bronzes,* no. 16.

Exhibited:

"An Exhibition of Ancient Chinese Ritual Bronzes Loaned by C.T. Loo," Detroit Institute of Arts, October 18 to November 10, 1940.

"Chinese Ritual Bronzes: Modern Technology Encounters Ancient Art," Cincinnati Art Museum, September 12–November 26, 1989.

Notes:

1. See Yang, "The Shang Dynasty Cemetery System," pp. 49–63.

2. See *Yinxu Fu Hao mu*, the complete archaeological report of this tomb.

3. Poor, "The Master of the 'Metropolis'-Emblem Ku." Unaware of its present location, Poor mentions in his postscript, p. 82, the Museum's *gu* with "Fu Hao" inscription, formerly in C.T. Loo's collection.

4. *Yinxu Fu Hao mu*, pp. 74–85, in pl. XLII–XLIII.

5. Bagley, *Shang Ritual Bronzes*, p. 236, n. 7, mentions the Museum's *gu* and its Fu Hao inscription, citing Chen Mengjia's suggestion that the inscription was incised rather than cast.

3. *Jue*

Shang dynasty, Anyang period, Yinxu III, 12th century B.C. Cast bronze. H. 22.4 cm.
Given in honor of Mr. and Mrs. Charles F. Williams by their children, 1952.112

Supported by three slender legs, the round-bottomed vessel has straight sides, a strap handle, a lip flaring to a point opposite the long, channeled spout, and two conical capped posts. Decoration consists of a spiral-filled blade design on the underside of the spout, spiral-filled triangles with arrow-tip designs below the rim, relief decoration of a disintegrated taotie around the vessel body divided by flanges, and a water buffalo head in high relief on the handle. The two-character graph is located beneath the handle.

The *jue*, a single-handled cup with three legs and a funnel-shaped rim with long, channeled spout, functioned as a warmer and server for fermented grain spirits. It is the oldest known shape in the ancient Chinese bronze vessel repertoire. Relatively crude cast-bronze *jue* found at Erlitou are the earliest bronze vessels yet unearthed in China and date to the first half of the second millennium B.C.[1] *Jue* remained important components in sets of bronze ritual vessels well into the Zhou dynasty.

The inscription consists of two characters. The first is a *yaxing*, a graph depicting the niche in a family's ancestral shrine in which ancestral tablets are stored. As a symbol of this particular clan, the *yaxing* contains a single-eye pictograph above a man. The second character also has the form of a man. The Museum's *jue* is nearly identical to the *jue* inscribed "*ri xin gong*" excavated in 1969 from Tomb GM907, and dated to Yinxu III.[2] A *fang lei* in the Shanghai Museum bears a similar inscription.[3]

Technical remarks: The vessel was cast in a single pour without the use of clay cores for the legs, which computed tomography (CT) scans revealed to be solid cast (Technical Appendix, fig. 5). Digital radiograph and CT scans disclosed extensive porosity in the rounded bottom of the vessel (TA, figs. 6 and 7). This concentration of trapped air bubbles is further evidence that such vessels were inverted during the pour so that the legs served as sprues for the molten metal. The greatest risk of pitting or casting failure occurred in the bowl of the vessel, where rising gases became trapped.

Provenance:

C.T. Loo

Published:

Archives of the Chinese Art Society in America, 9 (1955), p. 80.

Avril and Bonadies, "Non-Destructive Analysis," pp. 52, 54–56.

Bonadies and Avril, "Technical Examination," pp. 104, 106.

Sculpture Collection of the Cincinnati Art Museum, p. 107.

Exhibited:

On loan to the Cincinnati Art Museum, 1949–1952.

"Chinese Ritual Bronzes: Modern Technology Encounters Ancient Art," Cincinnati Art Museum, September 12–November 26, 1989.

Notes:

1. See Fong, *Great Bronze Age of China*, fig. 15 and pp. 2–3, 69–83.

2. *Yinxu qingtongqi*, pl. 75 and line drawing 71.

3. Bagley, *Shang Ritual Bronzes*, fig. 135. Also see *Shanghai Bowuguan cang bao lu*, pp. 19, 92.

4. *Fangyi*

Shang dynasty, Anyang period, 12th century B.C. Cast bronze. H. 29 cm.
Given in honor of Mr. and Mrs. Charles F. Williams by their children, 1948.75

The house-shaped, lidded vessel rests on a high rectangular foot. Surface decoration is divided into horizontal registers on the rectangular sides of the vessel. The main decorative motifs, in high relief against a spiral background, include addorsed dragons in profile around the base, large taotie, and pairs of confronted dragons. Inverted taotie adorn the surfaces of the pyramidal lid; at the top is a knob whose cap echoes the lid shape. Heavy flanges project from each corner and bisect each surface of the vessel and the lid. Two versions of the single-character graph were cast: one inside the lid, the other inside the vessel.

Superbly designed and flawlessly cast, this *fangyi* is among the most engaging objects in the Museum's collection because of its robust architectonic shape and the crisp *taotie* in high relief. The square shape is especially well suited to create an air of imposing monumentality. The flat (rather than curved) surfaces enhance the confrontational quality of the *taotie*, thereby intensifying the potency of the motif.

During Yinxu II the container types for alcohol increased in number, as did the variations of each type.[1] Among the innovations of this period was the introduction of *fangyi* and *guang* (see entry 5). *Fangyi* is one of the vessel types that did not derive from pottery shapes but apparently was devised for production in bronze alone.[2]

Much speculation surrounds the interpretation of Shang-dynasty iconography, especially that of its predominant motif, the *taotie*, because no written evidence dating from the Shang period exists to elucidate it. The term *taotie* was first identified by twelfth-century antiquarians and was based on the *Lushi Chunqiu,* a third-century B.C. text. Discussions in that and other, later texts have variously identified the animal mask as a bodiless monster punished for eating people,[3] a gluttonous monster whose abysmal behavior was viewed as a warning against overeating, or a guardian against evil spirits. The specific meaning assigned by the Shang to this intriguing creature is not known, however.

On the basis of passages in the *Guo Yu,* a fourth-century B.C. text that describes ritual activities, it has been suggested that animal motifs on Shang ritual objects may represent various agents invoked by the diviners to assist in contact with the ancestral spirits.[4] Considered in this context, the images on the Museum's *fangyi* are placed logically to aid such a dialogue. The four inverted *taotie* on the pyramidal lid of the vessel are oriented to be seen from above and thus provide a focus upward toward heaven, while the *taotie* on the sides of the vessel gaze directly at the earthbound viewer. Similarly, the *taotie* are placed effectively to enhance a possible guardian function, as if poised to avert evil from any direction.

The *ya yi* graph, namely the figure of a man immediately below an empty *yaxing* and holding a T-shaped object in one hand, occurs on more than fifty vessels and weapons from Anyang.[5] It has been associated with the diviner Yi of Zu Jia's reign.[6] A *fangyi* closely resembling this one is in the collections of the Sackler Gallery.[7]

Provenance:
   C. H. Yie; C. T. Loo
Published:
   Avril, "Highlights of Chinese Art," p. 66.
   Chang, *Shang Civilization,* p. 30.
   Chen, *Yin Zhou qingtongqi fenlei tulu,* no. A642.
   Cincinnati Art Museum Handbook, p. 58.
   Deydier, *Les bronzes archaïques chinois,* p. 216.
   Edwards, "Sophistications of Chinese Art," p. 84, fig. 5.
   Loehr, "Bronze Styles of the Anyang Period," p. 43, fig. 18.
   Loehr, *Ritual Vessels of Bronze Age China,* cat. no. 38, pp. 58, 90, 93, 128, 177, 183.
   Luo, *Sandai jijin wen cun,* 11.3.5
   Masterpieces from the Cincinnati Art Museum, p. 54.
   Mathes, *Treasures of American Museums,* p. 389.
   Sculpture Collection of the Cincinnati Art Museum, p. 108, illus. p. 109.
   Spiro, "Max Loehr's Periodization of Shang Vessels," fig. 5.
   White, *Bronze Culture of Ancient China,* p. 52.
Exhibited:
   "Ritual Vessels of Bronze Age China," Asia House Gallery, New York, 1968.
   "Chinese Ritual Bronzes: Modern Technology Encounters Ancient Art," Cincinnati Art Museum, September 12–November 26, 1989.
Notes:
   1. See Thorp, "Archaeology of Style at Anyang," pp. 50–51 for a discussion of the preference for vessels with square cross-sections.
   2. Thorp, "Archaeology of Style at Anyang," p. 49.
   3. Chang, *Art, Myth, and Ritual,* p. 57.
   4. See Wang, "A Textual Investigation of the Taotie," pp. 107–17.
   5. Bagley, *Shang Ritual Bronzes,* pp. 325–27. Although most of the *ya yi* inscribed bronzes are related to objects from Fu Hao's tomb, Bagley singles out several bronzes, including the Cincinnati Art Museum's, as appreciably later than Fu Hao's time.
   6. Loehr, *Ritual Vessels of Bronze Age China,* no. 38.
   7. Bagley, *Shang Ritual Bronzes,* no. 79, pp. 440–44.

5. *Guang*

Shang dynasty, Anyang period, 12th century B.C. Cast bronze. H. 23.6 cm.
Given in honor of Mr. and Mrs. Charles F. Williams by their children, 1948.78

The sauceboat-shaped vessel rests on a high ring-foot and supports a lid with a similar undulating profile. A bottle-horned dragon baring its teeth forms the front of the lid (covering the spout); the dragon's spine ends at the pair of projecting c-shaped horns of a taotie *that constitutes the lower half of the lid. The vessel proper is fashioned as a bird, whose beak is a prominent feature of the flange below the spout. The handle consists of a horned creature devouring a bird. Surface decoration on the vessel body, in high relief against a spiral ground, is divided into horizontal compartments that are bisected by flanges. The upper section contains animals in profile, the middle section includes disintegrated* taotie, *and the lower section contains pairs of confronted tigers in profile just above the ring-foot. The vessel is not inscribed.*

Vessels such as the *guang,* with an abundance of animal motifs covering the entire surface, and forming the vessel itself, are among the most alluring types of ritual vessel. The complex interrelationships of animals making up the profile of the vessel — the bottle-horned dragon of the lid, the bird of the vessel spout, and the dragon devouring a bird that forms the handle, as well as the numerous gaping-mouthed creatures and *taotie* covering the surface — create an overall sense of energy not seen on other vessel types.

In studying such compelling vessels, one cannot resist wondering what the preoccupation with animal motifs meant in Shang ritual practice. Because divination was such an important component of Shang rites, it seems plausible that motifs on ritual items would serve a communicative function. Perhaps, as Chang suggests, the animals depicted on ritual accoutrements represent spirits used by Shang shamans to aid the heaven-earth dialogue.[1] Or perhaps, as Thorp suggests, the various combinations of animal motifs formed messages that were meant to be "read" like rebuses, visual puns employed frequently in Chinese art of later periods.[2]

Sets of various vessel types were needed to conduct offering rituals. As a result, shapes evolved which complement or represent variations of one another. The precise regularity of ritual vessels would suggest that a rigid-profile template was used to produce a vessel model in clay. These templates also would have served as effective design tools because variations in the profiles could easily create new shapes or modify traditional ones.[3] The vessel type *guang,* designed for production in bronze alone, combines the round body of the *you* with the undulating spout of the *jue.* The lid of the *guang,* its most distinctive characteristic, relates to lids on animal *zun*; the form also was adopted for use on *jue.*[4]

A similar *guang* was unearthed at Lingshi, Shanxi province.[5]

Technical remarks: The *guang* was cast in several pours: one for the lid, one for the vessel, and one for the handle, which was cast onto the vessel over tenons extending out from the body. The handle was cast around a clay core, which is still visible on the inside surface. Evidence of metal overflow is also visible on the surface of the vessel where the handle is attached. Further confirmation of the casting method was revealed by a DR image (TA, fig. 8) and by three-dimensional replication achieved by first CT-scanning the entire vessel in increments of 508 microns and then reconstructing the data into a computer model. A full characterization of the join, as well as the shape of the clay core inside the handle, could be seen by slicing this model (TA, fig. 9).

Provenance:
   C.T. Loo
Published:
   Avril and Bonadies, "Non-Destructive Analysis," pp. 52, 56, 61–62.
   Bonadies and Avril, "Technical Examination," pp. 103–06.
   Chen, *Yin Zhou qingtongqi fenlei tulu*, no. A660.
   Cincinnati Art Museum Handbook, p. 59.
   Deydier, *Les bronzes archaiques chinois*, p. 222.
   Edwards, "Sophistications of Chinese Art," p. 84.
   Guide to the Collections of the Cincinnati Art Museum, p. 53.
   Hai-Wai Yi-Chen T'ung-Ch'i, p. 29.
   Munsterberg, *The Arts of China*, p. 39, illus. p. 28, pl. 3.
   Sculpture Collection of the Cincinnati Art Museum, p. 110, illus. p. 111.
Exhibited:
   "Chinese Ritual Bronzes: Modern Technology Encounters Ancient Art," Cincinnati Art Museum, September 12–November 26, 1989.
Notes:
   1. Chang, *Art, Myth and Ritual*, pp. 56–80. Cited is a passage from the *Zuo zhuan* (606 B.C.) that describes the early representation of *wu* (interpreted as "animals with power" or "animal offerings") in pictures and on ritual bronzes "so that the people might know [the distinctions] between the helping and harming spirits."
   2. Thorp, "Archaeology of Style at Anyang," pp. 56–59.
   3. Wood, "Ceramic Puzzles from China's Bronze Age," pp. 51–53.
   4. See a *jue* with a bottle-horn dragon-head lid, excavated from tomb M1713 in the western sector of Yinxu Anyang, illustrated in Rawson, *Chinese Bronzes*, p. 23.
   5. Now in the collection of the Shanxi Provincial Museum. See Yang, *Sculpture of Xia and Shang China*, pl. 173, p. 181.

6. *Gu*

Shang dynasty, Anyang period, Yinxu III, 12th century B.C. Cast bronze. H. 30.4 cm.
Given in honor of Mr. and Mrs. Charles F. Williams by their children, 1948.77

The trumpet-mouthed beaker has a slender, straight neck and a flaring base that rests on a high foot-ring. The flaring base is decorated with taotie *and* kui *dragons in profile, executed in relief;* leiwen *cover the relief as well as forming the background. The lower portion of the vessel is divided from its narrow neck by three smooth bands separated by simple raised lines; the bands are pierced by two openwork crosses. Taotie designs form the decoration of the waist. Vertical flanges project from the waist and the base, dividing the middle and lower sections into quadrants. Decoration on the vessel's upper section consists of a horizontal band of curly-tailed birds in profile and* leiwen-*filled blades rising to the flared rim. The vessel is inscribed inside the base with a* yaxing *above the image of a bird.*

This *gu* typifies the late Anyang style in its attenuated form and in the filling of high-relief surfaces with *leiwen* spirals similar to those in the background.[1] The success of the minutely detailed surface exemplifies highly refined casting and also results in a disintegration of the *taotie;* the individual components relate less cohesively as a unit. A band of long-tailed birds on the neck reflects the growing popularity of bird motifs after Yinxu II.

The *gu* inscription is composed of a *yaxing* and a bird. The bird (*chui*) may indicate that the vessel was cast for the official keeper of birds.[2]

A somewhat similar *gu*, but with flanges that extend all the way to the rim, was excavated in 1979 from an Anyang tomb.[3] A *gu* of identical size, surface decoration, and inscription, formerly in a private collection in California, was sold at auction in 1978.[4]

Provenance:
   Orvar Karlbeck; Robert Woods Bliss; C.T. Loo
Published:
   Avril and Bonadies, "Non-Destructive Analysis," p. 51.
   Chen, *Yin Zhou qingtongqi fenlei tulu*, no. A485.
   Revue des Arts Asiatiques, 8, no. 3, p. 160.
   Sculpture Collection of the Cincinnati Art Museum, p. 110.
Exhibited:
   "Chinese Ritual Bronzes: Modern Technology Encounters Ancient Art," Cincinnati Art Museum, September 12-November 26, 1989.
Notes:
   1. See Bagley's discussions of the Style V[a] relief on vessels from Fu Hao's tomb. He points out that it does not appear on *gu* until later than on other vessels; thus a date after the thirteenth century B.C. is warranted. See *Shang Ritual Bronzes*, nos. 36 and 37, pp. 248-253.
   2. See Chang, "Ku kung Shang-dai."
   3. Tomb 2508, West Zone Tract 1, Anyang. *Yinxu qingtongqi*, pl. 65. Also illustrated in Thorp, "Archaeology of Style at Anyang," fig. 16.
   4. Sotheby Parke Bernet, New York, 11 May 1978, lot 16.

7. Double-Owl *You*

Shang dynasty, 12th century B.C. Cast bronze. H. 18.9 cm.
Given in honor of Mr. and Mrs. Charles F. Williams by their children, 1948.73

The lidded vessel, in the form of two addorsed owls whose heads make up the lid and whose bodies form the vessel proper, is supported on four feet formed as the legs of the birds. The surface is decorated sparsely with features of the owls in soft relief against a smooth background: curved beaks, upward-gazing eyes, C-*shaped horns, and wings. Between the tips of the wings on both sides of the vessel are animal masks in high relief. Simple intaglio decoration appears on the conical cap of the lid knob, on the lower part of the vessel body and on the four feet. The graph is located on the bottom of the vessel interior.*

You functioned as storage vessels for liquid offerings. They vary in shape from long-necked, pear-shaped vessels to squat, round vessels with lids, often with attached swing handles. A particularly interesting variation is the squat *you* in the sculptural form of two owls standing back-to-back. In the late Anyang period *you* became an increasingly popular vessel type, as did other more rounded forms. Some double-owl *you* have heavily decorated surfaces; others, such as this one, exemplify a tendency in the late Shang to leave much of the surface smooth and to model relief forms more softly.

A similar owl-shaped *you* with only scant decoration was unearthed in 1957 at Shilou, Shanxi province.[1] The profile of its lid differs from that of the Museum's, whose owls gaze upward; their beaks are rendered more organically.[2] The owl heads of the excavated example gaze straight ahead and have stiff, downcurved beaks.

The graph is composed of the character *wang*, meaning "ruler," above an anthropomorphic figure with crossed legs.

Technical remarks: Industrial computed tomography revealed that the legs of this vessel were cast around clay cores (Technical Appendix, fig. 10). A digital radiograph of a portion of the lid shows in rather dramatic detail the fracture, which continues longitudinally through the lid (TA, fig. 11). The break had been repaired and the surface reworked to conceal it.[3]

Provenance:
　C. T. Loo
Published:
　Ackerman, *Ritual Bronzes of China*, pp. 81, 88–89, 104, pl. 4.
　Avril and Bonadies, "Non-Destructive Analysis," pp. 52, 56–58.
　Bonadies and Avril, "Technical Examination," pp. 105, 107.
　Chen, *Yin Zhou qingtongqi fenlei tulu*, no. A 572.
　Sculpture Collection of the Cincinnati Art Museum, p. 113.
Exhibited:
　"Chinese Ritual Bronzes: Modern Technology Encounters Ancient Art," Cincinnati Art Museum, September 12–November 26, 1989.
Notes:
　1. *The Chinese Exhibition*, no. 87.
　2. The profile of the Museum vessel's lid relates to that of a double-owl *you* with fully decorated surface in the Fitzwilliam Museum, Cambridge. See Bagley, *Shang Ritual Bronzes*, fig. 63.3.
　3. Avril and Bonadies, "Non-Destructive Analysis," pp. 56–58; Bonadies and Avril, "Technical and Examination," pp. 105 and 107.

8. Axle Caps

Shang dynasty, 13th to 11th century B.C. Cast bronze. L.16.9 cm.
Bequest of Mrs. J. Louis Ransohoff, 1965.176,177

The pair of cylindrical tubes tapers slightly from the open end to the flat closed end. Two aligned rectangular openings are located near the open end of each cap. Surface decoration, which covers the front half of the cap, consists of blade designs on the shaft and whorl designs on the ends.

Bronze in ancient China was equated with political authority not only by its association with ritual, but also as an important component of military might. The most formidable weapon of the Shang military was the two-wheeled chariot, which was made of wood with fittings of bronze for the vehicle as well as for horse trappings.

Cylindrical bronze fittings such as these capped the ends of the axle. They were fastened by a bronze linchpin, which passed through the pair of rectangular perforations near the open end and thus held the chariot's large-spoked wheels in place.

Provenance:
　Mrs. J. Louis Ransohoff

9. *Ge* Dagger-Axe

Shang dynasty, Anyang period, Yinxu II, 13th to 11th century B.C. Cast bronze. L.29.6 cm.
Gift of Dr. and Mrs. B. Kemper Westfall, 1980.52

The halberd has a slightly curved blade with a central ridge running its length. The tang has the form of a long-snouted animal in profile whose details are rendered in simple raised lines.

One of the most common types of weapons used in ancient China from the Shang to the Han dynasties was the *ge* dagger-axe. Hafted to a wooden pole, this battle-axe was attached by inserting the tang through a split in the top of the pole and then lashing it with cord.[1]

Numerous *ge* dagger-axes with tangs in the form of fantastic animal heads in profile were excavated from the tomb of Fu Hao. Rawson has suggested that their appearance is evidence of foreign contact, which stimulated the adoption of new forms and motifs.[2] The Fu Hao *ge* exhibit minor variations in form and decoration; some have openwork in the tangs, while the tangs of others are solid. *Ge* no. 1154 from this tomb is nearly identical to the Museum's *ge*.[3]

Provenance:
　Dr. and Mrs. B. Kemper Westfall
Notes:
　1. Loehr, *Chinese Bronze Age Weapons*, p. 49; Chang, *Shang Civilization*, pp. 196–98.
　2. Rawson, "Late Shang Bronze Design," p. 82.
　3. *Yinxu Fu Hao mu*, plate 72.

10. Bell, *Bo*

Eastern Zhou dynasty, 6th century B.C. Cast bronze. H.42.4 cm.
Given in honor of Mr. and Mrs. Charles F. Williams by their children, 1948.76

The bell, a pointed oval in cross-section, has a curved base and gently curved sides tapering toward the flat top. The looped handle is supported by a pair of addorsed felines, their crouched bodies S-curved in profile. Surface decoration consists of repeated patterns of interlacing dragons in profile. These patterns fill the top surface of the bell; appearing in identical configurations on both sides, they fill a wide rectangular band on the lower portion of the bell. In the upper portion the pattern is repeated in four smaller bands alternating with rows of raised serpent-headed bosses. The bell is not inscribed.

After the invasion of the Western Zhou capital (near modern-day Xi'an) by nomadic peoples of northwest China in 771 B.C., the successor of the conquered king fled to establish a new capital at Luoyang, in Henan province. This event ushered in the Eastern Zhou dynasty, an era of gradual disintegration of centralized government and the rise of independent states controlled by powerful princes. Historians further subdivide the Eastern Zhou into two periods, the Spring and Autumn (770–476 B.C.) and the Warring States (475–221 B.C.), each named after the titles of early writings. The fragmentation of China into feudal states spurred the growth of regional bronze foundries as each ruler, hoping to strengthen the heavenly mandate for his government, performed state ceremonies requiring countless bronze items. As Zhou demands on the bronze industry increased, distinctive new styles evolved.

Music played on large sets of bronze bells was an important component of the state rites, and of entertainment at banquets. Chimes of bells varied greatly in size, the largest excavated to date consists of sixty-five bells.[1] Sound was produced by striking the bell with a wooden mallet. Each bell was designed to produce two distinct tones (a feature made possible by its pointed-oval cross-section), depending on whether the bell was struck near the bottom edge in the center or at a point halfway between the center and the side.

This ceremonial bell of the *bo* type is an example of the early Liyu style. This popular Spring and Autumn-period bronze style is named after the site of Liyu, in northern Shanxi province, where a local peasant unearthed a hoard of bronzes in 1923. Characterized by surface decoration of interlacing dragon motifs in relief against a plain ground, Liyu-style bronzes are often embellished further with naturalistic animals; frequently these are felines, which are rendered three-dimensionally. In general the interlace motifs on the Liyu bronzes evolve from low-relief types, in which the dragons are clearly discernible, to high-relief manifestations in which comma shapes and texture patterns dominate the designs. A major manufacturing center for the Liyu-style bronzes was discovered at Houma, in southwest Shanxi province. During the 1956–1961 excavations of this Eastern Zhou city site, archaeologists unearthed the remains of a large foundry with thousands of mold fragments and models bearing many motifs known from the Liyu-style bronzes. Many of these clay models were actually master stamps consisting of a single design unit. Such stamps played an important role in the production of matched sets, such as chimes of bells, and contributed to the overall efficiency of the mold-making process.[2]

Powerful addorsed felines supporting a loop handle, bosses in the form of coiled serpents, and panels of angular, dragon-headed interlace are characteristic features of the set to which the Museum's bell once belonged. A larger bell, which must have come from the same chime, is in the Indianapolis Museum of Art.[3] A similar bell is in the Winthrop Collection at the Sackler Museum, Harvard University; in its surface decoration it differs somewhat from the Indianapolis and Cincinnati bells, and is smaller. All bands of interlacing dragons on the Cincinnati and Indianapolis bells derive from the same design motifs; on the Winthrop bell the small bands

of decoration between the rows of bosses differ from the motifs of the larger band in the lower section of the bell. Huber noted the importance of these bells as products of the earliest phase of the Liyu style, by relating them to a similar bell now in the Shanghai Museum. The inscription on the Shanghai bell states that it was made in the state of Qi by the great-grandson of Duke Huan (r. 685–643 B.C.). Therefore, these bells can be dated to the early sixth century B.C.[4]

Provenance:
   C. T. Loo
Published:
   Avril, "Highlights of Chinese Art," pp. 66–68.
   Cincinnati Art Museum Handbook, p. 59.
   Mino and Robinson, *Beauty and Tranquility,* p. 116.
   Sculpture Collection of the Cincinnati Art Museum, pp. 112–13.
Exhibited:
   "Masterpieces of Chinese Art," Virginia Museum of Fine Arts, Richmond, 1954–1955.
   "Chinese Ritual Bronzes: Modern Technology Encounters Ancient Art," Cincinnati Art Museum, September 12–November 26, 1989.
Notes:
   1. Excavated in 1978 from the tomb of a marquis of Zeng, Sui Xian, Hubei province. *Wenwu,* 1979, no. 7, pp. 1–52; Thorp, "The Sui Xian Tomb," pp. 67–92.
   2. For a discussion of Liyu style and the Houma foundry, see So, "New Departures," pp. 257–63.
   3. Mino and Robinson, *Beauty and Tranquility,* pl. 33, pp. 116–17. Eli Lilly acquired the Indianapolis *zhong* from C. T. Loo.
   4. *Grenville L. Winthrop,* no. 38, pp. 36–37. Also, Huber, "Ancient Chinese Bronzes," p. 83; Mino and Robinson, *Beauty and Tranquility,* pl. 33, pp. 116–17.

11. Mirror

Tang dynasty, late 7th or early 8th century A.D. Cast bronze.
Diam. 21 cm.
Museum purchase: Gift of Mr. and Mrs. Leonard Minster, by exchange, 1989.101

The round mirror is smooth on the obverse. Its reverse is decorated in concentric bands of relief, organized in radial symmetry with a rotating viewpoint around a central rosette boss. These bands contain, from the center to the outer edge, four pairs of confronted lions; a thirty-two character inscription (partially obscured by incrustation); a band of scrolling grapevine entwining alternating lions and birds; and a narrow band of scroll design.

Early Chinese mirrors do not have handles; they were either held in the hand by means of a silk cord tied to their backs, or were supported in stands. Mirrors were cast in bronze in a two-part mold: one section for the smooth, reflective side of the mirror, and the other, more elaborate section for the decorated back.

In artistry and meaning, luxury mirrors dating from the Warring States period through the Tang dynasty are the most impressive Chinese specimens. Perceived as able to reflect not only the users' physical appearance but also their inner character, mirrors were endowed with supernatural powers, often suggested in their surface decoration. Iconographic programs exhibited on Han-dynasty mirrors, for example, emphasize Daoist deities and cosmic symbolism. Later, the decoration of mirrors revealed the popularity of Buddhism as well as an interest in secular motifs, particularly those reflecting the taste for foreign goods that characterized cosmopolitan Sui and Tang societies. The inscription on this mirror boasts of its superior quality and supernatural capabilities; it surely belonged to a person of wealth and status:

> *[This bronze mirror] of Lingqi is refined from a divine mint. Take it to the platform [at night], and you see the image of the moon in it. Display it against the sun [in daytime], and you see the radiation of light from it, shaped like the water-chestnut. Any object illuminated by it becomes brighter and clearer. It can be used to reflect one's appearance and to adjust one's adornment. It can also be used to straighten one's mind and to register one's loyalty.*[1]

The Museum's mirror is of the classic Tang "lion and grapevine" type, incorporating designs of foreign imports that came to China from the West. Neither lions nor grapes are native to China. Lions were presented by foreign delegations as tribute to the Tang imperial court. The lion's ferocity impressed the Chinese; contemporary poetry, written descriptions, and paintings emphasized its supernatural powers.[2] The lion's majesty was compared metaphorically to the Buddha's spiritual superiority. Where the Buddha sat was known as the "seat of the lion" (see entry 15), and the animal's roar symbolized the voice of the Buddha instructing all beings in his law. The lion also served as the vehicle of the bodhisattva Manjusri (see entry 26).[3] The Chinese styllization of the lion appears to be an adaption of the Persian *senmurv* as it appears in Sasanian art.[4]

Grapes were introduced to China during the Han dynasty but did not become popular until the Tang dynasty, when choice varieties, along with wine-making techniques, were introduced from the West. Wine made from grapes became popular at the Tang imperial court and was demanded, along with imports of raisins and grape syrup, as tribute from central Asia.[5]

Considered within the development of mirrors with lion and grapevine motifs, the Museum's example dates to the early Tang dynasty. It is similar to a mirror in the Minneapolis Institute of Arts,[6] whose central area of design also consists of pairs of confronted lions and a band of grapevine alternately entwining birds and lions. The Cincinnati mirror, however, differs in its retention of certain Sui elements, such as the inscription and the rosette boss, and is probably slightly earlier. A nearly identical mirror was unearthed in 1955 near Xi'an, the Tang capital.[7]

In the later, fully developed form of these mirrors the design is no longer compartmentalized into concentric bands. Instead the lions and grapevines fill the entire surface and spill over raised areas which, on earlier mirrors, divided one band of decoration from another. On the later mirrors, even the central boss has a lion's form.[8]

Technical remarks: Chinese mirrors are made of a bronze alloy that contains a high percentage of tin to create the silvery appearance necessary for reflection. Energy-dispersive X-ray analysis of this mirror disclosed an alloy of 70% copper, 27% tin, 2% lead, and 1% iron.[9]

Provenance:
  Alice Boney
Published:
  Avril, "Highlights of Chinese Art," pp. 67–68.
  Christy, "Alice Boney," p. 5.
Notes:
  1. trans. Nora Ling-yün Shih.
  2. Schafer, *Golden Peaches of Samarkand*, pp. 84–86.
  3. Schafer, *Golden Peaches*, p. 87.
  4. Nakano, *Bronze Mirrors from Ancient China*, p. 198.
  5. Schafer, *Golden Peaches*, pp. 141–45.
  6. Thompson, "Evolution of the Tang Lion and Grapevine Mirror," pp. 36–38, fig. 12. A similar mirror in a Japanese collection has also been published. See Kokubo, *Kaiju budokyo*, p. 169.
  7. *Shanxi sheng chutu tongjing*, p. 113, fig. 103.
  8. Thompson, "Evolution," figs. 12 (Avery Brundage Collection) and 14 (Denver Art Museum).
  9. Analysis was conducted at General Electric Aircraft Engines, Evendale, Ohio.

12. Tomb Relief Depicting a Carriage Procession

Possibly from Liaocheng, Shandong province, Han dynasty, 2nd century A.D. Limestone. H.45.5 cm.
Museum purchase, 1950.74

> *A rectangular dark-gray slab, carved and incised in monoplanar relief, depicts a procession composed of (right to left): a pair of equestrians; a chariot of solid chamber drawn by a single horse, above which a bird is flying; a pair of equestrians behind a canopied open chariot carrying two passengers and drawn by a single horse; a pair of equestrians following a single mounted rider who holds a parasol; and a canopied chariot with three occupants. This latter vehicle is cropped by the diagonal cut of the slab's left end. Above the procession is a frieze of repeating motifs of crouching dragonlike creatures from whose open mouths clouds arise.*

This panel, which once was part of the stone lining of an underground tomb chamber, depicts the right-hand portion of a long processional scene. Carriage processions, typically found on the ceilings or upper registers of tomb walls, were a common theme in Han funerary art; they reflected both Daoist metaphysical beliefs and Confucian social aspirations.

According to the *Huainanzi*, a Han compilation of mostly Daoist essays, the human soul is a unification of two parts, one originating from heaven and the other from the earth. Upon death, the soul divides: The *hun* soul, or vital life force, returns to the sky, while the *po* soul merges with the corpse and eventually vanishes into the earth.[1]

Processional scenes in tombs represent the *hun* soul's safe passage through a dangerous wilderness that lies between earth and heaven. Long carriage processions also indicated the exalted status that would enable the *hun* to join the bureaucracy on high; from there, it was believed, it would forever influence the prosperity and social status of surviving family members and their descendants.[2]

The economic prosperity of Shandong province, Confucius's homeland, during the first and second centuries A.D. made possible the widespread patronage of the funerary arts by lower-level bureaucrats. Funerals and memorial structures not only served the needs of the deceased and the grieving family, but also became important public statements of filial piety, a virtue essential for upward mobility in the Confucian bureaucracy.[3]

The Confucian discouragement of ostentatiousness is reflected in Shandong funerary art by a rather austere style of decoration based on silhouettes with simple incised details. A nearly black limestone, particularly well-suited to incising and polishing, was used. To meet the demands of numerous bureaucratic patrons, mortuary artisans developed modular systems of incised stones to line the walls of funerary structures. A respectable tomb required nine to thirteen stones; some had fewer; others contained as many as thirty or more. Competing workshops of artists existed, and the extant inscriptions, such as those touting the fame of the artist chosen to carve reliefs for a particular shrine, suggest that the artists varied in skill and repute.[4]

The Museum's panel belongs to a group of stones purportedly from Liaocheng, in western Shandong province, which exhibit similar processional scenes below a distinctive border of dragon-headed cloudbands.[5] Three slabs from this group were offered for sale in 1985: one was purchased by the Cleveland Museum of Art; the others, one of which is the adjoining half of the Cincinnati slab, are now in private collections.[6] If the Museum's stone were combined with its left-hand half, the retinue of riders and various types of horse-drawn carriages would be complete. The group moves from right to left toward a standing figure, who greets the procession.[7] Such greeters represent palace gatekeepers of Mt. Kunlun, the paradise ruled by Xiwangmu, Queen Mother of the West; she protects the *hun* soul on its journey and assists its entry into heaven.[8]

Provenance:
C. T. Loo
Published:
Adams, "Sculpture of the Far East," p. 6.
Cincinnati Art Museum Bulletin, 2, no. 1 (November 1951), p. 2.
Edwards, "Sophistications," p. 84.
Hayashi, "Go-Kan Jidai no Shaba Gyoretsu," fig. 14.
Sculpture Collection of the Cincinnati Art Museum, p. 114.
Shih, "Early Chinese Pictorial Style," p. 118, pl. 30.
Notes:
1. James, "An Iconographic Study of Xiwangmu," p. 21; Loewe, *Chinese Ideas of Life and Death*.
2. See Hayashi, "Go-Kan Jidai no Shaba Gyoretsu." Also, James, "An Iconographic Study of Two Late Han Funerary Monuments," pp. 335–36; Wu, *The Wu Liang Shrine*, pp. 62–63 and 145–47.
3. Recent exhaustive studies have shed new light on the patronage and symbology of Shandong funerary architecture in the later Han dynasty: Wu, *The Wu Liang Shrine*; Powers, *Art and Political Expression in Early China*. See also James's review of the latter in *China Review International*.

4. Powers, *Art and Political Expression*, pp. 67–71 and 124–26.
5. Shih, "Early Chinese Pictorial Style," pp. 115–18 and pl. xxx.
6. Sotheby's, New York, 3 June 1985, lots 30–32. According to C.T. Loo inventory records, a Han tomb slab with inventory number 80767, published in Loo, *An Exhibition of Chinese Stone Sculpture*, no. 5, was sold to the Cincinnati Art Museum. Indeed, CAM records refer incorrectly to this publication as illustrating the panel now in the Museum's collection. However, neither the relief published in the exhibition catalog nor the photograph in the C.T. Loo archives labeled 80767 represents the CAM panel slab. Rather, #80767 was sold to Hong Kong collector J.T. Tai and was sold again at Sotheby's, New York, 3 June 1985, lot 30. It is now in the Cleveland Museum of Art. I am grateful to Elinor Pearlstein for sharing her discovery of information on the CAM panel while conducting research at the C.T. Loo archive.
7. Sotheby's, New York, 3 June 1985, lot 31.
8. James, "An Iconographic Study of Xiwangmu," pp. 25–37.

13. Seated Buddha

Northern China, Northern Wei dynasty, dated A.D. 474. Gilt bronze. H. 22.7 cm.
The William T. and Louise Taft Semple Collection, 1962.429

The figure of Sakyamuni is seated in meditation (dhyana mudra) against a flaming mandorla. The deity wears a simple robe that drapes over the left shoulder, leaving the right shoulder bare, the left hand holds the excess of the garment. The image is supported by a pedestal base with lotus decoration that rests on a stand with four bracket legs. The reverse is decorated in low relief with a seated Buddha with one hand in the protective gesture (abhaya mudra) and the other hand holding his robe. The Buddha is flanked by two standing attendants. At upper left is a figure wearing monk's robes and riding an elephant; above and at upper right are four flying apsaras. An inscription covers the rear panel of the base.

Buddhism reached China as early as the first century A.D., via the central Asian trade routes linking Han dynasty China with Sogdiana and northwest India. It was practiced only in isolated pockets until the Northern Wei dynasty (386–535 A.D.), when the Tuoba rulers, thought to be of Turkic origin, firmly established the religion in northern China. Not all Tuoba emperors shared in the promotion of the faith and Buddhists were persecuted intermittently, but after a particularly violent suppression in the mid-fifth century, the emperor Wen Chengdi restored Buddhism to official favor. Under his chief of monks, Tanyao, the religion was advanced with zeal and enjoyed tremendous popularity among members of all social strata.

Buddhist missionaries traveling through central Asia brought small icons that introduced Indian and Gandharan sculptural styles to China. These imports inspired the production of gilt-bronze images that synthesize Indian, central Asian, and Chinese styles. Although written records attest to numerous gilt-bronze Buddhist images in China during the fourth and early fifth centuries, few of these early examples survived the period of persecution.[1]

This is a fine specimen of the resumed production of Buddhist bronzes in the second half of the fifth-century. It features Sakyamuni, the historical Buddha, and Dingguang Fo [*Dápankara*], the

Buddha who immediately preceded Sakyamuni.[2] On the front, Sakyamuni sits cross-legged in meditation, his simple robes draped elegantly over one shoulder and swagging in parallel folds to the base. A lotus-form halo surrounding his head symbolizes the Buddha's enlightenment. Animated tongues of fire form the border of the almond-shaped arch (*mandorla*) and represent the Buddha's impassioned energy. The overall rhythmic linearity is characteristic of the Northern Wei style.

The reverse of the mandorla depicts in shallow relief a joyful scene of Tushita heaven, presided over by Dingguang Fo. His name means "Creator of Light," and he is considered a protector of sailors. The figure is seated, and his right hand makes the gesture of reassurance (abhayamudra) while his left hand holds the excess of his garment. He is flanked by two bodhisattvas.[3] Above, Sudhana rides an elephant, a reference to his gift of sixty elephants to an enemy country; this is only one of the many acts of charity that earned his rebirth in the Tushita heaven.[4] Flying apsaras, the celestial beings of the heavenly realm, descend from above, their scarves trailing in the wind. An inscription on the base reads:

> *Liu Jin, wife of Mou Cong of the upper village of Weichang, at Zhong-shan, in Dingzhou, built a statue of Buddha Sakyamuni on the 17th day of the second month of the fourth year of the reign of Yanxin during the rule of the Grand Wei [dynasty].* She wished to be reborn into the kingdom of Buddha. This is to note her cause.[5]

Buddhism offered a universally possible salvation that contributed to its popularity among women, merchants, and farmers, who were generally excluded from the social benefits of Confucianism. Whether members of the imperial family, nuns, or wealthy lay devotees from other social strata, women figured prominently among the patrons of Buddhism. Their names and pious dedications have been preserved in numerous inscriptions that accompany rock-cut caves at Yungang, Longmen, and other sites, as well as in the inscriptions on portable icons such as this.[6] Although nothing other than the information in this inscription is known about the patron Liu Jin, she must have been a woman of considerable financial means. Her act of devotion is recorded here as occurring in the year equivalent to 474 A.D.[7]

Provenance:
Nasli Heeramaneck; William T. and Louise Taft Semple
Published:
Avril, "Highlights of Chinese Art," p. 67.
Edwards, "Sophistications of Chinese Art," p. 84.
Munsterberg, *Chinese Buddhist Bronzes*, pp. 27, 40, figs. 7-a, 7-b.
Ridley, "When Is a Fake Not a Fake?" p. 43.
Sculpture Collection of the Cincinnati Art Museum, p. 116.
Notes:
1. Soper, *Literary Evidence*; also Rowland, "Notes on the Dated Statues of the Northern Wei Dynasty."
2. Frédéric, *Buddhism*, pp. 117–18.
3. Frédéric, *Buddhism*, pp. 117–18.
4. Ch'en, *Buddhism in China*, pp. 176–77.
5. trans. Nora Ling-yün Shih.

6. For a summary of recent studies of Northern Wei patronage of Buddhism, especially by women, see Caswell, *Written and Unwritten*, pp. 35–39.

7. A previous incorrect reading of the inscription equated the date to 528 A.D. Scholars observing that the sixth-century date did not fit with the fifth-century style of the bronze concluded that the inscription was a spurious later addition. See Munsterberg, *Chinese Buddhist Bronzes*, and Ridley, "When Is a Fake Not a Fake?" The correct reading dispels any doubt about the authenticity of the inscription or the information it provides, which is completely consistent with the late fifth century style of the sculpture.

14. Stele

Henan province, Northern Wei dynasty, dated A.D. 521. Sandstone.
H. 25 cm.
Gift of Mr. and Mrs. Philip R. Adams, 1958.549

> *The stele depicts the Buddha dressed in a long-sleeved garment, the voluminous skirt draping over the crossed legs and falling in regular pleats over the front edge of the stele. The figure is seated in meditation, with clasped hands resting in the lap. Behind the figure is a flaming mandorla of pointed almond shape. Parallel lines representing flames diverge around the Buddha's head and unite at the apex of the arch. Two standing attendants, one at each side of the Buddha, wear long robes; their hands are joined in adoration. The inscription fills the back and sides of the stele, and continues on the front.*

This small stone stele dedicated by the Yen family exhibits aspects of the popular transformation of Buddhism in China. Not only do the elongated figures and crisp linearity reflect sinicization of imported Buddhist sculptural styles; the inscription reveals a uniquely Chinese adaptation of the faith, in which filial piety plays an important role:

> *On the 13th day of the 7th month of the second year of the reign of Zheng-Guang (521 A.D.), Yen Xiaole, in expressing his gratefulness to the beneficence of Buddha, built this stone statue as a profession of his wishes to be [Buddha's] follower and be reborn into the seventh generation under the bodhi tree, revisiting the auspicious occasion at which Buddha was born. Pure and innocent, I am. Pure and faithful male disciple Yen Xiaole; his son Azhun; pure and faithful female disciple Du Ayao. The late father Yen Xiangnan; the late mother Sun Xiaoling.*[1]

Whereas Indian Buddhism promoted renunciation of family and social ties, inscriptions on Chinese votive sculptures often express the wish for the whole family, including past generations, to receive blessings and salvation.[2]

The Northern Wei court repeatedly attempted to control the rapidly expanding power of the Buddhist clergy by issuing decrees designed to restrict the indulgences of Buddhist devotees. These regulations had little if any effect on the burgeoning popularity of the faith, nor could they thwart the determination of newly prosperous segments of society, such as the merchant class, to gain entry into the Buddhist paradise through public acts of piety.[3]

Provenance:

   C. T. Loo; Minkenhof collection; C. T. Loo; Philip Rhys Adams

Published:

   Archives of the Chinese Art Society of America, 13 (1959), p. 90.

   Loo, *An Exhibition of Chinese Stone Sculpture,* no. 11.

   Sculpture Collection of the Cincinnati Art Museum, p. 116.

Exhibited:

   "An Exhibition of Chinese Stone Sculpture," C. T. Loo and Co., 1940.

Notes:

   1. trans. Nora Ling-yün Shih.

   2. Ch'en, *Buddhism in China,* p. 179.

   3. See Caswell, *Written and Unwritten,* pp. 21–28.

15. Stele

Henan province. Northern Wei dynasty, dated A.D. 522. Limestone.
H. 202 cm.
Museum purchase, 1946.11

On the front of the dark gray, arch-shaped stele is a large image of the seated Buddha. Wearing loose-fitting robes that fall in parallel folds over the body, the deity sits in a meditative pose. The remnants of the damaged right hand form a gesture of reassurance (abhaya mudra); *the left hand points downward in the gesture of blessing* (varada mudra). *Also in high relief, two attendants stand on bases supported by lions, one on each side of the central deity. Each attendant wears a high headdress. The larger clasps both hands around a lotus bud, while the smaller holds a lotus bud in one hand and a vase in the other. Behind each figure is a halo in monoplanar relief: the Buddha's is a double halo of lotus petals and seated icons of the seven Buddhas of the past; the halo of the smaller attendant has the form of leaping flames; and the halo of the larger attendant is composed of palmette scrolls.*

Monoplanar relief decoration continues above the figures to include four flying apsaras bearing offerings and flanking an incense burner held by a dwarf caryatid. Above this is a pair of intertwined dragons, whose heads are somewhat obscured by surface losses toward the apex of the stele. A border of leaping flames frames the background for the main figures. The band of monoplanar relief at the base includes a gingko tree with a clinging infant beside a jar and a series of seven donor figures holding censers and standing under canopies held by male servants. The donor figures, each identified by an inscription, approach a large censer in the form of a lotus bud.

Monoplanar relief decoration covers the sides and back of the stele. One side bears a scene of a tiger attacking a deer, five donor figures, and a guardian animal below a dragon writhing toward the apex. On the other side are seven donor figures, a snake in pursuit of a toad, and a caryatid figure holding the tail of a dragon writhing toward the apex. The back shows numerous donor figures in rows along the lower portion of the stele. In the upper center, the figure of Xiwangmu sits cross-legged in a pavilion with tied curtains. To the left is the main inscription. Above the roof of the pavilion, a naked infant on the left holds a disk containing a bird with outspread wings; on the right a male figure with straddled legs holds a disk containing a toad. Above is a mulberry tree with pendant fruits. At the apex of the stele is a crane holding a snake in its mouth.

The prominent Shang family, representing generations of district magistrates and governors, dedicated this grand stele in 522 A.D. as a public statement of filial piety and in memory of Shang Tianze, patriarch of the Shang clan of Ji county. Though partially damaged, the long inscription rather than the iconography provides the most important clue to the stele's significance. The images on the front of the stele form a standard Buddhist sculptural group, but the inscription on the back makes no reference to Buddhism. Instead it invokes the blessings of Sheng Mu, "Sacred Mother," referring to Xiwangmu, the Queen Mother of the West. In the upper portion of the back of the stele, the goddess is shown seated in a pavilion beneath a mythical tree, but hers is not the most prominent image on the stele.

Such seemingly incompatible juxtapositions are not uncommon in Chinese religious art. They reflect the commingling of Buddhism and Daoism that shaped popular beliefs.[1] Apparently any deities who were perceived to meet basic concerns about protection, offspring, longevity, prosperity, immortality, or who could be considered useful in the practice of filial piety, were fit for the people's devotion, regardless of their doctrinal origins. Deities of foreign origin evolved into uniquely Chinese gods and goddesses through adaptation from indigenous religions.

In Chinese art the appearance of Xiwangmu together with the Buddha dates back to the Eastern Han period (25–220 A.D.). At that time the two deities, both of whom were believed to dwell in the West, were considered equal in their powers to assist people. The Queen Mother, embodiment of the female principle *yin*, had been paired with a male counterpart, the King Father, representing *yang*, to represent the harmony of forces that would assure peace and prosperity.[2] With the introduction of Buddhist iconography, figures of Xiwangmu and the Buddha began to appear together, and Xiwangmu's depiction followed an iconic form similar to the Buddha's. Also, there was a notion that the Daoist sage Lao Zi's preaching to barbarians living west of China returned as the Buddha's teaching. This idea gained recognition and was promoted in the fourth century. Such melding of Daoist with Buddhist deities culminated in Buddhist/Daoist votive sculptures of the Six Dynasties period. In the minds of some Daoists, the Buddha and Lao Zi were one and the same, so that an image of one could serve as an image of the other.[3] This intermingling continued until the seventh century, when religious Daoism established itself as a distinct cult.[4]

Xiwangmu dwelled on Kunlun, the mountain connecting earth with heaven, and welcomed the *hun* soul of the deceased into heaven. She was also seen as an omnipotent messianic figure who someday would descend to earth to save her followers, deliver justice, and bestow blessings such as wealth, children, and protection from danger. On the back of this stele she appears enthroned in a pavilion beneath the sun, represented by a disk containing a bird, and the moon, signified by a disk containing a toad. Growing above the roof of the pavilion is the mythical *fusang* tree (leaning mulberry) which also represents an *axis mundi*. The *fusang* is related to the mythical dragon trees (*nagavirksha*) of the Tushita heaven, where Maitreya waits for his rebirth as a Buddha.[5]

Images on the edges include a tiger attacking a deer and a snake pursuing a toad; toward the apex of the stele, confronted dragons represent the guardians of the gate to heaven. The veneration of the lotus bud, depicted on the front of the stele just below the seated Buddha, is a subject of Buddhist origin that was also adopted in Daoist cosmology.[6]

Provenance:
C. T. Loo

Published:
Adams, "Sculpture of the Far East," p. 2.
Avril, "Highlights of Chinese Art," p. 67.
Davidson, "Great Chinese Sculptures in America," p. 74, figs. 10–13.
Edwards, "Sophistications," p. 84.
Loo, *An Exhibition of Chinese Stone Sculpture,* no. 16.
Sculpture Collection of the Cincinnati Art Museum, p. 115.
Sirén, *Chinese Sculptures in the von der Heyt Collection,* p. 56.

Exhibited:
"An Exhibition of Chinese Stone Sculpture," C. T. Loo and Co., 1940.

Notes:
1. James, "Some Iconographic Problems," pp. 71–76.
2. For a thorough discussion of the evolution of Xiwangmu beliefs in the Han dynasty, see Wu, *The Wu Liang Shrine,* pp. 108–41; also Wu, "Xiwangmu, the Queen Mother of the West."
3. James, "Some Iconographic Problems," p. 72.
4. James, "Some Iconographic Problems," p. 72.
5. See Birrell, *Chinese Mythology,* pp. 10, 38, 231, 234.
6. Wu, "Buddhist Elements in Early Chinese Art," pp. 270–71.

16. Dog

Northern Wei dynasty, 6th century A.D. Gilt bronze. H. 13.8 cm.
The William T. and Louise Taft Semple Collection, 1962.430

The short-eared dog turns toward the left with wide-eyed alertness, its long snout with open mouth and curled lip exposing the teeth. Rearing back slightly, the animal places its weight on the splayed rear legs; its taut ribs are exposed beneath the smooth skin of the narrow back. Wavy hair, indicated by incised lines, covers the neck, the broad solid shoulders and the hind legs. The figure is gilded overall, but in some areas the gilt is concealed beneath green and red patination.

The artist has captured the intense energy of a dog confronting an adversary by emphasizing features such as curled lip, bared teeth, taut muscles, and exposed ribs.

Ceramic figures of dogs commonly appear among the furnishings of Han and Six Dynasties tombs, but animal figures made of gilt bronze are rarer. Popular beliefs of the period suggest that such figures not only serve a protective function but also convey a more complex cosmological significance.

The dog is one of the twelve animals of the Chinese zodiac, based on the pairing of animal symbols with an ancient duodenary series known as the "earthly branches." Combined alternately with ten "heavenly stems" to make a cycle of sixty, they designated hours, months, seasons, years, lunar phases (*xiu*), and compass directions. By the late Han dynasty the twelve animal symbols had been incorporated into astrology and popular religion. The belief that the calendrical animal corresponding to one's birth year influenced one's personality and fate was prevalent by the fifth and sixth centuries. The zodiac was also consulted to determine the date of burial.[1]

In popular religion, the twelve animals of the Chinese zodiac were worshipped as potent spirits able to avert evil and ward off disease. Daoists believed that the duodenary animals could transform themselves into humans and perform magic on the days of their branch signs. Buddhism also played a role in promoting the worship of the calendrical animals' images. The *Dafangdeng Dajijing,* a Buddhist text translated into Chinese in the early fifth century, contains a story of twelve animals who lived in caves formerly occupied by bodhisattvas. Each animal traveled the world, performing miracles and saving those born under its sign. A Tang-dynasty commentator viewed this passage as proof that belief in the Chinese calendrical animals agreed with Buddhist teaching, because bodhisattvas themselves relied on those animal transformations to save sentient beings.[2]

Images of the calendrical animals have been found on the painted ceilings of sixth-century tombs, where they appear as cosmic symbols. There is also archaeological evidence for placing a set of duodenary animal *mingqi* in niches surrounding the coffin.[3] By the eighth century the twelve animals were depicted anthropomorphically as animal-headed civil officials.

Provenance:
Nasli Heeramaneck; William T. and Louise Taft Semple

Published:
Archives of the Chinese Art Society of America, 17 (1963), p. 58.
Cincinnati Art Museum Bulletin, 7, nos. 3/4 (1965), n.p.
Sculpture Collection of the Cincinnati Art Museum, p. 118.

Notes:
1. Ho, "Twelve Calendrical Animals," pp. 60–62.
2. Ho, "Twelve Calendrical Animals," pp. 65–66.
3. Ho, "Twelve Calendrical Animals," p. 72–76.

17. Seated Maitreya

Northern Wei dynasty, late 5th century A.D. Sandstone. H. 35.6 cm.
The William T. and Louise Taft Semple Collection, 1962.451

The slender, youthful figure with high, arched eyebrows and archaic smile gazes downward meditatively. He sits with legs crossed at the ankles; his right hand is raised in the gesture of assurance (abhaya mudra), while the left hand rests on the left knee in the gesture of charity (varada mudra). The bodhisattva wears a tall straight-sided crown, a loose-fitting robe that drapes over the legs in parallel folds, and a shawl-like scarf that wraps around the shoulders, crosses at the waist, and drapes over the forearms. Traces of red pigment remain on the figure's garment.

Among the most popular sutras in China during the Northern Wei period were those devoted to the bodhisattva Mi-Le (Maitreya), who waits in the Tushita heaven for his rebirth on earth as the future Buddha. Souls reborn into this heaven would find an environment conducive to their further progress toward nirvana. The numerous images of Maitreya carved into rocky cliffs of Buddhist pilgrimage sites throughout China attest to the widespread patronage by devotees hoping to gain spiritual merit and rebirth into this paradise.

This small fragment was once part of a complex sculptural program carved into the wall of a rock cave. It purportedly came from Longmen, Henan province.

Provenance:
    S. H. Mori; William T. and Louise Taft Semple
Published:
    Archives of the Chinese Art Society of America, 17 (1963), p. 58.
    Cincinnati Art Museum Bulletin, 7, no. 3–4 (February, 1965), n.p.
    Sculpture Collection of the Cincinnati Art Museum, pp. 114–15.

18. Head of a *Pizhifo*

Purportedly from Longmen, Henan province, Northern Wei dynasty, 6th century A.D. Limestone. H. 27.9 cm.
The William T. and Louise Taft Semple Collection, 1962.454

The face has high-arched eyebrows that extend to form the line of the nose, an introspective down-turned gaze, and a slight smile. The hair, parted at the center of the forehead, is smooth where it covers the crown. Then it is drawn up in a high chignon of twisted locks that form a spiral at the peak.

This head, severed from the rest of the figure at mid-neck, comes from a figure of a *pizhifo,* a buddha who appears between the disappearance of one true Buddha and the arrival of the next. This unusual type is characterized by its distinctive chignon of "twisted hemp," another meaning of the word *pi.* A full-length standing figure of this semi-buddha is in the Detroit Institute of Arts.[1] A Sui-dynasty bronze altarpiece of Amituo in the Boston Museum of Fine Arts includes attendant figures with similar twisted chignons.[2] A *pizhifo* also appears on the entrance jamb to the Lu Dong cave, Longmen.[3]

Provenance:
    Nasli Heeramaneck; William T. and Louise Taft Semple
Published:
    Archives of the Chinese Art Society of America, 17 (1963), p. 44.
    Cincinnati Art Museum Bulletin, 7, no. 3–4 (February, 1965), n.p.
    Hai-Wai Yi-Chen Buddhist Sculpture 2, p. 33.
    Sculpture Collection of the Cincinnati Art Museum, p. 114.
Notes:
    1. *Hai-Wai Yi-Chen Buddhist Sculpture 2:* p. 98.
    2. Sickman and Soper, *Art and Architecture of China,* fig. 84.
    3. *Longmen Shiku,* pl. 113.

19. Hand Holding a Lotus Bud

Northern Wei dynasty, early 6th century A.D. Limestone with traces of color. H. 59.9 cm.
Museum purchase, 1952.109

The right hand, which was severed at the wrist from the original figure, is bent back to reveal the palm. The hand grasps a lotus bud with thumb and three fingers; the extended index finger supports the bud from behind.

This hand probably comes from an image of Guanyin (Avalokitesvara), bodhisattva of compassion, who is generally depicted holding the attributes of a lotus bud and vase. The lotus is one of the most important symbols of Buddhism and is equated with Buddha's purity: the plant grows in muddy waters but produces unsullied blossoms. The lotus bud symbolizes the heart, wherein the virtues of Buddha are formed.

Although its origin is not known, the Museum's hand is made of dark limestone associated with the Longmen caves. It closely resembles the hands of large bodhisattva figures *in situ* at the sixth century Binyang and Lianhua caves, Longmen.[1]

Provenance:
    C. T. Loo
Published:
    Adams, "Random Notes," pp. 2, 6.
    Arts of the T'ang Dynasty, no. 45.
    Sculpture Collection of the Cincinnati Art Museum, pp. 120–21.
Exhibited:
    "The Arts of the T'ang Dynasty," Los Angeles County Museum of Art, 1957.
Notes:
    1. *Longmen Shiku,* pls. 55, 60, 73. See also a fragment of a hand possibly from cave XIX, Longmen, in the Metropolitan Museum of Art, publ. Priest, *Chinese Sculpture,* no. 44.

20. Guanyin and Da Shizhi

Hebei province, Northern Qi dynasty, circa A.D. 575. Marble with remains of pigment. H. (Guanyin) 173.9 cm, (Da Shizhi) 175.3 cm.
Museum purchase, 1952.110,111

Each of the sculptures in this pair is carved of fine-grained stone and was made in two parts. The hemispherical bottom of each standing, columnar figure sits within a pedestal formed of deeply cut inverted lotus blossoms on a cylindrical drum decorated in high relief with scrolling plant motifs; everything rests on a plain square base. Each bodhisattva wears a dhoti that is gathered at the waist and falls in straight pleats to the undulating hem, a simple upper garment with rounded neckline, and scarves that drape across the shoulders and abdomen, and over the forearms. Each is richly adorned with pendants, belts, buckles, and chain necklaces that criss-cross through a disk just above the waist. The crown of each figure bears a distinctive diadem, one of a vase, the other of a buddha figure. Traces of red and blue pigment remain in the hair and on the base of each figure. Each sculpture is missing its forearms and hands.

During the rather short-lived Northern Qi dynasty (550–577 A.D.), a wave of foreign influence from Gupta-period (320–600 A.D.) India resulted in the appearance of a new sculptural style. Emphasizing corporeality and roundness of form, the Northern Qi sculptors rejected the earlier reliance on linearity. Instead they achieved an elegance and restraint through the contrast of plain surfaces punctuated with ornate embellishments.

On the basis of similarity of their facial features and ornamentation, Sirén matched this pair of bodhisattvas with the Buddha image they once flanked, an Amituo (Amitabha) dated by inscription to 575 A.D.[1] Its inscription indicates that the sculpture was commissioned by two military officials:

[Erected in] the 6th year of Wu Ping of the Great Qi dynasty, cyclically called zhiwei (575 A.D.), on the 8th day of the 4th month by two men who were adjutants on the board of armaments in Renzhou, called Song Si-jing and Zhao Bao, for his Imperial Majesty, the Imperial family, the prime minister, their fathers and mothers, and all living beings most respectfully, of white stone, in order that they all may receive the benefits of the Noble Way and thus become illuminated. The promoters (or patrons) of the statue were the pacifier of the South, general Bo Ren with his good wife Zhu, and the pacifier of Bo (i.e., Liaocheng in Shandong), general Han Ning(?) with his mother and his wife Sun. The master presiding at the unveiling (i.e., giving light by opening its eyes) was the abbot Daoxun and his mother Yuan, and the lay disciple of Buddha Xu Wenzheng with his wives Jin and Wang, and the female lay devotees Xu Zhanger and Xu Cui(?)er.[2]

The Museum's pair of bodhisattvas, together with the Buddha image, would have formed a triad known as the Holy Ones of the Pure Land: Amituo, Buddha of Infinite Light, the celestial buddha who presides over the Western Paradise, also known as the Pure Land; Guanyin (Avalokitesvara), the bodhisattva of compassion, who meets the faithful upon death and guides them to the Pure Land; and the bodhisattva Da Shizhi (Mahasthamaprapta), representing Amituo's power and wisdom, who greets those entering the Pure Land with a gesture of offering and veneration. Each bodhisattva is identified by a distinctive diadem. Guanyin's bears an image of his spiritual father Amituo (partially damaged on this sculpture), and Da Shizhi's is decorated with a vase. Pure Land doctrine, whose popularity increased in the mid-sixth century, offered rebirth into Amituo's paradise to faithful individuals calling on the deity's name. In the Pure Land reborn souls would dwell in an environment conducive to attaining the ultimate goal of enlightenment.

The mention of specific women in the dedicatory inscription is noteworthy, because it indicates that the Pure Land sect allowed women of spiritual merit to be reborn into Amituo's paradise. The sutras, however, vary in their accounts of this phenomenon. Some indicate that only devout women of special virtue will be welcomed and that they will be reborn as men, while others explain that all female believers must be reborn into the paradise.[3]

Provenance:
    C.T. Loo

Published:
    Adams, "Sculpture of the Far East," p. 13.
    Archives of the Chinese Art Society of America, 7 (1953), p. 84.
    Edwards, "Sophistications," p. 84.
    Hai-Wai Yi-Chen Buddhist Sculpture 2, no. 61.
    Loo, *An Exhibition of Chinese Stone Sculpture*, no. 25.
    Sirén, "Chinese Marble Sculptures," pp. 471–78, pl. 1b,c.
Exhibited:
    "An Exhibition of Chinese Stone Sculpture," C.T. Loo and Co., New York, 1940.
Notes:
    1. Sirén, "Chinese Marble Sculptures," 475–78, pl. 1. The Amitabha was once owned by D. Kelekian of New York; its present whereabouts are unknown. Before it had been cleaned, it was covered in dark pigments as illustrated in Sirén, *Chinese Sculpture*, vol. 3, pl. 256.
    2. Sirén, "Chinese Marble Sculptures," p. 476.
    3. See Frédéric, *Buddhism*, p. 140.

21. Bodhisattva

Hebei province, Sui dynasty, circa A.D. 581–590. Limestone.
H. 76.4 cm.
Museum purchase, 1950.72

The bodhisattva with softly modeled face has high arched eyebrows, a narrow nose, a slight smile, a pointed double chin, and a thick cylindrical neck. The sloping shoulders are concealed beneath a shawl tied in a knot in the front. Another scarf falls over the forearms and down the sides of the figure; both ends are broken off. The fragmentary figure is broken off just above the hem of the garment. The slender, high-waisted figure has an undulating profile and holds a leaf-shaped object in the left hand. The right forearm is broken off, and the hand is completely missing. The bodhisattva wears jeweled chains that cross in a roundel at the lower abdomen. A sash hangs from the roundel. A pointed tiara and a scarf cover the head. The figure stands against a halo with relief decoration of a lotus-form roundel in the center. Surrounding the center are seven images of seated Buddhas in meditation, spaced evenly around the perimeter. Traces of gilt remain.

After some 350 years in which splintered kingdoms vied for dominance in northern China, Wen Di (r. 581–601), first emperor of the Sui dynasty, unified China in the late sixth century. The Sui not only overhauled the central government but also patronized Buddhism with renewed vigor, restoring temples destroyed during the Northern Zhou persecutions of 574–578.

Early Sui sculptures such as this continue the style of the Northern Qi sculptors of Hebei province (see entry 20). This style is characterized by an overall simplicity and a symmetrical placement of linear details that yield to the predominance of smooth surfaces. Because Hebei was somewhat remote from the political turmoil, it enjoyed a relatively peaceful transition to the Sui rule.

Characterizing this earliest phase of Sui sculpture are the three-sectioned crown and the tall, squarish head with high-arched eyebrows. The body features sloping shoulders, a short upper body, a spreading midsection adorned with jewel chains that cross in an x, and elongated lower body and legs.[1]

The bodhisattva holds a leaf-shaped object in the left hand; the right hand is missing. A companion piece, wearing a similar crown and cloth head covering, and shown against a halo with seven seated Buddhas in relief, is in the Freer Gallery of Art.[2]

Provenance:
   Belle Da Costa Greene; C.T. Loo
Published:
   Adams, "Sculpture of the Far East," pp. 10–13.
   Edwards, "Sophistications," p. 85.
   Guide to the Collections of the Cincinnati Art Museum, p. 32.
   Hai-Wai Yi-Chen Buddhist Sculpture 2, no. 85.
   Masterpieces from the Cincinnati Art Museum, p. 52.
   Sculpture Collection of the Cincinnati Art Museum, pp. 118–19.
   Sirén, *Chinese Sculpture,* vol. 1, p. 83, no. 306; vol. 3, pl. 308.
Notes:
   1. Rhie, "Aspects," pp. 98–99.
   2. Sirén, *Chinese Sculpture,* vol. 3, pl. 307.

22. Head of a Bodhisattva

Five Dynasties or Northern Song dynasty, 10th-12th century.
Molded glass. H.30.5 cm.
Gift of Drs. Martin and Carol Macht, 1991.275

The opaque white glass of the head has a surface "skin" of mottled beige and red brown with sandy incrustation in folds of the hair. The head, with fleshy face, full lips, wide flat nose, downcast eyes, and arched eyebrows, has elongated earlobes and upswept hair gathered into a high chignon. The base of the head, directly below the chin, is unfinished.

This head of a bodhisattva, the largest known example of early Chinese glass sculpture, is a complete anomaly. The head does not represent a fragmentary portion of a larger figure, but was purposely made without a neck or any other visible means of attachment to a body. An unusual example of soda-lime glass (see technical remarks below), for many years it has defied confident assignment of place and date of manufacture, or even of original function. The head relates to Tang stone sculptures from Tianlongshan,[1] whose style continues to appear in Song and later bodhisattva figures.

It is known that glass was used to produce items for Buddhist temples in the Tang dynasty. Recent archaeological finds include cups, bowls, and flasks unearthed from reliquary chests and pagoda sites.[2] In addition, small glass figures of Buddhist deities thought to date from this period are preserved in Western collections.[3]

Scientific analysis has shown that most glass produced in the Tang dynasty has a high lead content, representing long-standing traditions of glass technology dating back to the Han dynasty. Indeed, lead glass continued to be produced well into the Song dynasty. Recent archaeological evidence,[4] however, as well as analytical studies of objects of unknown provenance,[5] shows that soda-lime glass, known for a long time in the Middle East, was produced in China (though in much smaller quantities) during the Sui and Tang periods. The small quantities are believed to be due to insufficient do-

mestic sources of sodium carbonate; Chinese glassmakers thus were forced to rely on imported natural soda from the Middle East.

Textual and archaeological evidence suggests that glassmaking was largely under the control of the imperial court from the Northern Wei dynasty (386–535 A.D.) to the early Tang. Recorded experimentation with soda lime glass by imperial artisans in the Northern Song period, as described in the *Tiewei shan congtan* [Collected Discussions at Mt. Tiewei], sheds new light on our understanding of the Museum's bodhisattva head:

> At this time (the fourth year of the Zhengde reign period [1114]), among items presented to the Imperial stores were found two glass jars of Longxian perfume and two large baskets of 'glass matrix.' This material resembles today's iron slag in lumps about the size of a fist. No one knew what it was for and for years there had been no record of it; the origin was also unknown, though some said it had been presented in tribute by the Dashi [identified in some sources as Tajiks, but here probably a generic title for Arab peoples — Trans.] during the Xiande reign period of Shizong [A.D. 954–960, of the Hou Zhou dynasty of the Five Dynasties period]. It was also said to be material from the Muslim court. The eunuch craftsmen attempted to smelt and mould the raw glass, but were only able to make things like inferior jade; nor did the colour turn out as expected, being green, red, yellow or white at random.[6]

The above description of unsuccessful results can also be applied to the Museum's head, with its pitted surface, adherence of the mold material, and mottled colors. Undoubtedly this unusual head exemplifies experimentation with an unfamiliar material. Although one can only speculate about the intentions of the artist who produced it, the head reminds us of the crucial role of trial and error in creating innovative works of art.

Technical Remarks: Extensive scientific analysis has been conducted on this object. In a 1962 study published by Werner and Bimson,[7] the opacifying agents were found to be a mixture of calcium fluoride and sodium fluoride. In other examples of Tang glass analyzed by Werner and Bimson in the same study, calcium fluoride was the only opacifying agent. Before that time, it was believed that fluorides were not used as opacifiers until the nineteenth century; this was found not to be the case with Chinese glass, however. In 1986 the head received further examination and scientific analysis at the Corning Museum of Glass. Quantitative chemical analysis conducted by atomic absorption and emission spectrography revealed that it was made of a soda-lime-silica glass decolorized with manganese. X-ray diffraction, employed to identify the opacifier, corroborated Werner and Bimson's finding of calcium fluoride and sodium fluoride.[8] The presence of both opacifiers is consistent with other known examples from the period. Because the lead oxide content of the head is only .08%, no lead-isotope analysis was conducted. The lack of evidence of weathering on the surface or in the crevices is not unusual for molded glass. Surface incrustation was identified as remnant refractory (i.e. ceramic mold material) which adhered to the glass during cooling.[9]

Provenance:

Private collection, Macao; Dr. Louis Joseph, London; Sotheby's London, 25 and 26 November, 1974, lot 347; Drs. Martin and Carol Macht

Published:

Archives of Asian Art, 46(1993), p. 112.

Avril, "Highlights of Chinese Art," pp. 68–69.

Brill, Tong, and Dohrenwend, "Chemical Analyses," pp. 37, 41, 46.

Cincinnati Collects Oriental Art, no. 82.

Werner and Bimson, "Some Opacifying Agents," pp. 303–05.

Exhibited:

Exhibited on loan to the Cincinnati Art Museum, 1982–1991.

"Cincinnati Collects Oriental Art," Cincinnati Art Museum, March-April, 1985, no. 82.

Notes:

1. For example, see Sickman and Soper, *Art and Architecture of China,* fig. 98.

2. An, *Early Chinese Glassware,* pp. 10–11, 17–20.

3. For a set of twelve small Buddha images, tentatively dated to the Tang dynasty, see Dohrenwend, "Glass in China," pp. 433–436. A standing Buddha image in glass, also assigned to the Tang dynasty, is in the British Museum; it is referenced but not illustrated in the above article. Results of technical analysis of two of the small ROM Buddha images are discussed in Brill, Tong, and Dohrenwend, "Chemical Analyses," pp. 46.

4. An, *Early Chinese Glassware,* pp. 25–26.

5. Brill, Tong, and Dohrenwend, "Chemical Analyses," pp. 13–16.

6. Quoted in An, *Early Chinese Glassware,* p. 26.

7. Werner and Bimson, "Some Opacifying Agents," pp. 303–05.

8. Brill, Tong, and Dohrenwend, "Chemical Analyses," p. 46.

9. Brill, "Comments on a Chinese Glass Head in the Cincinnati Art Museum," unpublished report of analysis conducted at the Corning Museum of Glass, Corning, New York, 1986.

23. Water and Moon (*Shuiyue*) Guanyin

Xixia or Jin dynasty, 12th or early 13th century. Wood with traces of pigments and gilt. H.99 x W.79.1 x D.55.5 cm.
Museum purchase, 1950.73

Seated in a relaxed pose, the deity leans on the left arm while the flexed left leg rests horizontally on the ground. The right knee is bent to support the extended right arm. Gazing downward with a calm expression, the face is fleshy and full; the hair, upswept in an elaborate coiffure and a heavily jeweled tiara, falls in ropelike trails across the shoulders and upper arms. The figure wears a loose-fitting dhoti, whose deeply cut drapery covers the legs but leaves the feet exposed. Heavily jeweled necklaces and long fluttering scarves falling diagonally from the left shoulder across the high waist adorn the otherwise bare upper body and arms.

Guanyin seated in the pose of "royal ease" (*maharajalila*) represents a uniquely Chinese form known as *Shuiyue* (Water-and-Moon) Guanyin. According to Buddhist scriptures, this bodhisattva lived on Potolaka, an island located in the seas south of India. The Chinese, however, associated Guanyin's island home with Mount Putuo, off the coast of Zhejiang, and it became a major Buddhist pilgrimage destination. Drawing on their own tradition of sages and immortals, the Chinese devised a form of Guanyin who lived in seclusion in a grotto on the island and meditated on the illusory nature of phenomena, metaphorically linked to the moon's reflection in water. Many indigenous Chinese Buddhist writings enriched and enlivened Guanyin into a deity capable of aiding people in any one of numerous manifestations. Other forms relating to the bodhisattva's residence at Mount Putuo include White-Robed (*Baiyi*) Guanyin and Guanyin of the Southern Seas (*Nanhai Guanyin*).[1]

The Chinese transformation of Guanyin involved the feminization of a being who (according to original Mahayana Buddhist doctrine) transcends all dichotomies such as gender. In Xixia, Song, and Jin dynasty sculptures, gender remains ambiguous, although the inclination toward a female form is detected in the softer modeling of the face and arms, and the delicate hands. Emphasizing Guanyin's feminine aspects underscored the deity's tenderness and compassion. A graceful, relaxed pose and a calm expression contributed to the humanization and emotional appeal of an approachable deity.

The faded pigments and the isolation of the sculpture from its original temple setting convey a somewhat misleading impression of aesthetic restraint. The deeply carved drapery and the heavy ornamentation only hint at the original sumptuousness and overwhelming visual effect that awaited temple visitors. They would have encountered this image in an elaborate stage set that included a carved wooden base in the form of rockery, a high backdrop representing the grotto dwelling, painted murals covering the walls, and many other sculptures of deities and arhats, all brightly colored and gilded.

The finest sculptures of this period were carved of wood, covered with gesso, painted with bright pigments, inset with jewels, and gilded to create elegantly animated, richly adorned figures. Glass eyes conveyed a sense of life and immediacy. Demand for large images, often greater than life-size, led to the development of construction methods involving multiple blocks of wood, assembled after carving with bamboo or wood pins. So many of these splendid works survive today largely because the artists used sophisticated joining techniques that prevented shrinkage.[2]

The late Tang persecutions of Buddhism left the religion weakened in central and southern China, but northern China, under the rule of the Khitan Liao (907–1125) and Tangut Xixia (ca. 928–1227), remained a Buddhist stronghold. In Shanxi province especially, many temples from the Buddhist revival of the eleventh through thirteenth centuries survived intact into this century, testimony to the glorious integration of architecture, painting, and sculpture that characterizes Buddhist temple art.

Provenance:

C.T. Loo

Published:

Adams, "Sculpture of the Far East," p. 17.

Cincinnati Art Museum Bulletin (November, 1951), p. 3.

Edwards, "Sophistications," p. 85.

Hai-wai Yi-chen Buddhist Sculpture 2, p. 151.

Masterpieces from the Cincinnati Art Museum, p. 51.

Record of the Art Museum, Princeton University 12(1953), p. 33.

Sculpture Collection of the Cincinnati Art Museum, p. 121.

Notes:

1. See Yü, "Guanyin: The Chinese Transformation of Avalokiteshvara," pp. 156-60.
2. See Larson and Kerr, *Guanyin,* for a thorough technical study of a circa 1200 seated wood Guanyin.

24. Head of a Buddha

Possibly Shanxi province, Ming dynasty, late 15th or early 16th century. Cast iron. H. 49.2 cm.
Bequest of John J. Emery, 1977.21

The squarish, fleshy face with a narrow nose and pursed lips, has large downcast eyes. The eyebrows are rendered as a continuous undulating raised line that trails across the lower edge of the forehead. Thin raised lines also define the eyelids, lips, and pierced earlobes. In the center of the forehead is a circular indentation lacking its jeweled urna *(third eye). The conical cranium is covered with a coiffure composed of regular rows of spiky curls, save for the pointed tip of the ushnisha and the oval bald spot. The ears, with their elongated, fleshy pierced lobes, bend outward from the cheeks. The head, once part of a larger sculpture, was cut off at the top of the neck.*

This head comes from what must have been a large and impressive figure of a Buddha. All but the tiniest traces of paint and gilding have been lost, leaving a rough, rusty surface that belies the sumptuousness of its original appearance.[1] Cast iron images were produced as early as the Tang dynasty, but most of those which survive today come from later periods.[2] The features of the Museum's head closely resemble a cast-iron image of a seated Buddha dated 1520.[3] The spiky hair curls, pointed *ushnisha,* and bald spot are all Chinese adaptations of a Buddha's physical marks and relate stylistically to depictions of Buddhas in Chinese paintings of the fifteenth century and later.[4] Hair curls are considered a sign of the Buddha's divine nature; the cranial protuberance *ushnisha* and the third eye *urna* signify wisdom; the joined eyebrows indicate a fortunate man.[5]

Provenance:

Purportedly from a temple in Northern Shanxi; Mathias Komor; D'Oiseau collection, Glendale, Ohio; Frank Caro; John J. Emery

Notes:

1. A cast-iron head of Guanyin in the Ackland Art Museum (88.29) retains much of its original polychrome and gilding. See Lee, "Asian Art," pp. 42–43, fig. 12.
2. Lee, "Asian Art," p. 43. See Kerr, ed. *Chinese Art and Design,* pp. 94–95, for a discussion of scientific analysis that prompted attribution of a cast-iron head of a Buddha in the Victoria and Albert Museum to the Tang dynasty. This analysis caused some controversy; see Whitfield, "Exhibition Review," pp. 789–90.
3. The Avery Brundage Collection, Asian Art Museum of San Francisco, B60 S335.
4. Compare a painting of Yaoshi, the Medicine Buddha, dated 1477, in the University of Oregon Museum of Art (MWCH 32.11), publ. Weidner, *Latter Days of the Law,* no. 5.
5. See Pal, *Light of Asia,* pp. 146–51.

25. Seated Sakyamuni Buddha

Sino-Tibetan, 18th or 19th century. Gilt brass with lapis lazuli pigment. H. 10.5 cm.
Gift of C. D. Lindhjem, 1992.59

The Buddha is seated cross-legged in meditative posture with the proper right hand in a gesture of touching the earth and the proper left hand in a gesture of contemplation. The figure wears a simple robe draped over the left shoulder, spreading over the left arm and legs and resting on a lotus-form pedestal. The coiffure is styled in tight curls painted blue; the exposed tip of the ushnisha *is gilt. A painted metal plate inserted in the hollow base has an incised decoration showing a pair of crossed vajras with a central auspicious yinyang sign.*

A Lamaist (Tibetan Buddhist) icon of a Buddha is considered an Artistic Emanation Body Buddha that can transmit the deity's living presence. Consecrational rituals performed upon the completion of icons empowered them for use in visualizations: devotees seeking enlightenment practiced envisioning themselves as the archetypal Buddha who embodies perfect wisdom and compassion. In this context temple images, intended to inspire devotees and remind them of their potential to achieve Buddhahood, came to be treasured for their aid in energizing the visualization.[1] Small images such as this one may have functioned in a more intimate way to assist the individual devotee. They may also have belonged to a set of images forming a three-dimensional *mandala,* or diagram of the spiritual universe.[2]

Seated in the lotus or diamond posture, with his right hand in the gesture of earth witness and his left hand in a gesture of contemplation, this image represents the historical Buddha Sakyamuni at the moment when he achieved enlightenment while meditating under the bodhi tree. Responding to the evil Mara's challenge of his fitness to become a Buddha, Sakyamuni touched the earth, calling on the Mother Earth goddess to witness his spiritual advancement and qualification for enlightenment.

Tibetan Buddhism was practiced at the imperial court, and fine gilt bronze images of this type were produced in large quantities under the patronage of the Qing dynasty emperors Qianlong (1736–1795), Jiaqing (1796–1820), and Daoguang (1821–1850). It is likely that this hollow-cast image contains a consecrational deposit (perhaps a sutra fragment, an incantation, or some other document)[3] held in place by the painted copper plate inserted in its base.

Notes:

1. Thurman, "Tibet, Its Buddhism, and Its Art," p. 37.
2. For similar images of Buddhas and other deities produced as a set to form a mandala, see Rhie and Thurman, *Wisdom and Compassion,* no. 134.
3. See contents of an image of Amitayus, Rhie and Thurman, *Wisdom and Compassion,* no. 144.

3. *Jue*
Shang dynasty, 12th century B.C.

4. *Fangyi*
Shang dynasty, 12th century B.C.

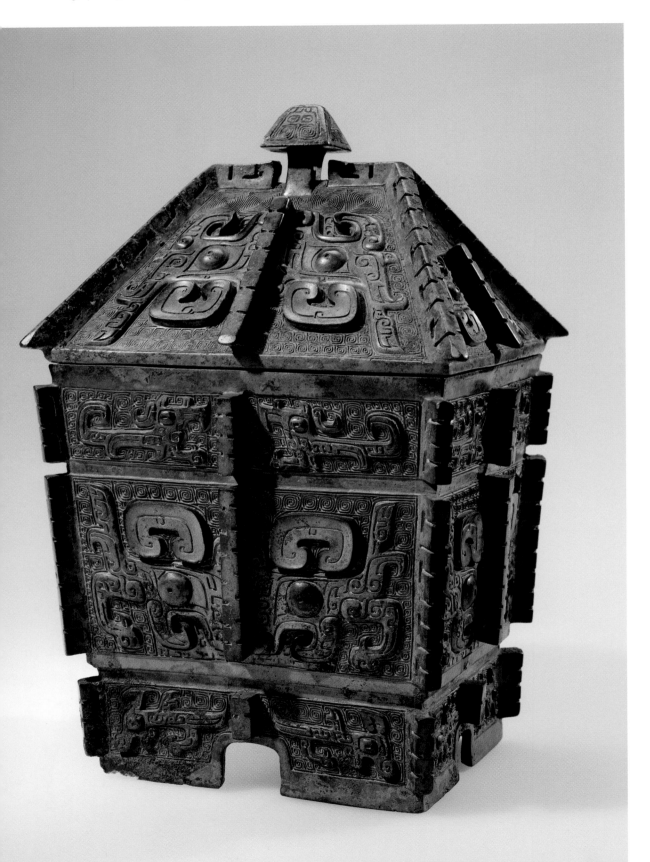

Lid

Vessel

5. *Guang*
Shang dynasty, 12th century B.C.

6. *Gu*
Shang dynasty, 12th century B.C.

7. Double-Owl *You*
Shang dynasty, 12th century B.C.

33

8. Axle Caps
Shang dynasty, 13th to 11th century B.C.

9. *Ge* Dagger-Axe
Shang dynasty, 13th to 11th century B.C.

10. Bell, *Bo*
Eastern Zhou dynasty, 6th century B.C.

11. Mirror
Tang dynasty, late 7th or early 8th century A.D.

12. Tomb Relief Depicting a Carriage Procession
Han dynasty, 2nd century A.D.

Reverse

13. Seated Buddha
Northern Wei dynasty, dated A.D. 474

14. Stele
Northern Wei dynasty, dated A.D. 521

15. Stele
Northern Wei dynasty, dated A.D. 522

Line drawing from reverse

15. Stele
Northern Wei dynasty, dated A.D. 522, reverse

16. Dog
Northern Wei dynasty, 6th century A.D.

17. Seated Maitreya
Northern Wei dynasty, late 5th century A.D.

18. Head of a *Pizhifo*
Northern Wei dynasty, 6th century A.D.

19. Hand Holding a Lotus Bud
Northern Wei dynasty, early 6th century A.D.

20. Guanyin and Da Shizhi
Northern Qi dynasty, circa A.D. 575

21. Bodhisattva
Sui dynasty, circa A.D. 581–590

22. Head of a Bodhisattva
Five dynasties or Northern Song dynasty, 10th to 12th century

23. Water and Moon (*Shuiyue*) Guanyin
Xixia or Jin dynasty, 12th or early 13th century

24. Head of a Buddha
Ming dynasty, late 15th or early 16th century

25. Seated Sakyamuni Buddha
Qing dynasty, 18th or 19th century

26. Prayer Sheet

Gansu province, Dunhuang, Mogao caves, circa A.D. 950. Woodblock print on paper. H. 29.8 x W. 18.7 cm.
The Albert P. Strietmann Collection, 1992.139

The composition of this prayer sheet follows a standard format for early Buddhist votive prints known as *shangtu xiawen* ("image above, text below"). Depicted in the upper portion of the page is Wenshu, bodhisattva of wisdom (Sanskrit: Manjusri), riding on a lion. To the bodhisattva's right stands a bearded Central Asian man. To the deity's left, in a posture of adoration, is the child pilgrim Shancai (Sanskrit: Suddhana). A single line of text in a cartouche to the right of the deity reads "The very holy Bodhisattva Wenshu"; the cartouche on the left is inscribed "Universal exhortation to worship and maintenance of the faith." The main portion of text contains instructions for worship, a short prayer, and incantations.[1]

This woodcut, the oldest work of art on paper in the Museum's collection, comes from a cache of early paintings, sutras, and prints that were discovered at the Mogao caves in the early twentieth century. Also known as Qianfodong, Caves of the Thousand Buddhas, this pilgrimage site is located near the Dunhuang oasis, Gansu province, at the eastern merger of two main trade routes that followed the perimeter of the Taklamakan Desert. An arduous journey through harsh deserts awaited those who traveled these central Asian trade routes, known collectively as the Silk Road. Buddhist cave-temple sites near Silk Road oases provided spiritual repose to pilgrims and weary travelers.

Votive prints were purchased by pilgrims both for their instructive devotional texts and for the images of deities that could be left as offerings. Making multiple copies of sutras and images of Buddhist deities was considered an important act of devotion; the popularity of this pursuit spurred the development of printing in China during the Tang dynasty (618–906). Among the hundreds of paintings and prints found inside Mogao cave 17 was the earliest dated woodcut in existence, a Diamond Sutra scroll dated 868 A.D. and now in the British Museum.[2]

Buddhist woodblock printing flourished in the tenth century. The appearance of numerous votive prints reflects an increased emphasis on private devotional practices and the popularity of bodhisattvas in the quest for personal salvation.[3] Prayer sheets like the Museum's are generally dated to the mid-tenth century based on their stylistic similarity to votive prints that were commissioned by the Imperial Commissioner at Dunhuang, Cao Yuanzhong, in 947 A.D.[4]

Two versions of the Wenshu prayer sheets from Dunhuang are extant. Both show the deity against a double flaming halo from which ribbons of light radiate, but the compositions differ slightly: In one the halo is shown as two full disks,[5] while in the other the upper disk is cropped just below the apex of the flames.[6] The Museum's print is of the latter type, which is further distinguished from the former by greater attention to detail, especially in the lion and the faces of the figures.

Because of their relatively remote location and a period of Tibetan control from 781 to 847, the Dunhuang caves survived the late Tang-dynasty persecutions of Buddhism that destroyed nearly all temples and monuments in central China. Chinese control of the area was restored in the second half of the ninth century, and the construction of caves at Dunhuang continued into the eleventh century. Cave 17 originally was constructed as a memorial chapel to Hongbian, the chief of monks who was honored for his role in restoring the area to Chinese control. Sometime in the early eleventh century it was cleared to store bundles of rolled sutras, paintings, and documents so numerous as to fill the room from floor to ceiling.[7]

The carefully sealed repository, hidden behind a wall of Northern Song-dynasty paintings, remained undisturbed until the turn of the twentieth century, when it was discovered by a Daoist priest, Wang Yuanlu. British explorer-archaeologist Sir Marc Aurel Stein, who arrived at Dunhuang in 1907, acquired a large portion of the library's contents from Wang. (Stein's acquisitions form collections now in the British Museum and the Museum of Central Asian Antiquities, New Delhi.) The Cincinnati print allegedly was collected by the French sinologist Paul Pelliot, who visited the Mogao caves only months after Stein left. Spending three weeks there in 1908, carefully studying and culling the contents of Cave 17, Pelliot purchased everything he considered to have quality and historical significance, about one-third of the remaining manuscripts, paintings, and prints. These are now housed in the Musée Guimet and the Bibliotheque Nationale, Paris. Pelliot informed Chinese scholars of the Dunhuang finds, which led to the government's transfer of several thousand manuscripts to the Library of the Capital in Beijing.[8] Later the remaining manuscripts, which Wang had hidden inside modern images, were taken to Japan by the Otani expedition.[9]

Recent provenance:
  Han Shan Tang

Published:
  Durrell, *Selection of New Acquisitions*, pp. 10–11.

Notes:
  1. See Whitfield and Farrer, *Caves*, nos. 82, 85 and 86; also Whitfield, *Art of Central Asia*, 2: figs. 140–43, and 147, for other examples of the type found at Dunhuang.
  2. Whitfield, *Art of Central Asia*, 2: figs. 144, 145; also see Wood, *Chinese Illustration*, pp. 8–11.
  3. Whitfield, *Art of Central Asia*, 2: pp. 20–21.
  4. See Whitfield and Farrer, *Caves*, nos. 83–85.
  5. Examples of this version in the British Museum are illustrated in Wood, *Chinese Illustration*, p. 17; Whitfield, *Art of Central Asia*, 2: fig. 142; Whitfield and Farrer, *Caves*, no. 86. Impressions also are found in the Museum of Fine Arts, Boston (BMFA), published in Edgren, *Chinese Rare Books*, pl. 2a; pl. 2b is another variant in the BMFA. A print in the Metropolitan Museum of Art is cited but not illustrated.
  6. An example of the cropped version is in the Stein collection, published in Whitfield, *Art of Central Asia*, 2: fig. 143.
  7. Whitfield and Farrer, *Caves*, pp. 15 and 20.
  8. Thote, "Paul Pelliot," pp. 39–41.
  9. Whitfield, *Art of Central Asia*, 1: pp. 9–11.

27. The Four Sages of Shangshan

Ma Yuan (active circa 1190–circa 1225). Southern Song dynasty, circa 1225. Handscroll; ink and light colors on paper. H.33.6 x L.307.3 cm.
Anonymous gift, 1950.77

In the right-hand section of the painting a stream emerges from a rocky ravine to join a larger body of water in a torrent of high-surging waves. The stream runs diagonally through the painting from left to right in a long straight channel past a high cliff with a cavern. Short bamboo and bare plum trees grow along the cliff. The near shore is obscured by a rocky precipice inhabited by four elderly men and a servant. One of the men looks out in search of mushrooms. The other three are gathered under the dense, protective canopy of an old pine tree; two are playing chess while the other looks on. Behind them, large jagged boulders partially obscure the pine tree.

This rare handscroll by Ma Yuan, one of the preeminent court painters of the Southern Song dynasty, depicts the mountain retreat of four aged scholar-officials known as the Four Sages of Mount Shang (sometimes referred to as the Four Greybeards), who chose a life of reclusion, rather than to serve the first Han emperor Gaozu, because they disapproved of his treatment of scholars.[1]

The story of Master Dongyuan, Scholar Luli, Qi Liji, and Master Xiahuang involves the intrigues of imperial succession and is recorded in Sima Qian's *Shiji*.[2] When the first Han emperor, Gaozu (r. 206–195 B.C.), resolved to disinherit the heir apparent, his eldest son by Empress Lu, in favor of Ruyi, Prince of Zhao, his son by Madame Qi, many ministers advised against his decision, but to no avail. The distressed Empress Lu turned to Zhang Liang, one of the emperor's trusted counselors to devise a plan. Zhang suggested sending for the Four Sages of Shangshan, who were known to be admired by the emperor. The four men arrived in the capital and first managed, through Empress Lu, to prevent the emperor from sending his eldest son into a battle that he would not have survived. The emperor himself led the army instead and returned victorious. Still determined to disinherit his eldest son, the emperor attended a banquet where the heir apparent waited on his father, accompanied by the Mount Shang recluses. The four men, who then were more than eighty years old, already had refused to serve Gaozu because of his arrogance.

The emperor, who did not recognize the scholars, inquired about their identity. They introduced themselves and explained that although they had declined to serve him, they had been induced to leave their mountain retreat by his eldest son's reputation for benevolence, filial piety, reverence, and respect for scholars. Their presence and counsel quickly convinced the emperor that the mandate of heaven was with the Empress Lu's son, so he summoned Madame Qi and informed her, "I had hoped to change the heir apparent, but these four men have come to his aid. Like a pair of great wings they have borne him aloft where we cannot reach him. Empress Lu is your real master now!"[3]

Ma Yuan was a resident of the Southern Song capital, Lin-an (modern Hangzhou), and served in the Imperial Painting Academy, as had members of three previous generations of his family. Little is known of his life — when he was born, when he retired, or when he died — except that he was active in the Academy under the emperors Guangzong (r. 1190–1194), Ningzong (r. 1195–1224), and into the reign of Lizong (r. 1225–1264).

The theme of the introspective scholar recurs often in Ma Yuan's paintings. He produced exquisite fans and album leaves depicting a single scholar in the mountains: watching deer,[4] drinking by moonlight,[5] viewing a waterfall,[6] or gazing at plum blossoms. Each has a lyrical, poetic quality; indeed, many originally were accompanied by poetry. Ma's paintings of scholars show them engaged in leisurely pursuits that are metaphors for neo-Confucian self-cultivation. In the Museum's painting, Ma shows the four recluses playing chess and gathering mushrooms. This painting seems to illustrate a song about purple mushrooms recorded in the *Gaoshi zhuan [Biographies of Recluses]* that came to be identified with the scholar Luli, who purportedly sang it after he fled to Shangshan:

> Silent is the lofty mountain;
>> Long is the deep valley.
> Bright are purple mushrooms;
>> They can still my hunger.
> The ages of [the emperors] Yao and Shun are gone forever;
>> Whither shall I go?
> A carriage and four, and lofty roofs,
>> All bring great worries [to the inmates].
> If riches and honors entail submission to others,
>> I would rather be poor and lowly in order to live happily.[7]

Ma Yuan depicts the long valley as a straight channel that cuts diagonally from left to right across the painting. The turbulent water must have been inspired by a geographic feature well known to the artist: the Qiantang tidal bore, a high wave front that occurs where the mouth of the Qiantang River meets the Eastern Sea, in the southern area of Hangzhou. Around the time of the autumn equinox the waves could reach a height of 12 meters as they passed through the river narrows. Large crowds gathered annually along the riverbank to view the spectacle by moonlight, and the bore became a frequent subject of paintings, poetry, and legend.[8]

The water symbolizes political turmoil, and at the same time buffers the scholars from the world outside their retreat. Ni Zan, in his colophon following the painting (see entry 27d), compares the waves to the Wuling torrent, the famous gateway to paradise in Tao Qian's (365–427) story of utopia, the *Peach Blossom Spring*. The Shangshan retreat was also a Daoist paradise; the scholars who lived there ate only purple mushrooms, which were a favorite ingredient in Daoist elixirs of immortality. The retreat also suggests Confucian morality and responsibility for upright governance. As evidenced by the numerous colophons following the painting, it had important instructional value for scholar-officials serving in China's civil service in the Yuan and early Ming periods.

The painting is signed with *chen*, meaning "your servitor," preceding the artist's name. This indicates that Ma Yuan intended it for the emperor, although it is not known which one, for Ma Yuan served under three emperors. The subject, in view of the problems of succession to the throne in the late twelfth and early thirteenth centuries, suggests that this is a work of Ma's late career. The Emperor Guangzong reigned only from 1189 to 1194 when he was deposed because of mental illness. Ningzong (r. 1195–1224) died without an heir; his successor Lizong (r. 1225–1264), with the aid of Ningzong's empress Yang Meizi (1162–1232), came to power as the result of a palace coup. In an effort to legitimize his rule, Lizong embraced the Neo-Confucian philosopher Zhu Xi's school of Dao and the concept of an orthodox lineage that traced its roots from the ancient sage kings Yao and Shun, the philosophers Confucius and Mencius, and the Northern Song Neo-Confucianists. Lizong appointed scholars of this school to his government and adopted its tenets as the official philosophy of the state.[9]

Elements of the story of the Shangshan four have connections with Lizong's rise to power: the role of the empress in the succession; the reference in the purple mushroom song to the sages' philosophy, descended from that of Yao and Shun; and the attempt to persuade lofty men of principle to serve the emperor and thus endorse the legitimacy of the succession. These political circumstances suggest that the painting probably was made for Lizong; thus a date of around 1225 is proposed. In addition, the painting, which was produced with a blunt brush, appears to be the work of a mature artist.

This scroll once was owned by the noted Ming-dynasty collector Xiang Yuanbian (1525–1590); the scroll displays 100 of his seals throughout. A letter from Wen Zhengming's (1470–1559) elder son, Wen Peng (1498–1573), who advised Xiang on matters of authenticity, price, and sources, seems to refer to this painting:

> It is very rare for Ma Yuan to paint on paper. If it were painted on silk, the brushwork would be more powerful. The figures seem to have not been painted by Zhang Guan[10] The signature, "Painted by your servant Ma Yuan," is very good, and a forger could not write like that. Also it is wonderful to have many colophons by famous people.[11]

One possible explanation for the relative sketchiness of the painting, as well as its having been done on paper, is that it was a *gaoben*, or preliminary compositional design, presented for approval to the emperor (or to whomever the emperor granted authority to officially approve paintings) before the completion of a formal, polished painting on silk.[12] This may also explain the lack of any colophon or seal of the Song emperor on the scroll. Ma Yuan seems to have painted several versions of this subject,[13] but if a formal version of the Cincinnati painting was ever completed by the artist, it has not survived.

The painting later entered the Qing imperial collection, where it remained until the early twentieth century. It is listed in Qianlong's painting catalogs and still has its Qianlong-period inscribed imperial silk wrapper and jade clasp. Two inscriptions by the emperor Qianlong (r. 1736–1795) are written directly on the painting. A later version in handscroll format, which follows the composition of the Museum's painting, was in a private collection in California.[14]

Artist's Signature:
  chen Ma Yuan

Collectors' Seals:
  Xiang Yuanbian (1525–1590); Wang Du; Bian Yongyu (1645–1702); Qianlong (r. 1736–1795); Jiaqing (r. 1796–1820); Xuantong (r. 1907–1911); Chu Jinsheng; Tan Jing (twentieth century); and others, unidentified.

Colophons

Colophons and Seals:
  On painting: Qianlong (r. 1736–1795), two colophons, dated 1754, with two seals, and 1765, two seals; following the painting: Yang Weizhen (1296–1370), three seals; Lu Juren (?–after 1377), three seals; Jiang Jian, one seal; Xie Jun, one seal; Han Jiang Ju Shi; Qian Nai, two seals; Zhao Ji, one seal; Jiao An, one seal; Qing Yang Zi; Gao Yuan; Wu Zhe, two seals; Peng Haogu; Zhu Jing, four seals; Yu Zhong, two seals; Zhou Jihan, two seals; Qing Chu, two seals; Chen Wendong; Ju Mian, three seals; Qian Weishan; Chen Di, one seal; Wang Feng (1319–1388), five seals; Ni Zan (1301–1374), dated 1371; Zhang Shouzhong (16th century); Cheng Yu, one seal; Zheng Pan, one seal; Zhang Jun, two seals; Chen Wendong, four seals; Guan Ne, one seal; Jin Jianli; Zhu Fu, dated 1370, four seals; Gao Wanjie; Yuan Kai; Fan Gongliang, five seals; Cao Zongru, one seal; Yu Jiyue; Hu Yen (1361–1443), dated 1392, three seals; Gu Lu, one seal.

Thirty-seven colophons, either prose or poems by men of letters of the Yuan and Ming dynasties, follow the painting and apparently had been added by the time the scroll entered Xiang Yuanbian's collection. (See complete list of colophons above.) Most of the writers came from the Yunjian or Songjiang area (between Shanghai and the border of Jiangsu and Zhejiang provinces). Among the colophons, three are dated: no. 30, by Zhu Fu, dated 1370; no. 22, by Ni Zan (1301–1374), dated 1371; and no. 37, by Hu Yen (1361–1443), dated 1392. Thus the colophons by the Yuan scholars must have been written during 1370 and 1371.[15]

Special gatherings of poets, painters, scholars, or officials were often organized for the purpose of viewing a private art collection. On such occasions, guests were invited to write down their thoughts, feelings, or comments about the subject of a particular painting or about the artist and the quality of brushwork. The writing of such commentaries, known as *colophons*, is a tradition that began around the seventh century. On handscrolls, colophons sometimes were inscribed on the painting itself; usually, however, they were written on a separate piece of paper that was added to the painting when it was mounted. On hanging scrolls, colophons frequently appear on the painting or its mounting. Comments included in an album are usually found on the page opposite the painting, although occasionally they appear on the painting itself.

Often the author of a colophon is an accomplished calligrapher. Thus colophons, in addition to their historical or documentary significance, can be appreciated as works of art in their own right. Four exceptionally fine colophons are illustrated and discussed here. All four calligraphers, Yang Weizhen (1296–1370), Lu Juren (?–after 1377), Ni Zan (1301–1374) and Wang Feng (1319–1388), were contemporaries and members of the same circles of literati. Some were close friends and colleagues. Yang Weizhen, Lu Juren, and Qian Weishan (?–1368), author of colophon no. 19, were intimate friends; often they composed poems together, and after their deaths they were buried in the same vicinity.

Wang Feng, although a generation younger, was also a close friend of Yang Weizhen and the Yuan-dynasty master painter Huang Gongwang (1269–1354). A rare painting by Huang, *Nine Pearl-Like Verdant Peaks*, is in the collection of the National Palace Museum, Taipei. Made for Yang Weizhen in 1347, it illustrates the relationship of the three friends. Yang inscribed a poem on the upper middle surface of the painting, just above the mountains. Sometime in the 1360s, Yang asked Wang Feng to write a poem on the upper right-hand side of the painting. After the poem Wang wrote: "Inscribed by Wang Feng of Wuxi for Caoxuan Daoren on a painting by the noted teacher Dachi." Yang used the name Caoxuan Daoren after he finished building his studio, Caoxuan Hall, in the spring of 1363. Dachi is the *hao* of Huang Gongwang.[16] Therefore Wang Feng's colophon on the painting is historical as well as documentary.

There may originally have been a colophon by Yang Zai (1271–1323) following the Museum's painting, but it was not recorded in the catalogs of Wang Koyu, Yu Fengqing, or Bian Yongyu that mention the Museum's painting, and it was considered lost by the time the scroll entered the Qing imperial collection. The colophons by Lu Juren (see entry 27b) and Ni Zan (see entry 27d) claim to follow Yang Zai's rhyme scheme, and the colophons by Qian Nai and Zhu Jing both refer to two Yangs (Yang Zai and Yang Weizhen). Qianlong, in his first colophon on the painting, accepted the explanation of the editors of the *Shiqu Baoji* that the missing colophon had been cut out.[17] A poem entitled "On the Wind-screen Depicting the Four Old Men of Shangshan," is preserved in Yang Zai's collected works:

> Flying snow-flakes sprinkle the wide terrain
> > Angry waves surge on an expanse without banks
> Amidst coiled hills and vales
> > There dwelt these four old men
> They were preceptors of the people
> > They were guests of the imperial house
> Wide went their cool breezes [i.e. lofty influences]
> > My mind longs for the desolate banks[18]

The subject of the four Shangshan recluses would have been a particularly poignant allegory for late Yuan dynasty scholars, whose political situation in many ways paralleled that of the Qin-Han transition. The first Ming emperor, Hongwu (r. 1368–1399), after the final defeat of the Mongols and the restoration of the country to Chinese rule, encouraged many disaffected Yuan officials to return to public life. However, perhaps because of his peasant background, Hongwu soon began to display an innate distrust of intellectuals. Many of the literati, who joined the new government in the belief that it represented a return to Confucian tradition, ultimately came to tragic ends: Many were purged as suspected traitors. Thus the commentary that follows the Shangshan story includes some criticism, for although the recluses, convinced that they should defend the rightful heir, had lofty motivations, their visit to the em-

peror ultimately played into the hands of the conniving duke and the Empress Lu, who eventually usurped the throne.

— NLYS and EA

27a. Poem by Yang Weizhen (1296–1370)

High was Shangshan,
and up there grew purple mushrooms.
By picking the mushrooms they could still their hunger
Why should the ferns of the Western Hill be exclusively favored?
The Hegemon of the West [Wen-wang] took good care of the
aged in his domain, but that was a long time ago;
The lawless tyrant [Qin Shihuangdi] killed literati, under
whom should they find protection?
The son of the Liu clan [Liu Pang, the emperor Gaozu of Han]
came to lord over the empire;
What did his persuasion and threat avail him?
In their scheme of life they did not know that fellow from Xiapi;
And so they became willing to betake themselves to the heir-
apparent's palace of Han [as frivolously] as if it were child's play.
Nobody seems to know Mr. Lu li or Qi li.[19]

Yang Weizhen (1296–1370),[20] from Guiji [modern Shaoxing], Zhejiang province, was an accomplished historian and painter, but he made his greatest contributions as poet and calligrapher. He earned his *jinshi* degree in 1327[21] and thereafter held minor civil service positions. In 1359 he moved from his home in Zhejiang province to the Songjiang area, where he lived until his death in June 1370. As leader of the Songjiang school of poetry, Yang had many followers, whose free style came to be known as *tieyai*, after Yang's *hao*. He revived the *yuefu* tradition of the Tang poet Li Bo (701–762).

An innovative calligrapher, Yang developed one of the most distinguished individualistic styles since the time of Huang Tingjian (1045–1105). Yang's eccentric, boldly expressive calligraphic style was not well received by many of his contemporaries, who preferred the conservative elegance associated with Zhao Mengfu (1254–1322).

Two examples of Yang Weizhen's calligraphy from the 1340s reveal the roots of his discipline. His earliest known work is a colophon datable to 1344 written in both regular and running scripts on the painting *Spring Landscape*, by Ma Wan (ca. 1310–1378), dated December 12, 1343.[22] This colophon shows that Yang looked to the rubbings of Northern Wei steles such as *Niu Jue xiao-xiang ji*, dated 495, as his models. Sharp, chisel-edged brushstrokes that seem to penetrate the surface of the paper, especially apparent in the right diagonal strokes with their knifelike silhouettes, exemplify the Northern Wei influence. A poem and calligraphy by Yang on Huang Gongwang's painting *Nine Pearl-Like Verdant Peaks*, mentioned above, was executed in cursive script when he was fifty years old. This script shows the influence of the elegant cursive of Wang Xizhi (303–361), especially as seen in his *Ji sheng jiao xu*.

Among Yang Weizhen's twenty or so extant calligraphies, seven are dated from 1360 to 1369, during his residence in the Songjiang area. There his rather indulgent lifestyle earned him a reputation for eccentricity and arrogance.[23] Many of his undated works show a stylistic maturity similar to those dated works produced in Songjiang during his late years.

Yang Weizhen's brushstrokes generally begin with the sharp point of an exposed brush tip; often the beginning of the stroke looks like the silhouette of a nailhead. Although Yang also used the center part of his brush, more often he preferred the folding tip.[24] This resulted in a chiseled appearance reminiscent of Northern Wei stone steles, as if the ink strokes could penetrate through the paper. Using the same brush, Yang could create strokes ranging from a single hair's width to more than ¾ inch wide, which he accomplished by laying down the whole brush sideways. He could make ink rich and heavy, or "flying-white" to extremely dry, by rubbing the brush forcefully on the surface of the paper. The sizes of the characters vary from medium to very large; often one large character occupies as much space as three columns of medium-sized characters. Although Yang's strokes are expressive, they remain structurally sound. On the whole, his calligraphy has the animation of a battlefield filled with moving blades. These features are illustrated in his colophon, dated 1361, after Zou Fulei's handscroll painting "A Breath of Spring" in the collection of the Freer Gallery of Art.[25]

Yang's medium-sized characters usually were written in rich ink; often, in a particular character, he extended the last vertical strokes to a taillike long stroke that occupied a space of four or five characters vertically. An example appears on his *Running Script* album, dated 1363, in the collection of the Shanghai Museum.

The poem following Ma Yuan's painting was written with rich ink in a relaxed, beautiful manner. The chisel-stroke effect is subtly present, but without the animated battling; there is only the beauty of lines and rich ink. This is undoubtedly one of his great masterpieces on the medium scale. Although Yang did not date his poem, he signed it "Old man of holding tradition *[baoyi laoren]* from Guiji, Yang Weizhen inscribed at Caoxuan Hall in Yunjian (Songjiang)." Yang wrote this shortly before his death in June 1370, sometime before the colophon by his close friend Lu Juren, which is datable 1370 or 1371. (See entry below.)

A few of his paintings, though amateurish, are still extant, such as *Wintry Pine* and *Spring Mountains* in the collection of the National Palace Museum, Taipei.

— NLYS

27b. Four poems by Lu Juren (?–after 1377)

1. With their cool breezes *[lofty influences]* they formed wings for the Han;
    [The wings] extending to the shores of four seas.
    Feeding on mushrooms, they refused to take emoluments;
      For a thousand years they have been admired.
    Unrolling the painting I see the grey eyebrows;
      I burst out in laughter, forgetting my role as host.
    Far away is the mountain of Lantian [Shangshan];
      Desolate is the water-margin dotted with pines.

2. Long is the valley of Shangshan;
      There hover dense clouds without bounds.
    There dwell mushroom-picking gray-heads

    More exalted in fame than those who planted peach trees.
    When they came out of retirement, it was in order to rectify the Han line;
      Yet the Son of Heaven could not make subjects of them.
    Let's laugh at the expense of the old man who "cleansed his ear,"
      For it was to no purpose that he grew old on the bank of Ji.

3. In the Han palace a woman was made into a pig;
      At the foot of Lishan the female pheasant is crowing.
    Who could have averted this calamity?
      The men of Lantian.
    They were generous enough to respond to the summons [of Empress Lu]
      accompanied with jewels and silk;
    But the whole scheme was hatched by the inmate of the tent
      [Zhang Liang].
    Unrolling the scroll I heave three long sighs,
      While cool breezes are rising on the river bank.

4. The corvée imposed by the Qin was fiercer than tigers;
      Yet there always was a way out if one could flee.
    Corvée nowadays is all-pervading, even over hills and in swamps;
      There's none can escape it.
    There being no Lu Zhonglian these days,
      The Eastern Sea has no one to welcome a visitor.
    Let me go and find friendly seagulls,
      With whom I shall live on the coast of Canglang.[26]

Lu Juren (?–after 1377),[27] from Shanghai, Songjiang, Jiangsu province, became a *juren* in his native area, in 1326, but chose to teach rather than join the civil service. A poet and close friend of Yang Weizhen, Lu was a leading calligrapher of the Songjiang school and was known for his running and cursive script. His calligraphic styles derive from Wang Xizhi (ca. 303–ca. 361).

Two calligraphies known to be the work of Lu Juren are dated 1371. One of these, inscribed in the late spring, is a poem colophon after a calligraphy handscroll by Xianyu Shu (ca. 1257–1302) now in the collection of the Shanghai Museum.[28] Here Lu's calligraphy shows such strong influence from Xianyu Shu[29] that stylistically it is nearly identical to Xian's bold and powerful strokes. However, it exhibits Lu's own slightly softer touch; few of the characters have long, taillike strokes.

The other 1371 calligraphy is a poem executed in late December, the "Water from Tiao River" handscroll in the collection of Palace Museum, Beijing. This poem bears Lu's signature: "Old Man of Yun-Song." Many aspects of "Water from Tiao River" also appear in Lu's colophon following the Ma Yuan handscroll: the free and fluid cursive script produced with a soft-fur brush in ink that ranges from wet to dry, and the execution of some characters with long, taillike strokes. These similarities argue that Lu wrote his four poems here at about the same time, in 1370, as Yang Weizhen wrote his colophon. Stylistically, both calligraphies seem to be influenced strongly by the Tang-dynasty cursive script of master and monk Huaisu (ca. 735–ca. 799), particularly his small cursive script "Thousand-Character Essay."[30]

— NLYS

27c. Poem by Wang Feng (1319–1388)

Five-colored clouds and nine-stalked mushrooms [are to be
on Mount Shang];
Ten thousand years and Heaven and Earth are a game of chess.
The Han emperor having fallen into Zhang Liang's calculation,
They [the four old men] were willing to climb down the mountain
to remonstrate with him [the emperor].[31]

In Jiangyin, Jiangsu province, Wang Feng's career in the civil service spanned 26 years. In 1367 he retired to Wujin, near Shanghai. There he built a house, named himself *Zuixian yuandin* ("the most unoccupied gardener"), and wrote poetry.

During his later years, while living in Songjiang, Wang was the youngest of a group of friends that included such literati as Zhu Deren (1294–1365), Yang Weizhen (1296–1370), and Huang Gongwang (1269–1354). Wang said theirs was a "friendship that forgets their ages."

There are only a few known calligraphies by Wang Feng. One is a colophon on Huang Gongwang's painting *Nine Pearl-Like Verdant Peaks*, composed for Yang Weizhen and perhaps produced in the 1360s, when Wang was in his forties.[32] Wang also wrote a poem on Zhu Deren's painting "Playing the *Chin* under a Tree," in the collection of the National Palace Museum, Taipei. A third poem appears on an album leaf, "Groom and Horse" by Zhao Mengfu (1254–1322), on loan to The Art Museum, Princeton University.[33] The style of all three poem calligraphies by Wang Feng derive from Wang Xizhi; their characters are tightly written, with sharp-edged strokes. All seem to come from a young hand and a fresh mind.

The poem by Wang Feng on Ma Yuan's painting is executed loosely and expressively in an elongated, slightly clumsy cursive script. Although it is not dated, Wang Feng probably wrote it in 1370 or 1371, when he was in his early fifties. His calligraphy here demonstrates a more mature style.

— NLYS

27d. Poem by Ni Zan (1301–1374)

In the original rhyme of the Biejia Yang [Yang Zai]

The greyheads of Shangshan
Pervade the Eight Extremities [of the universe] with their cool breeze.
The consolidation of the foundation of the Han
Owes to these subjects of the bygone Qin dynasty.
High ranks they did not covet;
Tall pines were their companions.
There are also the men who planted peach trees
On the banks of the torrent of Wuling.[34]

Ni Zan (1301–1374), from Wuxi, Jiangsu province, was a gentleman scholar from one of the few well-to-do families in Wuxi. Because of his inherited wealth he led a fairly comfortable life, devoting his time to poetry, painting, and calligraphy. He is known as one of the four great painting masters of the Yuan dynasty.

Many of Ni Zan's paintings and calligraphies are dated. Ni's calligraphy is based primarily on that of Zhung Yu (151–230), the founder of regular script, with a strong influence from Han-dynasty clerical script. Most of Ni's calligraphic works are executed in small regular script, with distinctively thin, dry strokes. The stroke *na*, the right-hand descending diagonal, always extends longer than the others and ends with the silhouette of a sharp knife, which is quite expressive. Other strokes "begin with sharp exposed heads and end with a firm emphasis giving his lines a tensile style quality."[35] The squarish form characteristic of Ni's script in the 1360s becomes slightly squat in the 1370s, as seen in his works in the collection of National Palace Museum, Taipei,[36] and shows greater firmness and power. Cincinnati's colophon by Ni Zan, dated 1371, exhibits the same mature qualities.[37]

— NLYS

Recent Provenance:
   C.T. Loo

Published:
   Archives of the Chinese Art Society of America, 5 (1950), p. 71.
   Avril, "Highlights," pp. 70–71.
   Bian, *Shigutang shuhua huikao*, chapter 14, fol. 50b–54b.
   Cahill, "Ch'ien Hsuan and His Figure Paintings," p. 24.
   Cahill, *Index*, p. 159.
   Cincinnati Art Museum Bulletin (March 1953), p. 14.
   Edwards, "Sophistications," pp. 86–87.
   Moore, *Eastern Gate*, pp. 53–55.
   Munsterberg, "Collection of Chinese Paintings," pp. 307–09, 311.
   Nakata and Fu, *Masterpieces*, nos. 12–17.
   Shiqu Baoji [1745], vol. 16, chapter 14, fol. 71a–86b.
   Sirén, *Chinese Painting*, 2: p. 76.
   Suzuki, *Comprehensive Illustrated Catalog*, 1: no. A24–001.
   Wang, *Shan-hu-wang hua-lu*, chapter 5, fol. 7b–11a.
   Yu, *Yu Shi shuhua tibaji*, chapter 2, fol. 3b–6a.

Notes:
   1. There are differing views of which emperor's unworthiness prompted the Four Sages into seclusion. Sima Qian's account indicates that they retired in protest to Han Gaozu's treatment of scholars. Ban Gu's biography of Zhang Liang, while following Sima Qian's account, also asserts that they retreated into the mountains to escape government service under the Qin dynasty (221–206 B.C.) and its first emperor Qin Shihuangdi, a ruthless tyrant and notorious persecutor of Confucian literati. Later writers' opinions varied as well. See Vervoorn, *Men of the Cliffs*, pp. 96–100.
   2. *Records of the Grand Historian*, pp. 145–49.
   3. *Records of the Grand Historian*, p. 149.
   4. Album leaf in the Cleveland Museum of Art; see *Eight Dynasties*, no. 52; also Barnhart, *Along the Border*, fig. 31.
   5. *Eight Dynasties*, no. 53.
   6. Barnhart, *Along the Border*, fig. 32; also see Fong, *Beyond Representation*, pl. 51.
   7. trans. Achilles Fang, from the *Gaoshi zhuan* [Biographies of Recluses] in Fang, "Some Observations."
   8. Allee, "The Qiantang Tidal Bore," pp. 61–68.
   9. See Fong, *Beyond Representation*, pp. 233–35, 247.
   10. Zhang Guan was a painter from Songjiang who was active at the end of the Yuan and the beginning of the Ming dynasties. He followed in Ma Yuan's style.
   11. Wong, "Hsiang Yuan-pien and Suchou Artists," p. 156.
   12. I am grateful to Richard Barnhart for pointing out evidence of this practice, especially the first colophon following Xia Gui's "Pure and Remote Views of Streams and Mountains," a long handscroll on paper in the National Palace Museum, Taipei, in which the painting is refered to as a *gaoben*. Cahill refers to the Cincinnati painting, in his discussion of Xia Gui's handscroll, as an example of looser style

brushwork on paper practiced by Southern Song Academy painters; see Cahill, "The Imperial Painting Academy," p. 191.

13. Fang, "Some Observations," notes two paintings in addition to the Cincinnati scroll: a hanging scroll recorded in *Yuxueluo shuhua lu*; and a painting depicting three of the four old men standing and one gazing up at the sky, on which Wu Hai (early Ming) wrote a colophon recorded in his collected works *Wenguozhai ji* and quoted in *Nan Song Yuan hualu*, chapter 7, fol. 18b. It is not clear whether Yang Zai's (1271–1323) poem, "On the Windscreen Depicting the Four Old Men of Shangshan," purportedly a colophon once attached to the Museum's painting (see discussion of colophons), refers to the Cincinnati painting, or to another painting.

14. Present whereabouts are unknown. A photograph is in the Cincinnati Art Museum curatorial files.

15. See Nakata and Fu, *Masterpieces*, p. 142.

16. For more detailed information about this painting, see Chang, *Four Great Masters*, pp. 42–44.

17. Fang, "Some Observations."

18. trans. Fang, "Some Observations."

19. trans. Fang, "Some Observations."

20. Tzu: Lianfu. Hao: Tieyai, Tie Di Zi, Dong Wei Zi, Baoyiso, Bao Yi Laoren, Caoxuan Daoren, and five more.

21. From the seal at the top of the row just to the left of the colophon, which reads, "li fu bang di er jia jin shi," indicating the year when he received his *jinshi*.

22. Collection of the Princeton University Museum of Art. Publ. Fu, *Studies in Connoisseurship*, 73/I, 83/I.

23. Cheng, "The Calligraphy Art," no. 5, p. 59. Also, Nakata and Fu, *Masterpieces*, p. 129.

24. See Ecke, *Chinese Calligraphy*, figs. 9a, 9b, 9c.

25. Nakata and Fu, *Masterpieces*, nos. 6–11.

26. trans. Fang, "Some Observations."

27. zi: Zhezhi, Zhao song weng, Yun song ye he

28. See *Shanghai Museum*, 1, pls. 86–89.

29. See Fu, *Traces*, p. 102.

30. Monk Huai-su is one of the few masters of cursive script, a simpler form of Chinese writing. His styles have been models for later generations. Usually, all the horizontal and vertical strokes in a character are connected together and simplified as curved lines. Often characters with many strokes can be written as one or two lines, finished in an expressive way. Sometimes two or three characters can be finished in one long cursive line. As a result, cursive script is difficult to read and appears to be abstract.

31. trans. Fang, "Some Observations."

32. See Chang, *Four Great Masters*, p. 43.

33. Reproduced in Nakata and Fu, *Masterpieces*, no. 41.

34. trans. Fang, "Some Observations."

35. Fu, *Traces*, p. 142.

36. Chang, *Four Great Masters*, pls. 308–17.

37. Chang, *Four Great Masters*, pl. 309; Fu, *Traces*, p. 172, pl. 25a.

28. Sima Yu's Dream of the Courtesan Su Xiaoxiao

Liu Yuan (active 13th century). Jin dynasty, early 13th century.
Handscroll; ink and colors on silk. H. 29.2 x L. 73.6 cm.
John J. Emery Endowment and Fanny Bryce Lehmer Endowment, 1948.79

On the veranda of his study, a scholar and his servant are asleep. The scholar, dressed in official robes and still wearing his cap, reclines sideways in a yokeback chair, his right foot on the footrest, his left leg relaxed on the chair seat, and his arms draped across the back rail of the chair to cradle his head. The servant, leaning against a large jar on the floor, sleeps face down, his head resting on his knees. The severely cropped architectural setting shows a desk and a candle stand next to a column. To the left, a woman wearing a loose-fitting garment and long scarves emerges from thick mist. She carries a wooden clapper and approaches the mottled stone steps of the scholar's quiet study.

This handscroll illustrates a scene from the love story of the Northern Song scholar Sima Yu and the spirit of the fifth-century poet Su Xiaoxiao. A renowned singer in Qiantang (modern Hangzhou), Su was one of China's legendary beauties, second only to the Tang-dynasty imperial consort Yang Guifei. The site of Su's tomb, at the base of Xiling bridge, is one of the most famous places along Hangzhou's serene West Lake.

Su's best-known poem concerns an isolated woman yearning for a roaming, indifferent lover:

I ride in a red painted carriage.
You pass me on a blue-dappled horse.
Where shall we bind our hearts
In a love knot?
Along Xiling Lake under the cypress trees.[1]

Su Xiaoxiao died young. According to popular legend, on stormy nights one could hear wistful songs issuing from her grave. As the subject of works by Tang poets such as Li Shen (780–846) and Li He (790–816),[2] she represents a consuming passion that persists even in death.

The earliest written account of Su Xiaoxiao's encounter with Sima Yu (active late eleventh century), protégé of the scholar-official artist and poet Su Shi (1037–1101) and grandnephew of the philosopher Sima Guang (1019–1086), is found in the *Chunzhu Jiwen [Hearsay at the Spring Sandbank]*, an eleventh-century compilation of miscellaneous anecdotes. The plot was adapted in the Yuan dynasty (1279–1368) for a musical suite titled "Song of the Golden Threads."[3]

The Museum's painting illustrates an episode that takes place in Luoyang, where the singer appears to the young scholar in a dream. Adorned with billowing scarves signifying that she is a spirit, the melancholy Su Xiaoxiao, wreathed in mist and clouds, floats on a breeze that gently disturbs the flame of a candle beside the desk. Holding a wooden clapper in her right hand and employing the theatrical gesture of lifting her left sleeve to conceal her mouth, she sings "Golden Threads":

I used to live by the Qiantang River.
Flowers fall, flowers bloom,
Without regard for the passing of years.
The swallows are taking with them the colors of spring.
At the gauze window — how many bouts of yellow plum rain?

At the completion of her song, the courtesan foretells a future rendezvous with the scholar and then disappears. Later Sima Yu, with the encouragement of his mentor Su Shi, sits for a special examination, passes it with honors, and is posted to Qiantang[Hangzhou]. There, behind his official residence, is the grave of Su Xiaoxiao.

Sima's colleague Qin Shaozhang, the police chief of Qiantang, added a second stanza to the courtesan's song:

The horn comb is set at an angle in her hair, which is so like
    half-rising clouds,
Lightly marking time with her sandalwood clapper,
She pours her soul into the song of "Golden Threads."
The dream ends, colored clouds are nowhere to be found.
In the coolness of the night, the moon rises on the spring riverbank.

The story ends with the rendezvous of the two lovers on a boat. As the boatman approaches to greet them, fire breaks out. Fleeing to report the disaster, the boatman encounters family members already grieving the scholar's death.[4]

Shortly after Sima Yu arrived in Qiantang, he died in a boating accident under mysterious circumstances. In the legend surrounding him he is lured to another world by the dream, a device often employed in Chinese literature and painting for the interaction of spirits with mortals. That Sima Yu himself indulged in writing palace love poetry, at least according to one version of the story, made him all the more susceptible to the enticements of a courtesan poet's spirit.[5]

In the Museum's painting, the artist Liu Yuan conveys a subtle eroticism reminiscent of that employed in palace love poetry.[6] The union of the two lovers is expressed metaphorically by the gentle breeze on which the courtesan wafts into the scholar's chamber. Its effects pervade the scene, fluttering the singer's loose-fitting, diaphanous silk garment and scarves, sensuously tousling her hair, unsettling the candle flame, and rustling the long tassels of the scholar's hat. The intimacy of the scene is enriched by the careful attention to details of the studio interior, such as the patterned stone of the veranda, the inkstone, scroll, and ornamented sword on the scholar's desk, and the lovers' garments made of similar dotted silk.

What is known about Liu Yuan's life is based on information provided in the inscription on the Cincinnati painting, which is the artist's sole extant work. It is signed *Santang Wang menren zhiying si Pingshui Liu Yuan zhi* [made by Liu Yuan of Pingshui, in the Crafts Office, a disciple of Wang of the Three Studios] with one seal of the artist [Pingshui Liu Yuan]. Liu Yuan was a student of the portrait painter Santang Wang and came from Pingshui, a district in the Pingyang area of southern Shanxi province.[7] Liu was a painter under the Jin, as corroborated by the fact that by 1266 Pingshui was no longer called by that name, and that Liu served in the Zhi Yingsi [Crafts Office], which was established in 1196 by the merging of the Tu Hua Shu [Office for Painting] and the Wensi Shu [Office of Ornamentation]. The Zhi Yingsi remained as part of the Yuan imperial palace establishment (i.e. after 1260) and was responsible for providing skilled carpentry, silk embroidery, painting, scroll mounting, and other such services.[8]

The late Jin rulers' admiration for Northern Song literati culture is reflected in both the subject and the style of Liu Yuan's painting.[9] Bush suggests that such a romance would have appealed to the growing scholar class in the late Jin as the numbers of *jinshi* degree graduates increased. While illustrating the love affair between a Chinese scholar official and a singing girl would not have been considered an appropriate subject for a court painting in the early Jin period, by the end of the Jin moral standards had loosened somewhat and the court was more strongly influenced by popular culture.[10]

Artist's Seal:
    Pingshui Liu Yuan

Collectors' Seals:
    One seal undecipherable; two seals unidentified; Yang Zhongying; Liu Ting; Chang Ts'ung-yu (1915–63).

Colophons and seals:
    Yang Zhongying, two seals; Chang Ts'ung-yu (1915–63), four seals.

Recent Provenance:
    Chang Ts'ung-Yu; C. T. Loo

Published:
    Avril, "Highlights," pp. 70–71.
    Bush, "Five Paintings," pp. 196–202.
    Cahill, *Index*, p. 304.
    Cheng, *Wei-ta-ti*, 2: pl. 2.
    Cheng, *Yun-hui-chai-ts'ang*, pl. 6.
    Edwards, "Sophistications," p. 87.
    Handler, "Yokeback Chair," pp. 12–13.
    Lee and Ho, *Chinese Art under the Mongols*, no. 199.
    Li, "Dream Visions," pp. 69–72.
    Munsterberg, "Collection of Chinese Paintings," p. 313.
    Suzuki, *Comprehensive Illustrated Catalog*, 1: no. A24–003.
    Tausend Jahre Chinesische Malerei, no. 26.
    Wang, *Exhibition of Authenticated Chinese Paintings*, no. 3.

Exhibited:
    "Exhibition of Authenticated Chinese Paintings," C. T. Loo and Co., New York, 1948.
    "One Thousand Years of Chinese Paintings," Haus der Kunst, Munich, 1959; Zurich, 1960; The Hague, 1960; Cleveland Museum of Art, 1960.
    "Chinese Art under the Mongols," Cleveland Museum of Art, 1968.
    "Art Conservation: The Race against Destruction," Cincinnati Art Museum, 1978.

Notes:
    1. Su Xiao Xiao, "A Song of Xiling Lake," in Rexroth and Ling, *Women Poets*, p. 12. The poem was preserved in the sixth-century anthology of love poetry, *Yutai xinyong*. Also see Birrell, *New Songs*, p. 272.
    2. Li, "Dream Visions," pp. 70–71. Also see, Li He, "The Grave of Su Xiaoxiao," in Graham, *Poems of the Late Tang*, p. 113.
    3. The following is based on a translation of the original story from the *Chunzhu jiwen*, in Lee and Ho, *Chinese Art under the Mongols*, no. 199.
    4. Translations from Li, "Dream Visions," p. 72.
    5. Li, "Dream Visions," p. 72.
    6. For a discussion of the early palace poetry aesthetic, see Birrell, *New Songs*, pp. 1–28.
    7. Bush, "Five Paintings," pp. 198–99.
    8. Hucker, *Dictionary of Official Titles*, nos. 1099, 7350, and 7723; Bush, "Five Paintings," pp. 198–99.

9. See Bush, "Literati Culture"; also Franke, "The Chin Dynasty," pp. 304–13.
10. Bush, "Five Paintings," pp. 199–200.

29. Doves and Pear Blossoms after Rain

Qian Xuan (circa 1235–after 1300). Yuan dynasty, late 13th century. Handscroll; ink and colors on powdered paper. H. 30.5 X L. 97.8 cm. John J. Emery Fund and Fanny Bryce Lehner Endowment, 1948.80

Two doves sit on the limb of a blossoming pear tree,[1] one with its head nestled as if resting, the other alertly leaning over and looking downward. The limb which extends from the lower left-hand side of the painting, is composed of two branches. The shorter branch has a broken end, and clusters of leaves surrounding fully opened blossoms. The longer branch, also with a short, broken end, supports the two birds; emerging from the twigs are five clusters of leaves and flowers in various stages of bloom.

Before the Mongols established the Yuan dynasty in 1279, China was divided into a northern territory, ruled by the Jurchen Jin dynasty, and a southern area under Chinese rule, known as the Southern Song dynasty. Many scholar-officials who had served the Southern Song regime viewed with disdain the reunification of the country under Mongol governance as foreigners gained positions of authority in the imperial court and at the local level. The Southern Song loyalists, known as *yimin* (literally "leftover subjects"), came to terms with their social and political situation in various ways. At the Mongols' invitation, some Chinese scholars accepted civil posts in the new government and had successful careers; others joined the bureaucracy but became disillusioned by Mongol corruption and resigned; still others altogether refused to oblige the foreigners and chose an eremitic life of personal protest.

Qian Xuan, in his forties at the time of the Mongol conquest, was among the most famous of the reclusive group of *yimin* painters who renounced government service to devote themselves to painting and poetry. Qian's loyalty to the Song, as expressed in his paintings, is legendary in the history of Chinese art. Born around 1235, Qian Xuan had earned the *jinshi* degree (awarded upon passing the highest-level civil service examinations) sometime during the Jingding era of the Song (1260–1264).[2] He may never have served in an official post; little is known of his life beyond his association with a group of scholars known as the "Eight Talents of Wuxing." The group was disbanded when another of its renowned members, Zhao Mengfu (1254–1322), accepted a request from Beijing to serve the Yuan emperor Khubilai Khan. In later writings, Qian's decision to remain in Wuxing and devote himself to his art is often contrasted with the actions of Zhao and others as a model of *yimin* allegiance to the Song.

For Qian, painting was an important means of expressing his dissatisfaction with the social and political climate. In this respect Qian was following a tradition that began in earnest in the late eleventh century, when Northern Song scholar-artists such as Su Shi (1037–1101) advocated amateur painting and poetry as vehicles of self-expression for intellectuals. For the scholar-artist, painting and calligraphy were visual imprints of the mind and an outlet for articulating one's most deeply held values. Bird-and-flower painting played an important role in this tradition by tapping a vocabulary of visual and literary metaphors from the natural world that came to symbolize the ideals of the educated elite.

In the Yuan political climate, the Museum's handscroll *Doves and Pear Blossoms after Rain* exemplifies the *yimin* painters' practice of infusing subject matter with allegorical references to the glories of the previous dynasty. In itself, Qian Xuan's choice of this subject for his political protest refers to the former imperial painting academy, where bird-and-flower painting was the most highly regarded genre.[3] A *jue-ju* (truncated verse) poem, written by Qian's contemporary Mou Yen (1227–1311), works in tandem with the painting to express a yearning for the past:

> After the rain ceased
> doves began cooing among the pear blossoms.
> Gathering joyfully in the early hours
> they called for the coming of a clear day.
> Once the sky was clear
> the flowers had already faded.
> Yet the pear trees remain strong and brilliant.[4]

Multiple layers of meaning, drawing from traditional literary and visual symbolism, are interwoven in Qian's painting. The pear tree, an emblem of wise and benevolent administration, refers to the Southern Song regime and the Chinese ideals for which it stood. Doves, endowed with Confucian qualities of faithfulness, impartiality, and filial duty, symbolize the loyalist *yimin*. According to Chinese legend, doves leave their partners in bad weather, then reunite when the skies clear; this instinctive act is a metaphor for the eremitic scholar who would retreat into seclusion and await the restoration of a morally acceptable political climate before serving in an official capacity. When the doves return, they find broken branches and faded flowers, but the tree has survived the storm.

Qian's flat, archaistic treatment of the birds and flowers emphasizes their symbolic function. Even the physical properties of the painting convey the artist's sense of loss. The painting and Mou Yen's poem are executed on *feng jian,* a special powdered paper that softens the images and gives them a slightly faded appearance. Ink and pigments applied to this paper tended to flake.[5] This tendency was well known during the artist's lifetime, so that even the physical condition of the painting may have symbolized the fading glories of the Song government and its aging remnants. Qian seems to have deliberately destroyed his own scholarly writings; perhaps he also intended the self-destruction of his paintings.[6]

Exposure to light also contributed to the faded appearance of the painting; the doves were later partially repainted. The pear blossoms, however, remain unretouched and give us a true sense of the artist's breathtaking delicacy of form, brushwork and subtle coloring.

Forgeries of Qian's paintings proliferated even in his own lifetime. On an excavated handscroll depicting lotus, from the tomb of Prince Zhu Tan, Qian wrote that he was compelled to change his pen name to "make the forgers feel ashamed of themselves." This new signature, *Zha qiweng Qian Xuan Shunju* [*The old man of Zha river, Qian Xuan Shunju*] appears both on the Museum's painting and on a painting of pear blossoms in the Metropolitan Museum of Art. However, because of the demand for Qian's paintings, this attempt to foil the copyists was probably not effective for very long. As soon as clever forgers discovered the change, they surely would have churned out works with the new signature.[7]

This painting was owned by the famous Ming collector Xiang Yuanbian (1525–1590). In addition to dotting the scroll with his numerous seals, Xiang added an inscription at the end that includes his inventory number and the price he paid for the scroll. The price was later rubbed out and can no longer be deciphered.

Artist's Seals:
  Shunzhu; Qian Xuan zhiyin; Hanmoyuxi

Collector's Seals:
  Xiang Yuanbian (1525–1590); Zhang Hao (ca. 1700); Bi Yuan (1730–1797); Bi Long (18th century); Chang Ts'ung-yu (1915–1963); others, unidentified.

Colophons

Colophons and seals:
  On painting: Mou Yen (1227–1311), two seals; following the painting: Ko Jiusi (1312–1365), four seals; Bao Xun (ca. 1300–after 1382), two seals; Qian Liangyu (1278–1344), two seals; Zhang Wenzai, three seals; Sun Hua, three seals; Sun Xin, one seal; Shen Cun, one seal; Sun Xin, one seal; Zhang Tianying, one seal; Lin Fufeng, one seal; Zou Liang, three seals; Qiu Dayu, three seals.

29a. Poem by Ke Jiusi (1290–1343)

Just waking up and still wandering,
  I was attracted by the fresh pear flowers.
The appearance of the tranquil birds on the branch
  is indicative of the arrival of spring.
When it was getting murky in the courtyard,
  they started calling, signaling the coming of rain.
Ah! Ours is a world already full of anxiety and grief,
  but the birds are only beginning to apprehend.[8]

Under the Emperor Wenzong (r. 1328–29; 1332), Ke Jiusi, a painter who specialized in bamboo (as did his contemporary Gu An; see entry 31), held the rank of Office Manager of the Imperial Seals Commission (*dian-rui-yuan du shi*). In 1329 this department became the Kuizhang Ge [Hall of Literature], which provided literary reference service for the emperor (see entry 30).[9] On February 13, 1330, Ke was appointed Master Connoisseur of Calligraphy and became responsible for examining and authenticating calligraphy in the imperial collection.[10] In October of that year, he was censured and impeached by the Yu shi tai [the Censorate] because of purported misconduct.[11] In 1333 he left Beijing and settled in Jiangnan.

From 1330 to 1332, Ke wrote many colophons on paintings and calligraphies, although few of the signatures included dates. He signed many of these colophons with his official title, "Master Connoisseur of Calligraphy."

Ke's regular medium script, as written in the 1330s and 1340s (his later years), shows consistency of style, with only rare exceptions. One such exception is his colophon following "Summer Landscape," a handscroll painting by Dong Yuan of the Five Dynasties, now in the collection of the Liaoning Museum. This colophon dated 1330, is written carefully and elegantly in regular small script. Many of the *na* strokes (right-descending diagonal strokes), which have a wide, sharp, knifelike silhouette, are in the clerical style.[12]

Ke wrote a colophon following the calligraphy by Chu Suiliang (596–658) of the Tang dynasty, "Copy after the Calligraphy Feiniao [Flying Bird] by Wang Xianzhi (344–388)," which was in the imperial collection (and is now in the National Palace Museum, Taipei).[13] Ke signed this colophon "Master Connoisseur of Calligraphy of Kuizhang Pavilion at Scholar Academy." Though the colophon is not dated, Ke must have written it before 1332.

Ke's calligraphy following the Museum's Qian Xuan painting was created at about the same time as the colophon on the Chu calligraphy, and is datable to 1332. These two calligraphies have many similarities: Both show the energetic, exuberant quality in horizontal strokes and in the *na,* as seen in the right-descending diagonal strokes of the characters *da* and *ren.* The horizontal and vertical strokes, beginning with the exposed tip or sharp-edged folding tips, display the confidence of a master with a powerful hand.

Each calligraphy shows four seals of Ke Jiusi after his signature. Three of these seals are identical in the two works, with one exception: The third seal after Chu's calligraphy reads *Jing Zhong shu yin* ("Jing Zhong's calligraphy seal"), but the third seal on Qian Xuan's colophon reads *Yun zheng zhai* ("the Yun Zheng studio").

In contrast to Ke's colophon on the Museum's scroll, his "Palace Poem" in the collection of the Art Museum, Princeton University, exhibits strokes that are less sharp-edged, more subtle, more mellow. Though not dated, it was probably created in the late 1330s or 1340s.

Ke's calligraphy derives from Ouyang Xun (557–641), one of the Tang dynasty masters of *kaishu,* or standard script, whose style emphasized folding tip strokes of rigid structure and sharpness along with vertically elongated regular characters. — NLYS

29b. Poem by Bao Xun (circa 1300–after 1382)

Flowers blossom during the Han Shi Festival,
  and the entire branches are as if coated with snow.
Gentle doves in pairs have been resting there for quite some time.
They look at each other contentedly,
  and gladly there is neither wind nor rain.
They hope they won't have to experience the pains of long separation.[14]

Bao Xun's colophon, the second colophon following the painting, is beautifully written in *kaishu* (standard script). The characters are well balanced. Some of the strokes, such as those in the top two characters in the first and second columns, are thicker than others; the strokes of the third characters are thinner. This alternation of thick and thin strokes contributes to the variety and rhythm of each column. So far, no other calligraphy known to be by Bao Xun exists for comparison. Stylistically, Bao's standard script was influenced by the elegant calligraphy of Zhao Mengfu (1254–1322). This is especially apparent in the turning stroke and the right-descending *na* strokes.[15]

— NLYS

29c. Poem by Qian Liangyu (1278–1344)

A pair of doves stands side by side on the blossoming branch of the tree.
It is not clear whether they are contemplating separation because of bad weather, or have just answered each other's call and have come for reunion under a clear sky.
This painting was done casually following the painter's mood, and is meant only for amusement.
But its results are comparable to that of the late General Wu.
The late General Wu Yuanyu of the Song dynasty learned the painting of birds from Cui Bo. But his styles and skills were not confined to the prevailing school of his time. One of his works, titled "Pear Blossoms and Doves," was treasured by Xuan-ho [Emperor Huizong of the Song dynasty]. Now the author of this painting, Zha Qiweng of my clan, was able to model [himself] after General Wu and attain the same level of achievement. He is truly an extraordinary person of our time.[16]

Qian Liangyu was known for his seal, clerical, standard, running, and cursive scripts. He based his method of calligraphy on Zhao Mengfu's and intensively studied the ancient masters to develop his own style.[17]

In addition to this colophon, there are three other calligraphies from Qian Liangyu's hand: Two are in the National Palace Museum in Taipei. The third, dated 1322, is a poem on an album leaf in the collection of the Tokyo National Museum;[18] it is influenced so strongly by Zhao Mengfu that it could almost be mistaken for the work of Zhao himself. Qian's poem and inscription, which follow Bao Xun's, are written in his more personal, more elegant style. However, they exhibit the influence of *Ji wang sheng jiao xu* by Wang Xizhi (303–361?), compiled by Monk Huairen in 672. Qian's characters are squarish, the individual strokes thin and bony.

Qian Liangyu's seal *Qian shi Yizhi* appears twice, once after his signature and again in the left-hand corner of the painting. Apparently Qian owned the painting at one time and had the colophons mounted together in the 1330s or 1340s.

Zhao Mengfu, the most influential calligrapher of the Yuan dynasty, attempted to revive the styles of the Wei, Jin (317–420) and Tang (618–906) dynasties. Zhao's running script was influenced strongly by Wang Xizhi's *Ji wang sheng jiao xu*, one of his favorite models. Zhao intensively studied and copied this model from a rubbing made from a stele carved in 672. Many of Zhao's contemporaries and followers, including Bao and Qian, followed his ideas and studied early masters; however, their works show a stronger influence from Zhao than from the earlier masters.

— NLYS

Provenance:
   Chang Ts'ung-yu; C. T. Loo
Published:
   Adams, "Random Notes," pp. 11–14.
   Avril, "Highlights," pp. 70–71.
   Cahill, *Index*, p. 269.
   Cheng, *Yun-hui-chai*, pls. 7–9.
   Edwards, "Ch'ien Hsuan and 'Early Autumn,'" pp. 72–73.
   Edwards, "Sophistications," p. 87, fig. 10.
   Fong, "The Problem of Ch'ien Hsuan," pp. 179, 189.
   Fontein and Wu, *Unearthing China's Past*, no. 122.
   Guide to the Collections of the Cincinnati Art Museum, 1956, p. 35.
   Ho and Kohara, *Bunjinga Suihen*, 3, no. 62.
   Lee, *History of Far Eastern Art*, 4th ed., p. 407.
   Lee, "To See Big within Small," fig. 59.
   Lee and Ho, *Chinese Art under the Mongols*, no. 181.
   Lu, *Wu Yue sojian shuhualu*, 4, fols. 13–15.
   Munsterberg, *Arts of China*, pp. 158, 161.
   Munsterberg, "Collection of Chinese Paintings," p. 318, fig. 7.
   Robinson, "The Vitality of Style," pp. 75–83, 214–20, fig. 1.
   Sirén, *Chinese Painting*, 7, p. 109.
   Suzuki, *Comprehensive Illustrated Catalog*, 1, no. A24–006.
   Wang, *Exhibition of Authenticated Chinese Paintings*, no. 4.
Exhibited:
   "Exhibition of Authenticated Chinese Paintings," New York, C. T. Loo and Co., 1948, no. 4.
   "Masterpieces of Chinese Bird and Flower Painting," Fogg Art Museum, 1951.
   "Chinese Art under the Mongols," Cleveland Museum of Art, 1968, no. 181.
   "Unearthing China's Past," Museum of Fine Arts, Boston, 1973–1974, no. 122.
Notes:
   1. Robinson identified the doves depicted as a subspecies of *Streptopelia chinensis*, commonly referred to as Spotted Dove and characterized by the wide band of spots around the neck. He identified the blossoms as cherry, rather than pear, due to the presence of a single carpel emanating from the center of each blossom, indicative that the tree would bear fruit with a single pit, and thus could not be pear, the blossoms of which have many inferior carpels. See "Vitality of Style," pp. 216–217. However, due to the importance of the pear in Mou Yen's poem on the painting, and on the colophons that follow the painting, the traditional identification of the subject as pear is followed here. Qian's other famous painting of pear blossoms, in the Metropolitan Museum of Art, cleary depicts the same tree as in the Cincinnati painting; the artist's poem on it, though it does not mention the pear per se (nor cherry either; it does not mention the flowers by name), refers in its first lines to a Tang poem by Bo Juyi about pear blossoms. See Fong, *Beyond Representation*, pp. 307–11.
   2. According to Xia Wenyen, *Tuhui Baojian*, circa 1365, quoted in Cahill, "Ch'ien Hsuan and His Figure Paintings," p. 11.
   3. According to a list of painting genres in the 1120 catalog of the Sung-government art collection [*Xuanhe Huapu*], there were nearly 2½ times as many bird-and-flower paintings as the next largest category (see Barnhart, *Peach Blossom Spring*, p. 27). See also Robinson, "Vitality of Style," pp. 50–55. Qian Xuan's painting and poetry in relation to his bird-and-flower painting is discussed in connection with the bird-and-flower genre in Harrist, "Ch'ien Hsuan's *Pear Blossoms*," pp. 53–70.
   4. trans. Nora Ling-yün Shih.
   5. A handscroll, *Ink Flowers*, by the late fourteenth-century artist Zhao Zhong (now in the Cleveland Museum of Art), is also painted on powdered paper. Wai-kam Ho, in *Eight Dynasties of Chinese Painting*, pp. 91–92, cites the late fourteenth-century scholar Liu Chi on the fugitive nature of ink and pigments applied to paper with sizing of this kind.
   6. Wai-kam Ho, in *Eight Dynasties of Chinese Painting*, pp. 90–91, suggests that Qian Xuan's "obscurity in history was self-imposed." He substantiates this by referring to Chao Fang's (1319–1369) description of discussions with Tang Di and a visit

to Qian Xuan's nephew, Qian Guoyung. The latter presented him with a list of Qian's Confucian treatises, all of which had been destroyed by the author.

7. See Fontein and Wu, *Unearthing China's Past*, p. 235. Also see Cahill, *The Painter's Practice*, p. 135.

8. trans. Nora Ling-yün Shih.

9. Hucker, *Dictionary of Official Titles*, p. 62 and no. 3382.

10. Fu, *Yuan dai*, p. 47, pl. 30. It was recorded in the colophon following a calligraphy *Stele of Cao E* by an anonymous calligrapher of the Jin dynasty, in the collection of the Liaoning Museum.

11. Fu, *Yuan dai*, p. 49.

12. Fu, *Yuan dai*, pl. 40.

13. Fu, *Yuan dai*, p. 74.

14. trans. Nora Ling-yün Shih.

15. See Fu, *Traces*, p. 169, no. 15b.

16. trans. Nora Ling-yün Shih.

17. Huang Jin in Ma, *Shu-lin tsao-chien* 10, pp. 274–75.

18. See photo catalog of the Tokyo National Museum, *Chinese Calligraphy*, 1980, p. 28.

30. Portraits of Four Scholars

Yuan dynasty, circa 1323–1333. Handscroll; ink and colors on paper.
H. 28.6 x L. 76.2 cm.
John J. Emery Fund and Fanny Bryce Lehmer Endowment, 1948.82

Two pairs of similarly posed scholar-officials are shown in three-quarter view against a plain background. All four face toward the right and stand with feet apart. The two elderly gentlemen on the right wear the same type of long-sleeved robe: a plain, loose-fitting garment that wraps from the left shoulder across the chest to fasten under the right arm. One wears a beltless version; the other wears a belt with ring-and-hook clasp. Each holds his left arm pendant and completely concealed by the over-length sleeve. The right arm, with long sleeve pulled back, is bent across the abdomen, the right hand firmly holding a cane. Each of the two figures on the left is dressed in a loose white robe trimmed in black. They hold their crossed arms in front, completely concealed beneath the wide, long sleeves. Each of the four men wears a distinctive scholar's cap. In contrast to the rather generic poses and garments of the figures, each face is highly detailed and individualized.

The painting itself bears no inscriptions, but a colophon by Su Changling, dated 1354, follows the painting and identifies the four subjects:

There are many scholars in Lu state that I have seen —
Among them my teachers, of whom I always dream,
   whose ways I follow as an example —
But now they have passed away and I feel very sad.

Mr. Ning Zhuzhong showed me the four portraits: of my late teachers Mr. Wu Wenzheng [Wu Cheng], and Mr. Yu Meian [Yu Ji], Mr. Ouyang Guizhai [Ouyang Xuan], and Mr. Jie Manshi [Jie Xisi], and for a moment I saw my dear teachers in my mind's eye and felt very sad. So I wrote this to express my sorrow.

Fourteenth year of Zhi Zheng, eleventh month, first day [1354].
Su Danian, bowed twice and written [in deep humility].

Su Changling lists the four scholars in the order in which they would be viewed in the scroll — that is, from right to left. At the far right is the portrait of Wu Cheng (1249–1333), the preeminent neo-Confucian scholar of the Yuan dynasty and the eldest of the four men depicted. Although he passed the Jiangxi provincial examination at an early age, Wu Cheng avoided pursuing a government career, as did many young scholars during the decline of the Song, and did not attempt to attain the *jinshi* degree. Dedicated to scholarship from an early age, he produced many collations and textual studies on the Confucian classics while living a rather isolated life in Jiangxi. However, through the efforts of an imperial official and childhood friend, Cheng Jufu (1249–1318), who had tried unsuccessfully to persuade him to serve in the capital, Wu's writings were widely disseminated and brought him scholarly prominence and public recognition.

After several more attempts to enlist his services in the government, Wu finally agreed in 1309 to join the faculty of the National College. He was a popular teacher, but he left in frustration after less than three years. In 1323, after another period of prolific study and writing away from the capital Dadu (modern Beijing), Wu accepted the position of chancellor of the Hanlin Academy. In 1324 he taught in the hall for classical exposition, where emperors listened to lectures on Confucian principles. Once again he left the government after serving only two years. He continued to work energetically, producing commentaries until his death at age 85.[1]

Yu Ji (1272–1348), depicted to the left of his mentor, Wu Cheng, also grew up in Jiangxi and was Wu's principal biographer and disciple. Descendant of a Song general who had fought the Jurchen Tartars, Yu served the Mongol government loyally for more than 35 years. His career reached a high point under the emperor Wenzong (r. 1328–29; 1330–32), who in 1329 created the Kuizhang Ge Xue Shi Yuan [Academy of the Star of Literature] and named Yu Ji as the head. Among its various tasks, the academy tutored the emperor in the Confucian classics and Chinese history, and collected and compiled books. It became the imperial center for connoisseurship of calligraphy and painting. Yu Ji was primarily responsible for compiling the *Jing shi da dian* [Grand Canon for Governing the World], the Kuizhang Ge's most ambitious project. He was esteemed both for his astute aesthetic judgment and as a master of *ti hua shi*, poetry inscribed on paintings. His poems can be found on works by some of the most important painters of the period, including Zhao Mengfu (1254–1322).[2]

Ouyang Xuan (1283–1357) was a high official and famous scholar from Luling, Jiangxi,[3] who also served in the Kuizhang Ge. Ouyang was named director-general of the "three histories" project, a compilation of the histories of the three previous dynasties: Liao, Jin, and Song.[4]

Jie Xisi (1274–1344), who composed Wu Cheng's funeral tablet,[5] was also an eminent scholar in the Kuizhang Ge and worked among the compilers of the "three histories." He gained renown for his poetry, and is often grouped with Yang Weizhen (1296–1370) (see entry 27) and Yu Ji as one of the greatest Yuan poets.[6] As a calligrapher, his standard script was especially fine.[7]

The Museum's painting of these four men follows the conservative style associated with portrait painting and is unsigned. This is not unusual because portrait painters were considered artisans of rather low status. The exquisitely painted faces are highly individualized, compelling portraits drawn from life by a master painter, who may have been associated with the imperial court. These portraits must have been painted before Wu's death in 1333; in view of Wu's elderly appearance, they were likely executed around 1325 when all four men were serving in the capital, shortly before Wu left his last government post as lecturer in the Hall for Classical Exposition. Combining veneration for individual character and for the ideals of Confucian virtue, each countenance documents a lifetime of intellectual development and Confucian self-cultivation. Age is emphasized to show that they are men of mature wisdom and decorum.

Wang Yi (active 1360s), a slightly later contemporary of the anonymous painter of the Museum's scroll, is one of the few portrait painters of the period known by name. His work assists in placing the Museum's scroll in the artistic context of Yuan dynasty literati portraiture. Wang Yi's fame rests upon the dissemination of a circa 1360 treatise he wrote, the *Xixiang Bijue,* or *Secrets of Portrait Painting,* and on the existence of a painting in the Palace Museum, Beijing, a 1363 portrait of Yang Zhuxi, identified as the work of Wang by the scholar-painter Ni Zan (see entry 27d), who added the landscape setting on the painting.[8] The Beijing painting shares certain stylistic similarities with the Cincinnati painting in the treatment of the portrait, such as the stance of the figure and use of simple delineation to render a relatively generalized treatment of dress and overall physique. In both paintings this is sharply contrasted with a delicate, sensitive treatment of the face. Wang's painting displays even greater attention to minute facial detail; he must have employed a brush constructed of a single hair. In his treatise, Wang described his method for capturing inner character in the depiction of a face:

> Whoever paints a portrait must be thoroughly familiar with the rules of physiognomy, for the disposition of the parts of people's faces is like that of the Five Mountains or Four Rivers, each element being different. Even if there are symmetrical areas, their expression and color will differ according to the four seasons. Only during a lively conversation will they show their original and true character. Then I remain quiet and try to seek it, silently noting it in my mind. Even with my eyes closed, it is as if I had [the features] before my eyes and, when I release my brush, it is as if [the face] were already beneath the brush's tip. After that, I fix it down with pale ink and build it up in successive layers.[9]

Wang's statement about adhering to the rules of physiognomy refers to traditional Chinese study of facial appearance not only as a reflection of inner character, but for revealing an individual's destiny in terms of familial and professional success and prosperity. In fact, the Chinese word for portrait, *xiang,* sounds like the word for fortune-telling and the character for portrait includes an element referring to the earthly manifestation of heavenly images, connoting

a metaphysical revelation in the face that can be deciphered for purposes of prognostication.[10] The meticulously detailed description of methods for drawing and coloring the facial features that follows in Wang's treatise can best be appreciated in this context.[11]

The Museum's painting once was owned by the Korean salt merchant An Qi (ca. 1683–after 1744); his seals are on the scroll, although the work is not listed in his catalog, *Moyuan hui-kuan.* Despite this omission, the scroll must have been among the paintings that An sold to the imperial collection, because it is recorded in the *Shiqu Baoji,* the 1745 catalog of Qianlong's painting collection.

Collectors' Seals:
   Su Changling (fourteenth century); An Qi (ca. 1683–after 1744); Qianlong (r. 1736–1795); Fan Zengxiang (1846–1931); Tan Jing (twentieth century); Chang Ts'ung-yu (1915–1963).

Colophons and seals:
   Su Changling (fourteenth century), five seals; Fan Zengxiang (1846–1931), two seals.

Recent Provenance:
   Chang Ts'ung-yu; C. T. Loo.

Published:
   Cahill, *Index,* p. 370.
   Cheng, *Yün-hui-chai,* pp. 54–5.
   Lee and Ho, *Chinese Art under the Mongols,* p. 81.
   Munsterberg, "Collection of Chinese Paintings," pp. 314–17.
   Shiqu Baoji [1745].
   Suzuki, *Comprehensive Illustrated Catalog,* 1: no. A24–004.
   Wang, *Exhibition of Authenticated Chinese Paintings,* no. 9.

Exhibited:
   "Exhibition of Authenticated Chinese Paintings," C. T. Loo and Co., New York, 1948.

Notes:
   1. Gedalecia, "Wu Ch'eng," pp. 186–94.
   2. See Li, *Autumn Colors,* p. 27. Yu's biography is recorded in *Yuan Shih,* 181. Also see Sun, "Yu Chi," pp. 225–27.
   3. His biography is in the *Yuan Shih,* p. 182 and *Hsin Yuan Shih,* p. 206.
   4. See Chan, "Chinese Official Historiography," for a discussion of this controversial project.
   5. Gedalecia, "Wu Ch'eng," p. 186, note 1.
   6. Sun, "Yu Chi," p. 226, note 32.
   7. Fu, *Traces,* pp. 142, 291, notes 17 and 302, notes 72, 74, and 78.
   8. Published in Vinograd, *Boundaries of the Self,* figs. 14a and b.
   9. trans. Bush and Shih, *Early Chinese Texts on Painting,* pp. 271–72.
   10. Vinograd, *Boundaries of the Self,* pp. 5–6.
   11. A translation of the entire treatise is in Franke, "Two Yuan Treatises," pp. 27–32.

31. Bamboo

Gu An (circa 1295–circa 1370). Yuan dynasty, 14th century. Hanging scroll; ink on paper. H. 113 x W. 33 cm.
John J. Emery Endowment and Fanny Bryce Lehmer Endowment, 1948.81

A slender stalk of bamboo bends gently to the left, then to the right at its final joint, creating a subtle S-curved silhouette. Lush branches of varying length grow in pairs from each of the upper joints; their elegant leaves are formed of confident brushstrokes executed in rich, black ink.

The artist, Gu An, from Yangzhou, Jiangsu province, served as a district judge in Quanzhou, near Suzhou, during the Yuantong era (1333–1334). As a painter he specialized in ink bamboo, a category of painting that reached its zenith during the Yuan dynasty. Gu is usually classified as a master of this genre with his older contemporary Li Kan (1245–1320) and with Ke Jiusi (1290–1343) (see entry 29a) and Wu Zhen (1280–1354). Gu's birth and death dates are unknown. However, a painting of bamboo, rock, and old tree in the Palace Museum, Taipei, on which he collaborated with Zhang Shen (active 1368–1398) and Yang Weizhen (1296–1370) (see entry 27a), indicates that both Yang and Gu had died by 1373, when Ni Zan (1301–1374) added his inscription.[1]

Gu's oeuvre sensitively explores the qualities of bamboo through its various stages of growth and under assorted seasonal and weather conditions. In one of his greatest works, a large painting dated 1359 now in the National Palace Museum, Taipei, the leaves of several large bamboo growing by a rock are whipped by the wind. The multitude of leaves curl in unison to the wind's command and are echoed in their movement by scattered tufts of grass; the overall effect is a masterful choreography of Gu's disciplined brushwork.[2] In the Museum's painting Gu emphasizes the vigor, rather than the movement of the leaves, but their strength retains an innate pliability. This treatment compares with an album leaf dated 1365 in the National Palace Museum, Taipei, depicting a spray of new bamboo growing behind a rock.[3]

Bamboo was a favorite subject for literati painters, who equated it with the virtuous gentleman. Painting bamboo requires the same brushwork as writing. This practice is traditionally considered an intellectual art which, like calligraphy, reveals the artist's inner character. In his preface to Li Kan's (1245–1320) treatise *Zhu Pu [Manual of Bamboo]*, Ke Qian (1251–1319) explains the relationship of the Confucian scholar with painted bamboo:

> [I]f . . . on seeing the paintings and treatise we say that there is nothing but bamboo there, we really do not understand bamboo, nor do we understand the author, Master Li. A proverb says: "A gentleman is comparable to bamboo because of their similar virtues." What people may describe and paint are only the form, the color, and the type of bamboo; what neither description nor painting can encompass are the virtues for which bamboo stands. Bamboo stems are hollow ["empty hearted," i.e., humble]. When humility is applied in dealing with everyday life, it is Li's personality, which is neither proud nor selfish and obstinate. The nature of bamboo is to be straight. Uprightness is expressed in the cultivation of disposition; it is Li's lofty and pure nature, vast and open mind, and correct manner in getting along with people. Bamboo's joints are clear-cut. When this virtue is associated with efforts in carrying out serious responsibilities, it is expressed in Li's accomplishments at court as a model of human behavior . . .
>
> During his leisure time Li expressed his inspiration in his bamboo painting, and his paintings and treatise have become in turn the things which bamboo represents in itself. If one is able not to look at bamboo

as bamboo but to seek its supreme unborn nature beyond all form and color, then Li's own character can be visualized.[4]

Gu An's bravura signature and bold title illustrate the connection between brush writing and the directness and calligraphic quality of ink bamboo. The painting's title, two large characters in the upper right-hand corner (*wan jie*), literally means "late growth," and by extension can mean "coming to maturity late" as well as "integrity in old age." The phrase is a play on words: *Jie* means "joint" or "stage," and refers to the way bamboo grows in jointed sections that do not change form throughout the life of the tree.

The painting bears two colophons. The first, by Ju Yisheng, praises Gu An as a master of bamboo:

> Gu Dingzhi [Gu An] is well-known far and near.
> His bamboo paintings are particularly refreshing and exceptional.
> Unrolling this painting reminds me of the night scene on the Xiang River.
> Moonlight casting various irregular shadows of bamboo.

The second colophon, at the top left of the painting, is by Zhao Ziqiu:

> I am always fond of this gentleman [bamboo],
> who flutters gracefully in woods afar.
> Even after suffering the frequent rains of autumn nights,
> Still he endures the bitter cold of winter.
> Morning after morning I go to the place of instruction at dawn,
> and return to my study room each evening after dark.
> Whenever I have the opportunity to unroll this painting for a look,
> my worries dissipate for the rest of the day.

In his colophon, Zhao taps into another interpretation of the word *jie*, which refers to a lesson in school or a classroom session. Here the bamboo signifies perseverance in the face of difficulty and challenge, an attribute that inspires the anxious scholar.

Artist's seals:
Gu An; Dingzhi fu

Collector's seals:
Liang Zhangju (1775–1849), 1 seal; Cheng Daoji (19th century?), one seal; Xu An (20th century), one seal; Tan Jing (20th century), two seals; Chang Ts'ung-yu (1915–1963), three seals; three seals, unidentified.

Colophons and seals:
Ju Yisheng, two seals; Zhao Ziqiu, one seal.

Recent provenance:
Chang Ts'ung-yu; C. T. Loo

Published:
Cahill, *Index*, p. 293.
Cheng, *Yün-hui-chai*, p. 39.
Ch'ien, *Lu Yuan Tsung Hua*.
Chu, *Pao Shu T'ing Shu Hua Pu*.
Edwards, "Sophistications," p. 89.
Hai-wai yi-chen Painting 2, no. 40.
Munsterberg, "Collection of Chinese Paintings," p. 320, fig. 12.
Shiqu baoji.
Suzuki, *Comprehensive Illustrated Catalog 1*, no. A24–009.
Tausend Jahre Chinesische Malerei, no. 34.

Wang, "Chinese Ink Bamboo Paintings," p. 55.

Wang, *Exhibition of Authenticated Chinese Paintings,* no. 7.

Exhibited:

"Exhibition of Authenticated Chinese Paintings," C. T. Loo and Co., New York, 1948.

"Masterpieces of Chinese Art," Virginia Museum of Fine Arts, 1954–55.

"One Thousand Years of Chinese Painting," Haus der Kunst, Munich, 1959; Zurich, 1960; The Hague, 1960; Cleveland Museum of Art, 1960.

Notes:

1. Cahill, *Hills beyond a River,* pp. 175–76 and pl. 85.
2. Illustrated in *Ku Kung ming hua* 5, no. 40.
3. Illustrated in *Ku Kung ming hua* 5, no. 39.
4. Bush and Shih, *Early Chinese Texts,* pp. 274–75.

32. Wenshu, Bodhisattva of Wisdom, at a Writing Table

Shanxi province, from the Lower Monastery of the Guangshengsi [Temple of Vast Triumph]. Yuan dynasty, 1354. Glue tempera on clay size over mud and straw wall. H. 416.8 x W. 297.3 cm. Gift of C. T. Loo, 1950.154

The bodhisattva, seated in a fantastic thronelike chair, gazes intently at a blank scroll unfurled on the elaborate table before him. Stirred by the flaming sphere borne on clouds behind his head, he leans forward, rests his left elbow on the table, and holds a brush aloft, poised to begin writing. Neatly arranged on the desk are the accoutrements of a Chinese scholar: a brushholder with extra brush, a pile of books, an extra scroll, an inkstone with inkstick, and a water dropper. Next to the desk, a vermilion-skinned servant holds a bundle of scrolls.

The active engagement of the bodhisattva and the rhythmic linearity of forms throughout the mural create an overall sense of animation that is characteristic of Yuan dynasty Buddhist painting. The motion and brilliance of the flaming orb, the bodhisattva's downward gaze, his posture, and the flowing drapery of his robes, work in concert to lead the viewer's eye diagonally across the picture from upper left to lower right. Counterbalancing this are the strong diagonal lines of the chair and writing table. These features form the underpinnings of a dynamic composition and further serve to create a sense of spatial depth.

In Shanxi province, Buddhist temple construction flourished continuously from the Han through Ming periods. Surviving there today are many of China's oldest and best-preserved timber-frame buildings. Temple interiors inspired awe with impressive murals serving as backdrops for magnificent wood sculptures (see entry 23). This mural comes from the lower monastery of the Guangshengsi (Temple of Vast Triumph), located near Zhaocheng, in the Fen River valley of southern Shanxi province.[1]

An inscription in the upper right-hand corner of the Museum's mural is partially damaged but reads as follows:

South [?] wall.

[?] upper Zhang village [?]

Li Shih . . . [2 missing names] . . . Wang Renqi, Li Hengfu(?), Li Tong[?], (Buddhist) master Xiao[?]gui, Gao Youde.

May each of you protect your body from harm, may the family soon find tranquility, and may all members, whether senior or junior, be kept safe.

Fourteenth year of the Zhi Zheng reign in the cyclical year Jia Wu [1354], [?] month.[2]

The inscription follows a format similar to those of inscriptions dated 1358 in the Chunyang Hall of the Daoist monastery Yongle gong, in southwest Shanxi. The Yongle gong inscriptions list the names of the artists involved in painting the murals, and distinguish between master and assistant painters.[3] The Museum's inscription differs, however, in that it includes a dedicatory statement, which does not appear on the Chunyang Hall inscriptions. This would indicate that the names listed are those of the donors of the mural, rather than the artists who painted it.

Wall paintings were produced by teams of artists working under the supervision of a master painter, who designed the compositions and prepared the sketches and model drawings. Walls were prepared for painting by first installing wooden pegs tied with tassels of hemp fibers; next came an application of one or two layers of clay mixed with coarse sand and wheat stalks. Another layer of fine clay mixed with finer sand and chopped straw was added next. The wall received its final smoothing with coats of chalk and/ or alum, whose whiteness also would enhance the brilliance of pigments. The master painter made initial sketches directly on the wall surface with charcoal, then assistants transfered model drawings onto the wall by pouncing. The master painter was responsible for painting the ink outlines; assistants later filled in the colors.[4]

The Guangshengsi was built in 147 A.D. Originally it was named Ayu Wang (King Asoka) after the third-century-B.C. Indian king whose devout patronage of Buddhism secured its status as a major religion. In 769 the Tang emperor Daizong (r. 762–779) changed the name to Guangsheng [Vast Triumph]. The temple complex consists of two large compounds: an upper monastery located on a hillside and a lower monastery situated at the foot of the hill, about a mile away.[5] A subsidiary temple dedicated to Mingyingwang, the spirit of the Huo spring, is located to the southeast of the lower monastery, near the spring. Its hall contains wall paintings and enshrines an image of the deity.

The plan of the Guangshengsi lower monastery follows a north-south axial orientation for the principal structures: an entrance gate at the south end, the front hall in the middle, and the main hall at the northern end. The main hall was adorned with Buddhist paradise murals on each gable wall until they were removed in the 1920s; these are now in the Nelson-Atkins Museum and the Metropolitan Museum of Art.[6] The Cincinnati mural, acquired by C. T. Loo's agent around 1930, must have come from the main hall and originally would have flanked a doorway; the inscription states that it was located on a south wall. The front hall of the lower monastery was constructed in the Ming dynasty; its gable murals are now in the Museum of Art and Archaeology, University of Pennsylvania. The murals in the Nelson-Atkins Museum and the Metropolitan Museum of Art, considered the earliest of the group, have been assigned dates ranging from the late thirteenth century to about 1319.[7] The Cincinnati painting is dated 1354. The Pennsylvania murals are thought to have been executed after 1475, on the basis of an inscription stating that reconstruction of the front hall was completed in 1475.[8]

According to a stele located at the Mingyingwang hall, a severe earthquake in 1303 and subsequent fires destroyed nearly every building in Zhaocheng. Rebuilding of the monastery began in 1305. As indicated in the wall inscriptions of the Mingyingwang hall, new interior images and wall paintings had been completed there by 1324; they survive at the hall today. It is not known how severely this earthquake damaged other buildings of the temple complex, but Sickman asserted that complete destruction was unlikely.[9]

The frequency of earthquakes in this area influenced the choice of subject matter for the lower monastery's murals. Both the main hall and the front hall paradise murals include an Assembly of Tejaprabha, the celestial Buddha who protects from natural disasters.[10] In the Philadelphia mural depicting the Assembly of Tejaprabha, the attendant bodhisattva on the Buddha's right holds a book titled "Sutra Spoken by the Buddha, [Giving] the Mantra of the Gold-Wheel Buddha-Head of Great Virtue, Tejaprabha Tathagata, Which Dispels All Calamities." According to the Tejaprabha sutra, the bodhisattva to whom Tejaprabha revealed this mantra was Wenshu (Sanskrit: Manjusri), the bodhisattva of wisdom.[11]

Complementing the lower monastery's large paradise murals, the Cincinnati wall painting depicts Wenshu receiving Tejaprabha's mantra. Seated in an elaborate thronelike chair at a desk of equally fantastic design, the bodhisattva awaits the Buddha's revelation, symbolized by the flaming orb behind his head.[12] On the desk are the writing implements of a Chinese scholar-official, exemplifying the sinicization of the deity.

Wenshu was promoted in the Tang dynasty as a protector bodhisattva for China and its emperor. During *mofa*, the latter days when the Buddhist law was waning, he was believed to dwell on Mount Wutai in Shanxi province, a site that served as an important pilgrimage destination in China. Wenshu also was a monastic ideal, as evidenced by depictions of the bodhisattva in the sangha hall of Southern Song Chan Buddhist monasteries. The sangha hall, where monks meditated, ate, and slept, housed an image of Wenshu wearing monk's robes and seated in meditation; in this guise he is known as the Holy Monk.[13]

Wenshu gained the respect of China's scholar-officials for his willingness, when all other disciples of Buddha had refused, to debate the formidable lay devotee Vimalakirti on the doctrine of nonduality. Confucian scholar-officials who were also devout Buddhists admired in Vimalakirti a command of rhetorical discussion that embodied their own notions of intellectualism.

The depiction of Wenshu at a writing desk would have resonated

with civil service candidates seeking divine intervention as they strove to attain high-level government appointments by earning the coveted *jinshi* degree. From the beginning of the Yuan dynasty, the Confucian civil service examination system underwent changes that favored Mongols for government service in the capital. Beginning in 1333, however, the national examinations, held triennially under the Yuan, produced their full quota of *jinshi* degrees for all ethnic groups.[14] Half of these degrees were awarded to Mongols or western Asians, who sat for simpler examinations less rigorously judged. Although standards for Chinese candidates were higher, and northerners were officially favored over southerners in eligibility for bureaucratic posts, greater opportunities existed under the Yuan than previously.[15]

Finally, the Museum's mural reflects the Mongols' political use of Buddhism in legitimizing their rule over China. The Guangshengsi monastery played an important role during the Yuan dynasty as a temple associated with the Yuan imperial household; the Emperor Khubilai Khan's portrait was hung there each year during celebrations of the imperial birthday. In the same year as the Museum's painting was completed, a great architectural project in Beijing, the Juyong Gate, was also built. Its Mongol inscription (one of five inscriptions, all in different languages) bestows divine status on the Emperor Khubilai Khan by declaring him a reincarnation of Manjusri. Through this identification with China's protector-bodhisattva, religious authority was claimed for Mongol governance.[16]

Provenance:
    C. T. Loo
Published:
    Avril, "Highlights," pp. 68–69.
    Baldwin, "Monumental Wall Paintings," p. 242, n. 7.
    Edwards, "Sophistications," p. 87, fig. 12.
    Lippe, "Buddha and the Holy Multitude," p. 326.
    Steinhardt, "Zhu Haogu Reconsidered," pp. 5–20.

Notes:
    1. This information was supplied by the donor, C. T. Loo, whose agent purchased murals from the Guang Sheng temple in 1930. They were sold at that time to raise money for renovations (Cincinnati Art Museum curatorial files). For photographs of the lower monastery see Liang Ssu-ch'eng, *Pictorial History of Chinese Architecture*, pp. 100–101.
    2. Translated by Nora Ling-yün Shih.
    3. See Tsang, "Further Observations," pp. 96–98, figs. 4–5.
    4. See Tsang, "Further Observations," pp. 110–11.
    5. Jing, "Yuan Buddhist Mural," p. 147.
    6. Jing, "Yuan Buddhist Mural," pp. 147–48; Lin and Liang, "Jinfen gu jianzhu," p. 46.
    7. Qi, "Liangnian lai Shanxi sheng," p. 61, suggests that the main hall was rebuilt in 1309 (after 1303 earthquake), on the basis of the date 1309 inscribed on the ridge purlin of the hall. Jing, "Yuan Buddhist Mural," p. 159, on the basis of the Chinese archaeologists' find, believes that the murals were executed between 1309 and 1319, the date of the stele in the temple to Mingyingwang that describes the rebuilt Guang Shengsi as magnificent (i.e. having totally recovered from the earthquake); see Sickman, "Wall Paintings of the Yuan Period," pp. 56–59, for transcription and translation of the stele. Sickman dated the murals from the main hall to the thirteenth century; see "Notes on Later Chinese Buddhist Art," p. 15. Baldwin,

"Monumental Wall Paintings," p. 264, agrees with Lippe's and Sickman's suggestions that the murals were created before the 1303 earthquake.

8. Jing, "Yuan Buddhist Mural," p. 160, cites Qi, "Liangnian lai Shanxi sheng," p. 65, for an inscription in the front hall stating that the reconstruction of the front hall was completed in the eleventh year of the Ming emperor Chenghua's reign, or 1475.

9. Sickman, "Wall Paintings of the Yuan Period," p. 59, indicates that this portion of the stele inscription refers only to the Mingyingwang hall and that not all buildings were destroyed because some still surviving at the upper monastery appeared to be of Song or Jin date.

10. Jing, "Yuan Buddhist Mural," pp. 155–59.

11. See Lippe, "Buddha and the Holy Multitude," pp. 332–33. The bodhisattva who holds the book is identified as Samantabhadra because Manjusri is usually not shown on the Buddha's right, but in the place of honor on his left.

12. Donghua Mugong Qingting, Lord of the Way, sits on a similar thronelike chair before a similar table in the mural of Daoist deities in the Sanqing [Pure Trinity] Hall of Yongle gong, dated 1325. See Liao, *Yongle Palace Murals*, pp. 46–47.

13. Foulk, "Myth, Ritual, and Monastic Practice," pp. 183–84.

14. Dardess, "Shun-ti and the end of Yüan rule," pp. 564–66.

15. Endicott-West, "The Yüan Government and Society," pp. 637–40.

16. Berger, "Preserving the Nation," pp. 92–93, 105–06.

33. Lotus

Yuan dynasty, 14th century. Hanging scroll, ink and colors on silk.
H. 99 x W. 53.4 cm.
Gift of Mr. and Mrs. John J. Emery, 1964.700

Three large pink lotus flowers in varying stages of bloom emerge from a lush array of round leaves that twist and turn in all directions. A single stalk of smartweed hovers above, echoing the gentle curve of the lotuses. Below, brilliant white water lilies float in the pond.

The painting is executed in the style of the Piling school, a group of professional painters who worked in the area of modern Wujin, Jiangsu province and specialized in decorative floral paintings. The school flourished more-or-less continuously from the Song into the Qing period.

Yuan dynasty lotus paintings of this school are characterized by the pervasive use of opaque mineral pigments: pink or powder-white for the flowers and malachite for the leaves. Compositions follow a formula: The large lotus plant, usually shown bending in the wind, fills the scene but is placed to one side and is cropped severely. Additional plants and sometimes waterfowl, such as ducks or herons, are included, though these elements are usually subordinate to the lotus. In the Museum's painting, the silk has darkened considerably, causing the pink and white pigments to stand out more strongly than the artist probably intended. Piling-school paintings were especially popular in Japan, where they were preserved in the collections of Buddhist temples.[1]

Lotus, imported to China from India, is associated closely with Buddhism. Symbolic of the Buddha himself, this grand flower represents purity and transcendence, because its blossoms rise in unblemished splendor from the murky pond. Similarly, according to Pure Land beliefs, reborn souls enter Amida's Western Paradise as infants emerging from a lotus pond. Paintings of this phenomenon show each unfurled blossom containing a naked infant soul.

Provenance:
Mr. and Mrs. John J. Emery
Published:
Keppel, *China in 1700*, p. 16, no. 66.
Exhibited:
"China in 1700: Kangxi Porcelains in the Taft Museum," Taft Museum, Cincinnati, 1988.
Notes:
1. See Fong, *Beyond Representation*, pp. 381–87.

34. Wild Geese Descending to a Sandbar

Wang Zhao (active circa 1480–1540). Ming dynasty, late 15th or early 16th century. Hanging scroll; ink on paper. H. 147.3 x 73 cm.
Gift of Mr. and Mrs. John J. Emery, 1964.702

A line of geese descends on a marsh as the setting sun hovers above windswept grasses. In the middle ground, gnarled trees grow near a rock, partially obscuring a thatched hut. In the grasses of the nearest shore, a fisherman and his servant are asleep in their boat. It is the end of the day: The nets are tucked away, a rod with retracted line is propped against the side of the boat, and the fisherman rests on his oar. His young servant is asleep in the stern.

Wang Zhao, a native of Anhui province and follower of the styles of Dai Jin (1388–1462) and Wu Wei (1459–1508), employs the atmospheric effects, broad ink washes, and scribbly brushwork characteristic of the last generation of Zhe-school painters. The Museum's painting is signed Hai Yun ("Sea-Clouds"), the artistic name Wang took to convey his preference for brushwork that is "free and surging like the sea or the clouds."[1] Indeed, both the subject matter and the brushwork of the Museum's painting reflect notions of spontaneous creation and sudden transformation.

The hub of Zhe school activity was Hangzhou, in Zhejiang province (hence the name), and its style was based on that of the Southern Song Painting Academy, particularly the work of Ma Yuan (active ca. 1190–ca. 1225) (see entry 27) and Xia Gui (active ca. 1195–1230). By the early sixteenth century, many Zhe-school artists were producing formulaic works with little more than decorative appeal. Wang Zhao was categorized by late sixteenth century critics as one of the *xiexue*, "Heterodox school," and thus came to be associated with the provincial artists responsible for the decline of the Zhe-school style.[2]

The subject of this painting is the first scene from a traditional landscape theme known as the *Eight Views of the Xiao and Xiang Rivers*. One of the great wetland areas of China, the Xiao and Xiang region, in Hunan province, is a misty, marshy, ever-changing riverscape that came to be romanticized by painters and poets as one of the great sanctuaries for the mind. The theme originated in the eleventh century with the painter Song Di (circa 1015–1080), whose

Eight Views were given titles by his contemporary Shen Gua (1029–1093).[3] Using these titles as a departure point, the Chan Buddhist monk Huihong (1071–1128) composed eight poems, one to accompany each of the views. Huihong's first poem, "Geese Descending," describes the arrival of geese at the end of the day:

The lake's autumn colors of burnished bronze,
Late afternoon sun, white sand, nebulous light:
Fluttering, about to land, still more calling and crowding,
By fives, by tens, among dense rushes;
Not yet returned to Xixing, melancholy unto old age,
A cloudless evening sky, the heaven as if swept;
At the windborne sound of a flute, they rise alarmed,
Writing cursive script in space like Wang Xizhi.[4]

Here Wang Zhao illustrates the first half of the poem, when the birds descend. Through the agitated brushwork of his landscape, however, he also anticipates the flushing of the geese. The last line refers to the fourth-century calligrapher Wang Xizhi (ca. 303–ca. 361), who was revered for his ability to create elegant, fluid cursive script with seeming effortlessness in a moment. Wang Xizhi also was said to be inspired by watching geese: "He thought their flexing necks were like a calligrapher turning his wrist to form a character as he held a brush."[5]

"Geese Descending to Distant Sandbars" also became a popular tune to which many writers composed poetry. Yuan dynasty playwrights drew upon the poetic imagery of the Xiao and Xiang to create atmosphere or to set a mood; "Rain on the Xiao and Xiang Rivers" [*Xiao Xiang Yu*], by Yang Xianzhi, was a popular Yuan drama.[6] The Museum's painting exemplifies Zhe school artists' utilization of elements of popular song and drama in their works, which would have appealed to the tastes of the urban merchant class, who were patrons of popular culture and Zhe school art.

In the fifteenth century, sets of paintings of the "Eight Views of Xiao and Xiang" had become so commonplace that the connoisseur Huang Xing (1339–1431) wrote of his dismay that artists failed to adequately convey the scenic beauty and geographic panorama of the Xiao and Xiang rivers, opting instead for individual scenes that reduced the image merely to its poetic associations.[7]

Although dismissed by their critics as pretentious, the Heterodox artists were independent professional painters who, with varying degrees of artistic success, sought to break free from the limitations imposed by both academic (i.e. court painting) and literati traditions. They chose an unconventional approach to life and art, preferring Daoist spontaneity to Confucian decorum. The Heterodox artists pursued wildness and eccentricity in their behavior as well as in their brushwork; their artistic names often reflected notions of craziness, Daoist immortality, and drunkenness.[8]

Stories about Wang Zhao praise his creativity, cleverness, and spontaneity. In one episode described in the *Huizhou Fuzhi*, an Anhui gazetteer, he managed to gain release from jail by demonstrating his talents as a painter. Approaching the blank silk in an unorthodox manner — by pouring ink on it — he created a picture of dawn

with his brush, inscribed a clever poem, and impressed the jailer so strongly that he was freed. In another episode, he managed to escape from a pirate ship that he had boarded mistakenly by first painting a fan for each of his captors and then demonstrating his uncanny ability to drink wine by inhaling it through his nose. Wang Zhao fled when the pirate chief drank himself into unconsciousness.[9]

Artist's seal:
    One seal, undeciphered.
Recent Provenance:
    Mr. and Mrs. John J. Emery
Published:
    Avril, "Highlights," pp. 71–72.
    Hai-wai yi-chen Painting 2, p. 123.
Notes:
    1. *Xiuningxian zhi* [Gazetteer of Xiuningxian], quoted in Barnhart, "'Wild and Heterodox' School," p. 372, after Suzuki, *Seppa*, note 326.
    2. Cahill, *Parting at the Shore*, p. 128.
    3. For a summary of the origin of the theme, see Murck, "Eight Views," pp. 214–35. For a thorough study of Song Di and the Eight Views, see Shimada, "So Teki."
    4. Translation after Murck, "Eight Views," p. 224.
    5. From the writings of Kuo Hsi (after 1000–ca. 1090), in Bush and Shih, *Early Chinese Texts*, p. 179.
    6. Shih, *Golden Age of Chinese Drama*, pp. 114, 124–25, 134–35.
    7. Rogers and Lee, *Masterworks of Ming and Qing*, p. 112.
    8. Barnhart, "'Wild and Heterodox' School," pp. 365–71.
    9. Rogers and Lee, *Masterworks*, pp. 122–23.

35. A Quiet River at the Foot of Misty Mountains

Attributed to Wen Zhengming (1470–1559), Ming dynasty, circa 1500–1512. Hanging scroll; ink on paper. H. 59.2 x W. 31.2 cm. Inscribed in the upper left-hand corner of the painting: [painted by Ma Wenbi, from Fufeng].
John J. Emery Endowment and Fanny Bryce Lehmer Endowment, 1948.83

In a mountain setting after rain, an empty pavilion occupies a rocky precipice along the shore of a quiet river. A short footbridge straddles the mouth of a small stream feeding into the river. Trees on the distant shore, shrouded in mist, form a middle ground that separates the tall trees in the foreground from the distant peaks that rise above hazy clouds. The painting was executed in a relaxed manner with flat wet brushstrokes, wet moss dots, and washes on an absorbent paper.

The Museum purchased this painting as a work by the Yuan-dynasty landscape painter Ma Wan (ca. 1310–1378); it is signed in the upper left-hand corner with Wenbi, the artist's *zi* (a style name that he took at age twenty). Dong Qichang's colophon (1555–1636), on a separate piece of paper mounted directly above the painting, also assigns the painting to Ma. However, comparison of this painting with accepted paintings by Ma Wan reveals very little in common.[1]

Ma Wan's brushwork is dry and consists of round, linear texture strokes, clearly defined, compact massing of mountains, and dense strokes and dots for mountaintops and tree leaves. Ma seldom employed washes or wet strokes, and showed little interest in portraying the effects of mist. The Cincinnati painting, by contrast, is composed entirely of soft, wet strokes, creating a misty atmosphere that is especially apparent in the mid-distant trees. Likewise, the signature on this painting, though written somewhat in the *zhangcao* [draft-cursive] script employed by Ma Wan in his inscriptions, has no resemblance to signatures appearing on accepted works by Ma.[2]

Indeed, this painting has many more features in common with the style of Ming-dynasty Wu-school painters working in and near Suzhou in the fifteenth and sixteenth centuries than with Yuan painting. Although smaller in size and simpler in composition, in many respects it is similar to a painting by Wen Zhengming (1470–1559) titled "Huang Gongwang's Leisurely Living at the Stream Pavilion," in the Binney collection.[3] The same wet, gray horizontal strokes are used to depict the trees behind the pavilion in the middle ground of both paintings. Shapes, outlines, and the hemp fiber-textured strokes of mountains in the two paintings are so similar in execution that they must be the work of the same artist, as are the gray ink washes defining the silhouettes of distant mountains.

The style name Wen Bi was not used exclusively by Ma Wan, but was also the given name of Wen Zhengming, who signed that name to many of his early paintings. Beginning in 1512, however, he preferred to use his style name, Zhengming. The brushwork in this painting compares closely with Wen Zhengming in the first decade of the 1500s, when his style followed that of the Yuan master Huang Gongwang (1269–1354) and of his teacher, Shen Zhou (1427–1509).

Further inspection of the Cincinnati painting reveals that the entire upper left-hand corner of the painting has been replaced; the bottom seam of the paper repair is located just above the last two characters of the inscription. Over time the two papers have discolored such that the patched paper is now noticeably lighter than the original. When examined under a microscope, the original paper appears to overlap the patch along the middle of the curved seam, whereas toward both ends the two papers are patched as one. At the left edge, the seam occurs just above the character bi, Wen's given name. The top four characters have been matched skillfully to the style of the last two characters except that they lean slightly more to the right and were written in a different ink. In addition, the color of the artist's seal matches exactly that of Dong Qichang's seal in the colophon above the painting, and indicates that Wen Zhengming's painting was reattributed when Dong Qichang added his colophon. The size of the patch suggests that originally one or more lines of text could have preceded Wen's signature, perhaps providing the date and title of the painting, but these are now lost.

Dong Qichang, the late Ming painter, calligrapher, art theorist and connoisseur added the following colophon above the painting:

This painting by Ma Fufeng [Ma Wan] is very much after the style of Huang Gongwang. It creates the impression of an imaginary secluded place. Paintings done in this manner by other artists are inferior. Inscribed by Qichang for my old friend Meigong [Chen Jiru, 1558–1639].

Dong Qichang was a superb artist and calligrapher. As scholars have noted, however, Dong's widespread, erroneous reattributions of Ming and Yuan paintings to earlier masters[4] suggest that "he was an instinctive, arbitrary, unhistorical connoisseur whose views were grounded in the personal politics, economics, aesthetics, philosophy, and tastes of a deeply creative artist, but not in any actual art historical reality."[5] Yet in his own time and later, he wielded enormous influence as a theorist and connoisseur. His lifelong friend and confidant, Chen Jiru, for whom the colophon on the Museum's painting was written, proclaimed that Dong was

a masterly connoisseur. Even before he had unrolled half a scroll, he could judge its quality and authenticity. Occasionally when he wrote his colophons, he would pick up the brush and finish without a pause, and all the comments would be profoundly memorable.[6]

This accolade also can have a less flattering interpretation: that Dong's self-possessed judgment might have led him to make hasty, even erroneous pronouncements about the origin of a painting. If Dong Qichang gained a reputation for not examining carefully the works of art brought to him, one can imagine that an unscrupulous peddler of paintings, knowing that a work by the Yuan artist Ma Wan would be held in higher esteem than an early work by Wen Zhengming, might attempt to fool Dong with a cleverly altered painting such as this.

One of the greatest artists of Suzhou, Wen Zhengming came from a scholar-official family and had the good fortune to live in a city celebrated for its intellectual and artistic life. Following the tradition of studying the Confucian classics, literature, and history, he aspired to the ideal of a cultivated government official. This goal eluded him, however; ten times he sat for the civil service examinations and ten times he failed. Wen Zhengming eventually was assigned a minor post in Beijing but inordinate frustration with political life led him to retire in 1526 after serving only briefly. He returned to Suzhou in 1527.

Wen studied painting and calligraphy under Shen Zhou, the other pivotal artistic personality of the Wu school, and they remained close friends until Shen's death. Wen studied calligraphy from the works of earlier masters such as Wang Xizhi (303?–361?), Huang Tingjian (1045–1105), and Zhao Mengfu (1254–1322). He learned the painting styles of the great landscape masters Li Cheng (919–967), Zhao Mengfu, and the Four Masters of the Yuan dynasty: Huang Gongwang, Wu Zhen (1280–1354), Ni Zan (1301–1374) and Wang Meng (ca. 1309–1385). Gradually Wen developed his own styles and became one of the leading figures of Wu-school painting. He had many followers, including his son Wen Jia (1501–1583), his nephew Wen Boren (1502–1575), Lu Zhi (1496–1576), and Chen Chun (1483–1544). Wen was a diligent artist who remained prolific in both painting and calligraphy until his death at age ninety. Most of his numerous extant paintings are landscapes, though he also produced many paintings of bamboo and flowers.

— NLYS and EA

Artist's seal:
Ma Wan zhi yin

Colophon and seal:
Dong Qichang (1555–1636), one seal: Dong Qichang yin

Collector's seals:
Chang Ts'ung-yu (1915–1963); Tan Yu (20th century); two unidentified seals: jiuhua xianshi yin; tiaotian zhenshang

Recent provenance:
Chang Ts'ung-yu; C. T. Loo

Published:
Cahill, *Index*, p. 307.
Fu, *Studies in Connoisseurship*, p. 81, n. 9.
Sirén, *Chinese Painting*, 7: p. 125.
Suzuki, *Comprehensive Illustrated Catalog*, 1: no. A24–010.
Wang, *Exhibition of Authenticated Chinese Paintings*, no. 7.

Exhibited:
"Exhibition of Authenticated Chinese Paintings," C. T. Loo and Co., New York, 1948. no. 7.

Notes:
1. See Fu, *Studies*, pp. 74–81, for a thorough discussion of Ma Wan and his paintings. Six genuine works by the artist are listed (p. 81, note 9). The Cincinnati painting is listed in note 9.10 as "a late Ming painting by a follower of the Wen school."
2. See Fu, *Studies*, p. 79.
3. Edwards, *Art of Wen Cheng-ming*, p. 52.
4. Barnhart, "Tung Ch'i-Ch'ang's Connoisseurship."
5. Barnhart, "Tung Ch'i-Ch'ang's Connoisseurship," p. 11–13.
6. Quoted by Ren Daobin, "Ch'en Chi-ju as Critic and Connoisseur," p. 9–9.

36. Birds by a Stream

Zhang Hong (1577–circa 1652). Qing dynasty, dated 1648. Hanging scroll, ink and light colors on paper. H. 91.4 x W. 40.6 cm.
John J. Emery Endowment and Fanny Bryce Lehmer Endowment, 1948.85

Cascading water springs from a narrow crevice in the steep cliff alongside a stream. The dry rocks are bare of vegetation save for some bamboo, some grasses, and a small tree that emerges from the moist environment behind the rocks. Two birds sit on a tree branch extending to the right across the scene. A bird that apparently has just left this branch flies toward another bird, which looks up from its rocky perch.

Zhang Hong was one of the finest painters working in Suzhou in the first half of the seventeenth century, but only scant information survives about his life. Most of it comes from inscriptions on his paintings. Zhang was a professional painter born in Suzhou in 1577, who, though he may have come from a commoner family, moved in literati circles. His work exemplifies the merging of literati and professional painting in the late Ming period.[1] He had a long career, but evidently no followers, so the innovations he achieved were not carried on.

The Museum's painting is a work of Zhang's late years. He states in his inscription: "On a summer day in the *wuzi* year (1648) Zhang Hong playfully imitated the painting method of Shunju (Qian Xuan)." Comparison of this painting with (for example) Qian's *Doves and Pear Blossoms after Rain* (see entry 29), reveals little, if any, similarity between the artists' styles. Imitation, *fang*, implies an imaginative emulation that uses the source as a departure point for the artist's creativity, rather than connoting a direct copying of style or technique that might cause it to be mistaken for another work. In an album of landscapes after Song and Yuan masters in the Ching Yuan Chai collection Zhang imitated (*fang*) more closely the styles and brushwork of earlier masters.[2] Here though, Zhang takes from the Yuan master's approach only the focus on a detail of nature and a composition based on artistic conventions of Song and Yuan bird-and-flower painting.

The sketchiness of Zhang's brushwork contrasts sharply with Qian's precise, archaistic style. Unlike Qian, who used subject matter to convey hidden meaning or personal expression, Zhang paints a scene devoid of deeper significance: it is a work of *xieyi* ("idea writing") ink play. Zhang breaks free from the constraints of traditional literati brushwork and employs his own unique graded ink washes, sketchy strokes and flecks.

Zhang further distinguished his art from that of the literati painters of his time, who were steeped in the orthodoxy of Dong Qichang's emphasis on brushwork, through a greater interest in naturalism. Cahill identifies this approach as "descriptive naturalism" wherein Zhang textured the rocks and mountains as he knew them from his own observations, rather than relying solely on the utilization of conventional type-forms. Zhang produced topographic landscapes in which he incorporated European approaches to creating spatial depth. He was inspired by engravings brought to China by Jesuit missionaries, such as Matteo Ricci, to experiment with atmospheric perspective so as to create the optical illusion of recession into space.[3] Comparison of his early landscapes with landscapes of his late career clearly show his gradual adoption of such perspective techniques. In the early works, landscape elements are piled up in the traditional Chinese way and appear on a single plane at the painting surface. In the late landscapes there is convincing spatial recession as Zhang used atmospheric perspective to create optical depth.[4]

Even in the Museum's painting, which is a rare surviving example by the artist of a bird-and-flower subject, Zhang's interest in atmospheric perspective and his brushwork innovations are apparent. He models the rocks with washes, rather than outlining and texture strokes, to create the appearance of three-dimensional form. The cascading water pierces the picture plane, appearing to come from deep within the rocks toward the viewer. The birds likewise interact within a convincingly three-dimensional space.

Artist's seals:
Zhang Hong; Juntu shi

Collector's seals:
Chang Ts'ung-yu (1915–1963).

Recent Provenance:
   Chang Ts'ung-yu; C.T. Loo
Published:
   Hai-wai yi-chen Painting, p. 159.
   Suzuki, *Comprehensive Illustrated Catalog*, 1: no. A24–008.
   Wang, *Exhibition of Authenticated Chinese Paintings*, no. 24.
Exhibited:
   "Exhibition of Authenticated Chinese Paintings," C.T. Loo and Co., New York, 1948.
Notes:
   1. Shan, "Tendency Toward Mergence," p. 3–14.
   2. Ho, *Century of Tung Ch'i-Ch'ang* 1, pp. 314–15
   3. Cahill, *Compelling Image*, pp. 1–35.
   4. Compare, for example, Zhang's "Mount Shixie," of 1613 with his "Wing in the Pines at Mount Koqu," of 1650; Cahill, *Compelling Image*, figs. 1.6 and 1.1, respectively.

37. The Scenery of Mount Yu

Wang Jian (1598–1677). Qing dynasty, dated 1662. Handscroll; ink on paper. H. 30.8 x L. 445.4 cm.
Museum purchase: John J. Emery Endowment and the Edwin and Virginia Irwin Memorial, 1992.1

Entrance to the landscape begins at the right with the view of a broad expanse of water between rounded foothills. Beyond the hills is a valley of fishing villages along a small river. From there the viewer must climb ever-steeper ridges, passing small pavilions and a temple along the way toward the grand Mount Yu. The path follows the crest of rocky ledges that wind through forests and peaks. Two travelers are seen approaching a steep, narrow trail through a densely forested ravine; its rocky overhangs are covered in creeping vines that hover above tiny lookouts clinging precariously to the cliff. The path climbs higher, around the peak of the mountain, and out of sight, building anticipation as it ascends to the point where the heart of the mountain is revealed.

Suddenly, as if the viewer has entered a vast sanctuary, the viewpoint changes so that one is now completely embraced by the mountain. The viewer looks up to see overhanging rocks and thundering waterfalls that plunge into misty depths. Here and there dense vines have overtaken their hosts, providing scribbly accents to trees and rocks. The stream continues its tumble through an old-growth forest of stately pines.

Beyond another massive ridge the rocky ledges reappear, circling above the dark entrance to a cavern before descending steeply. Travelers on donkeys make their way down the mountain past a couple of dwellings in a narrow valley. Beyond another ridge a lone fisherman in a boat drifts past secluded pavilions nestled along the riverbank. From the wooden footbridge a fisherman carrying his pole views a watery expanse with sailboats in the distance. The path continues through a cluster of open pavilions built out over the water. A covered bridge crosses a tumbling brook and affords a view of another dramatic waterfall. The viewer ascends again into populated hills; there, huts and lookouts, winding paths and streams offer sheltered stops where one can linger and contemplate the beauty of nature.

The artist Wang Jian, one of the "Four Wangs" and one of the "Six Orthodox Masters of Early Qing," was a conservative painter often overshadowed in discussions of early Qing painting by his close friend Wang Shimin (1592–1680) and their student Wang Hui (1632–1717). Born into a prominent family of scholars in Taicang, Jiangsu province, Wang Jian was the great-grandson of the Ming scholar-official Wang Shizhen (1526–1590), from whom he inherited a collection of important paintings. Wang Jian passed the second-level civil service examinations in 1633; after serving in a government post in Beijing, he was named prefect of Lianzhou in Guangdong province. The appointment apparently was given to him in honor of his great-grandfather's meritorious service there. Frustrated by politics, however, Wang Jian served only two years before retiring to his home in Taicang in 1641. There he joined his friend Wang Shimin and devoted himself to painting and scholarly pursuits; he never held public office again.[1]

Wang Shimin and Wang Jian were followers of the pivotal Ming painter, calligrapher, and art theorist Dong Qichang (1555–1636) (see entry 36). Both men knew him personally; Dong tutored Wang Shimin in painting, and on several occasions Wang Jian had the opportunity to visit the master at his home and view his extensive collection of paintings. Dong encouraged and advised both young artists to imitate the styles of Dong Yuan (active ca. 945–ca. 960), Juran (active ca. 960–ca. 986), and the Four Masters of the Yuan dynasty: Huang Gongwang (1269–1354), Wu Zhen (1280–1354), Ni Zan (1301–1374), and Wang Meng (ca. 1309–1385). Wang Shimin and Wang Jian thus became the leading proponents of Dong's orthodox theories in the Qing dynasty. Through their close friendship, their mutual encouragement and admiration of each other's painting, and their devotion to numerous students, especially Wang Hui and Wang Yuanqi (1642–1715) (the former discovered by Wang Jian, the latter was Wang Shimin's grandson), they perpetuated the traditions of landscape painting proclaimed worthy by Dong Qichang. Indeed, Wang Jian and Wang Shimin applied Dong's theories more literally in their paintings than Dong did in his own.

In style and subject matter the Museum's painting is a classic early Qing orthodox landscape painting that demonstrates Wang Jian's admiration for Huang Gongwang. The artist's inscription reads:

Huang Zijiu [Huang Gongwang] dearly loved the scenery of Mount Yu; he travelled often to the foot of the mountain, and viewed as many misty, cloudy scenes as possible. I intend always to imitate him, but my brushwork is so dry and dull that my works are in no position to be compared with his. Yet I paint this handscroll in his style, and wonder what viewers' opinions might be.
   In the second month of the renyin year [1662] painted and inscribed while on a boat at the foot of Mount Yu, Wang Jian.

The pervasive use of long, hemp-fiber strokes and heavy accent dots for the mountains is inspired by Huang's brushwork and directed by Dong Qichang's interpretation of the Yuan artist:

In painting, mountains must show concave and convex forms. One begins by outlining the mountains first according to their outward forms and momentum, and proceeds, within the outlined forms, by applying straight texture strokes. This is the method of Zijiu [Huang Gongwang].[2]

The choice of subject matter is a tribute to Huang Gongwang as well, because Mount Yu is located near the Yuan painter's birthplace, Changshu. The whole area resonated with Huang's spirit and was a source of inspiration for Wang Jian, as indicated in his inscription. In executing this handscroll, Wang surely had in mind Huang's great masterpiece,"Dwelling in the Fu Chun Mountains," a handscroll that he had the opportunity to study in Dong Qichang's collection.[3]

Ten years after he painted this scroll, Wang Jian produced an album titled"Ten Scenic Spots in Mount Yu," now in the Suzhou Museum. In it he depicts specific places of historical and topographic interest, such as retreats of famous scholars and seasonal views of the landscape. Although these sites cannot be correlated directly with scenery depicted in the Museum's scroll, they provide additional perspective on the eremitic importance of Mount Yu in Chinese literati tradition.[4]

Wang Jian and his orthodox contemporaries painted most of their landscapes in the hanging scroll format. Their adherence to an established tradition in landscape painting often resulted in rather formulaic works. Wang Jian certainly produced his share of paintings lacking in splendor. However, the handscroll format provided greater potential for exploring composition and perspective creatively. In an undated handscroll now in the Tokyo National Museum Wang provides an impressive bird's-eye panorama of a mountain range. In the Cincinnati scroll, however, the viewer becomes an involved participant, experiencing the mountain from a variety of perspectives: looking down on broad expanses of water and villages; following persons nearly at eye level as they walk or sit in pavilions; being completely embraced and overwhelmed by the monumentality of the mountain's "heart." These changing perspectives create a rhythm and energy that Moss compares to music:

The handscroll format takes the arts of painting and calligraphy far beyond the mere image; like a musical experience, it allows development, variation, climax and anticlimax, the subtle relationship of one aspect of a theme to another, contrasting with another aspect here and another relationship there. Wang Jian's ink landscape of Mount Yu can be very well understood, I think, as a passage of music, and its effect is as stirring and soothing.[5]

Artist's seal:
Jian
Collector's seals:
Luo Ping (1733–99), three seals; one seal, unidentified.
Recent provenance:
Sydney L. Moss, Ltd.
Published:
Archives of Asian Art, 46(1993), p. 111.

Avril,"Highlights," pp. 70–73.
Durrell, *Selection of New Acquisitions*, pp. 22–23.
Moss, *Scrolling Images*, pp. 57–62.
"Recent Acquisitions," p. 63.
Exhibited:
"Scrolling Images," Sydney L. Moss. Ltd., London, 1991, no. 6.
Notes:
1. For biographical information on Wang Jian, see Hummel, *Eminent Chinese*, 2: p. 812; Sirén, *Chinese Painting*, 5, pp. 104–109; Rogers, *Masterworks*, p. 157.
2. From Dong's *Hua yen* [The Eye of Painting], as quoted in Fong,"Tung Ch'i-Ch'ang and Artistic Renewal," p. 45.
3. Illustrated in Cahill, *Hills beyond a River*, pl. 41.
4. Gong,"Ten Scenic Spots in Yushan."
5. Moss, *Scrolling Images*, p. 9.

38. Birds and Lotus Pond

Bada Shanren (1626–1705). Qing Dynasty, dated November 16,1690. Handscroll; ink on paper. H. 37.5 x L. 330 cm. Museum purchase, 1950.79.

The composition begins at the right with a large rock outlined in broad ink strokes. The rock, which consists of an unpainted surface contrasting sharply with dense, black ink shadow, sits precariously on the shore of a lotus pond. A lush section of lotus follows, composed of dense leaves surrounding two partially visible white blossoms. Extending upward and to the left are several long, leafy stalks. A full leaf below fills the foreground and cushions a dry rocky outcropping. On the rocks, two sparrows seem to chatter at one another. A third sparrow steps gingerly and peers over the edge of one of the rocks. Beyond are more large leafy stalks of lotus, one severely cropped by the top edge of the paper, and a full lotus bud that reaches upward and touches the lower edge of the large overhanging leaf. Beyond, the lower part of an overhanging rock formed of dry, circular strokes is almost touched by the bill of a wide-eyed duck. The duck seems rather reptilian; it even bares tiny teeth. The duck looks upward, stretching its neck as it looks out from behind a plantain leaf. Above the plantain leaf is a five-line poem, and beyond the stalk the scroll ends with the artist's signature and date.

Bada Shanren is a literary name used in later adulthood by one of the most enigmatic painters in Chinese history. Bada has often been referred to as Zhu Da, but this name is incorrect. Many scholars have tried to ascertain his real name, but it remains elusive. Whether it was Zhu Tonglin, as suggested in the most recent major study,[1] is not known for certain, but more important even than his real name are the circumstances of his life and times, which profoundly affected his art.

A descendant of the Yiyang branch of the Ming imperial family, Bada was born in 1626 in Nanchang, Jiangxi province, residence of the Yiyang prince. Bada spent his early life in the company of intellectuals and artists. His grandfather, Zhu Duozheng, was a scholar, poet, calligrapher and painter who led the life of a literatus; his father, believed to have been Zhu Moujin, Zhu Duozheng's fourth son, was mute from birth and was a painter of landscapes, birds and flowers.[2]

The peace and stability of Bada's youth disintegrated when the Ming dynasty fell to the Manchus, who established the Qing dynasty in 1644. Bada suddenly found himself in the category of *yimin*, or "leftover subject," (also see entry 27), and the new political climate threatened his safety and self-identity. When Manchu forces occupied Nanchang, Bada fled into the seclusion of Buddhist monkhood, as did other members of the Zhu family clan. Gifted with a keen intellect, Bada was admired and respected as a Chan Buddhist teacher, and had many students. He served as abbot of the Gengxian monastery, yet remained dissatisfied. In 1677 and 1678 he wrote several colophons on a portrait of himself painted by Huang Anping in 1674; in these writings he expressed doubt and frustration in his life as a Chan monk.[3]

At this time, Bada began to exhibit the eccentric behavior for which he became renown. Many biographers described his madness as manifested by fits of laughter, weeping, leaping and yelling. The insanity was probably feigned as were his intermittent bouts of muteness; Bada adopted these behaviors whenever he felt the need to maks his feelings or retreat from social confrontation.

When he left the Buddhist faith, Bada was already in his fifties. From that time he devoted himself to painting and poetry. He enjoyed his most prolific years as an artist from 1684, when he took the name Bada Shanren, "mountain-man of the eight great," to his death in 1705. This literary name seems to be a reference to the *Sutra of the Eight Great Human Realizations* (*Ba da renjuejing*); Bada had admired and inscribed a copy of this book by the famous Yuan painter, calligrapher and Song loyalist, Zhao Mengfu.[4]

The Museum's handscroll, signed "In the *gengwu* year [1690], sixteenth day of the tenth month [November 16], Bada Shanren painted and inscribed," was executed at a critical stage in the artist's development. At that time it seems that Bada was finally accepting his circumstances, and the compositions of his paintings are conceived for the first time as complete environments.[5] The poem on the Museum's painting had appeared before, on an album leaf of lotus painted in 1689:

> I once saw in the heart of the lotus seed
> That the lotus flower had its roots.
> At Ruoya splitting the lotus pod,
> It is the young gentleman in the painting.[6]

Bada equates himself with the lotus, which is the young gentleman (*langjunzi*). This image is also an allusion to the emperor, who is sometimes known as *Langjun*, and thus reflects Bada's imperial roots. In a Buddhist context, the lotus symbolizes purity and the Buddha, because it rises unblemished from the mud. Augmenting its rich traditional associations, the lotus became an important personal symbol for Bada, which he often incorporated in his paintings. Just as the lotus pod contained its own root, Bada carried in his heart the evidence of his heritage. Unable to change the environment in which he was forced to live, Bada created a world of brush and ink in which the lotus is dominant.[7]

The lotus is the botanical motif depicted most frequently in Bada's paintings. In 1690 alone he painted many versions of birds among lotus, plantain, and rocks; in each he explored greater abstractions and new juxtapositions of form and void. The dense blacks and the rich, wet grays of the bold, large brush strokes, which form the lotus, rocks and banana plant, transform the lotus pond, which is tranquil from the human perspective, into a dynamic, even threatening environment when viewed by the resident birds and duck. The cropping of the large elements of the composition imbues them with power to break free from the constraints of paper, brush and ink. As a painter Bada broke the bounds of convention, developing a personal artistic language completely unprecedented in Chinese painting. The handscroll format provided compositional challenges that intrigued Bada; he painted many handscrolls of lotus ponds during his lifetime, each one exploring the alternation of dense solids with spatial voids in powerful new ways.[8] The severe cropping increases the sense of energy and dynamism to create a bold, graphic work.

Artist's seals:
    kede shenxian; Huangzhuyuan; Bada Shanren (twice); lüwu renwu; Bada Shanren

Collector's seals:
    Zhang Daqian (1899–1983), four seals: bufu guren gao houren; Daqian haomeng; cangzhi daqian; Daqian zhibao.

Recent provenance:
    Zhang Daqian; C.T. Loo

Exhibited:
    "Master of the Lotus Garden: The Life and Art of Bada Shanren," Asian Art Museum of San Francisco, Yale University Art Gallery, 1990.

Published:
    Archives of the Chinese Art Society of America (1951), p. 72.
    Avril, "Highlights," pp. 72–73.
    Bunjinga Suihen, 6 (*Bada Shanren*), no. 75.
    Chang and Hu, *Selected Painting and Calligraphy of Pa Ta Shan Jen* 1: no. 25.
    The Cincinnati Art Museum Bulletin (March, 1953), illus. p. 11.
    Edwards, "Sophistications," p. 89, fig. 13.
    Munsterberg, "Collection of Chinese Paintings," p. 319, figs. 9–10.
    Munsterberg, *Crown of Life*, pp. 140–41.
    Sirén, *Chinese Painting* 6: pls. 383–384; 7: pp. 322, 325.
    Suzuki, *Comprehensive Illustrated Catalog*, 1: no. A24–005.
    T'Serstevens, *L'Art Chinois*, 74, illus., p. 69.
    Wang and Barnhart, *Master of the Lotus Garden*, no. 15, pp. 17, 115–18.

Notes:
    1. See Wang, "Life and Art of Bada Shanren," pp. 24–30, for a thorough discussion of the problems regarding Bada's given name.
    2. Wang, "Life and Art of Bada Shanren," p. 23.
    3. Wang, "Life and Art of Bada Shanren," pp. 38–40.
    4. Wang, "Life and Art of Bada Shanren," p. 32.
    5. Barnhart, "Introduction," p. 18, and "Reading the Paintings and Calligraphy," p. 112.
    6. Inscribed on Leaf b of an album of fish, lotus, globefish and bamboo, in the Rosshandler collection, Wang and Barnhart, *Master of the Lotus Garden*, no. 7, pp. 103, 115. Poem translated by Lee Hui-shu.
    7. Barnhart, "Reading the Paintings and Calligraphy," pp. 115.

8. Other handscrolls include *Lotus and Bird,* circa 1690, in the Metropolitan Museum of Art; *Fish and Rocks,* 1691, in the Cleveland Museum of Art; *Flowers by a River,* 1697, Tianjin Art Museum; published Wang and Barnhart, *Master of the Lotus Garden,* nos. 16, 22 and 40, respectively.

39. Sadaksari Lokesvara (Sibi Guanyin) as Savior from Perils

Northern China, possibly from Beijing, Qing dynasty, mid-17th century. Glue tempera and gold on gesso, mud, and straw applied to wood panel. H. 245 x W. 415.5 cm.
Annual Membership Purchase Fund, by exchange, and Museum purchase in honor of the Museum Shop's 20th anniversary, 1988.12

From his central position in this massive wall mural, the four-armed Sadaksari Lokesvara, a Lamaist form of Avalokitesvara known in Chinese as Sibi Guanyin ("four-armed Guanyin"), presides over a verdant landscape and a tempestuous sea. Seated in a contemplative posture on an elaborate gilt-edged, multicolored lotus blossom that rises from the waves, Sadaksari holds two hands together, concealing the wish-granting gem at his heart, while in the other two hands he holds a rosary and a lotus. In addition to his flowing green and red robes, the bodhisattva is adorned with gold jewelry: anklets, bracelets, armbands, belt, pendants, earrings, and a five-leafed crown, all of which stand out in three dimensions from the painted surface. His encompassing presence is further enhanced by the multicolored billowing clouds, dark halo, and rainbow-bordered backdrop of scrolling tree peonies. Above Sadaksari are three deities: the blue-skinned Bhaishajyaguru, the Medicine Buddha; ruby-skinned Amitabha, the transcendent Buddha of the West; and the white-skinned Sarasvati, goddess of learning.

Salvation from peril is the principal theme of the mural. Sadaksari (literally "The Six-Syllable One") personifies the liberating mantra *Om mani padme hum* ("Hail the jewel in the lotus!"), which emanates from the bodhisattva's vow to save all beings, and whose magical sound reverberates throughout the universe. To the left and the right of the bodhisattva, the peaceful White Tara and the fierce Green Tara emerge from the water on lotus blossoms, a reference to the legend that these female deities were born from Avalokitesvara's compassionate tears. Embodiments of the miraculous activities of all Buddhas, the Taras encourage Avalokitesvara to strive toward his goal of saving all beings.

The central deities are surrounded by scenes of salvation from specific perils, as described in the twenty-fifth chapter of the Lotus Sutra (also known in China as the Guanyin Chapter). A two-armed Avalokitesvara borne on clouds approaches each scene to intercede on behalf of those who call on the bodhisattva for aid. Of the twenty-nine dangers outlined in the sutra, ten are illustrated here, although not in the same order as they appear in the text. Clockwise, beginning at the upper right, the scenes in the mural illustrate these selected verses:

If a man is pushed off a peak of Mount Sumeru, he will dwell in space like the sun.
If threatened with thunder, hail, or lightning, he will remain dry.
If confronted with snakes or insects breathing fire, the sound of one's voice will dispel them.
If he faces execution, the executioner's sword will break.
If he is afloat on a great sea in which there are fish, dragons, and ghosts, waves will not drown him.
If he is surrounded by beasts with sharp claws and teeth, they will flee.
If someone harms him through spells, curses, or poisons, the victim can send them back to plague their authors.
If he enters the sea in search of riches and a black wind carries the ship to the realm of the rakshasas [cannibal trolls], he will be saved.
If a man falls into a great fire, he will not burn.
If he is surrounded by bandits waving swords, their thoughts will be transformed to kindly ones.[1]

In its original setting the mural adorned a wall in one of the principal halls of a northern Chinese Lamaist temple. Because the walls of the buildings were not load-bearing, they could be constructed of rather crude wood paneling; the Museum's mural is still attached to its original wood-panel support. To prepare a uniform surface for painting, the artist first applied to the wall a mixture of mud reinforced with chopped straw. This was followed by a layer of fine clay to provide a smooth surface that would readily absorb pigments. Finally, a primer of white lime was sometimes added to heighten the brilliance of the colors. In the Ming dynasty, the use of impasto and gold lacquer became widespread for depicting jewelry and other metal adornments worn or carried by the figures. This three-dimensional surface enhancement, combined with the application of delicate gold-painted patterns on the garments of figures, created a shimmering effect. The present division of the painting into sections in no way reflects the original function or artistic intention of the painting: Initially created as a unified composition, it was cut vertically into five unequal parts to facilitate removal from the temple.

Lamaism, the form of Buddhism practiced in Tibet, was not followed widely as a lay religion in China but was supported by the imperial court, beginning with the Yuan dynasty rulers. The Ming emperors continued this patronage, fully aware of the political ramifications of doing so: An alliance with the religious leaders of Tibet kept both Tibetans and Mongols from threatening China's border regions. From the time of the fifth Dalai Lama's visit to Mukden (Shenyang) in 1642, two years before the Manchus swept into Beijing to establish their rule over China, the Qing emperors ardently promoted Lamaism. Under Manchu patronage, new Lama temples mushroomed in and around Beijing and Chengde, and throughout the northern regions along the route followed by lamas who traveled regularly between Lhasa and Beijing.

Both the style and the subject matter of this mural argue for a mid-seventeenth century date. The mural exhibits many characteristics of a transitional style that combines features of Ming and Qing, as well as Tibetan Buddhist, painting. It retains elements of

Ming Buddhist wall painting, such as the gold-lacquered impasto (a technique that had disappeared completely by the eighteenth century), pastel polychrome clouds, and dark-green landscape elements reminiscent of murals that still survive at the Fa Hai temple, just outside Beijing.[2] In the depiction of deities, however, the light, flowing garments associated with Ming painting have been replaced with symmetrical drapery that rises in S-shapes from the sides of each deity, as in Tibetan painting.

An indication of early Qing style is the complete abandonment of heavy outlining in black; most shapes are defined instead with gentle outlining in lighter colors, while many are not outlined at all. Color is applied innovatively; variations in tonality and shading are employed to create volume and atmosphere. The result is an overall sense of spatial depth in which deities and setting no longer seem to be confined to the painting surface, but emerge and recede convincingly.

Finally, elements anticipating the more florid eighteenth century style are visible here, as in the backdrop of scrolling tree peonies and the multicolored pedestal outlined in gold. Many of the deliverance scenes follow standardized depictions that appear in Ming woodblock-printed versions of the Guanyin Chapter of the Lotus Sutra — for example, the travelers carrying umbrellas and crossing a bridge as the Chinese storm gods wreak havoc on them, or the scene of food poisoning inside a pavilion.[3] Although the peril scenes are Chinese in style, the depiction of deities derives from Tibetan Buddhist art of the period. Because of the patronage of Lamaism by some of the Ming and all of the Qing emperors, the imperial and temple workshops in China employed Tibetans and Nepalese who worked directly with Chinese artists.[4]

In 1642, the year when he visited Mukden, the fifth Dalai Lama defeated his opponents and was declared political as well as spiritual ruler of Tibet. In 1645 he built the magnificent Potala palace in Lhasa, on the site where Avalokitesvara allegedly meditated. The whole tract of land was ritually offered to him as the publicly recognized reincarnation of Avalokitesvara. Thus a depiction of Sadaksari Lokesvara, the form of Avalokitesvara incarnate in the Dalai Lamas, presiding over a vast land not only conveys religious meaning but also reflects important historical changes that occurred in Tibet in the mid-seventeenth century.

The fifth Dalai Lama's ambition of spreading peace throughout Asia prompted him to build an alliance based on equality with the Manchu emperor, and in 1652 he accepted the Manchus' formal invitation to visit Beijing.[5] In 1651, preparing for the visit of the fifth Dalai Lama, the Shunzhi emperor (r. 1644–1662) rebuilt a Ming temple in Beijing that had been destroyed by rebels in 1643, and converted it into the Huang Si [Yellow Temple] to provide temporary residence for his important guest. More buildings were constructed in 1653 for the Dalai Lama's staff. Throughout most of the Qing dynasty, this temple complex housed the highest-ranking Tibetan and Mongol lamas during their visits to Beijing. Today it lies in ruins in the northern suburbs of the city, having suffered damage and occupation as a military barracks at the hands of foreign soldiers during the Boxer Rebellion in 1900. In the ensuing decades it was used by Chinese military units.[6]

According to information provided at the time of acquisition, the Museum's mural allegedly was removed from a temple near Beijing during the Boxer Rebellion. Then it entered a European collection, where it remained until shortly before the Museum purchased it. Without documentation it is nearly impossible to identify the temple from which the mural originates. On the basis of its style, quality, and subject matter it would have been well suited for the decorative program of an important mid-seventeenth-century temple such as the Huang Si, which served visiting Tibetan dignitaries. Temple construction declined after the reign of Qianlong (1736–1795), and many temples have fallen victim to indiscriminate plundering and destruction through the numerous political upheavals of the last hundred years. The Museum is fortunate to possess this rare surviving fragment of the formerly widespread magnificence of Lamaist temple art in northern China.

Recent Provenance:
William Wolff

Published:
Archives of Asian Art, 42 (1989), p. 95.
Avril, "Highlights," pp. 68–69.

Notes:
1. The order of the scenes does not follow that of the chapter. The scenes illustrate perils described in both the prose and the verse portions of the sutra text. The translation here follows Tanabe, *Paintings*, pp. 15–17.
2. The murals are published in Wei, *Fa Hai si bihua.*
3. Compare the many similarities in overall composition and configuration of peril scenes in a woodblock-printed book dated 1586 in the Indianapolis Museum of Art, 1983.106; published in Weidner, *Latter Days*, no. 42.
4. See Rhie and Thurman, *Wisdom and Compassion*, pp. 61–63. The Museum's mural is closely comparable in style to a seventeenth-century Chinese tangka of the eleven-headed Avalokitesvara in the Boston Museum of Fine Arts; see Rhie and Thurman, *Wisdom and Compassion*, no. 34.
5. See Rhie and Thurman, *Wisdom and Compassion*, pp. 30–31.
6. For a description of the condition of the Huang Si complex in the early 1930s, see Arlington and Lewisohn, *In Search of Old Peking*, pp. 238–39. The complex suffered further damage in the twenty years following the publication of above mentioned guide. See *Nagel's*, pp. 574–75.

40. Spring Morning in the Han Palace

Qing dynasty, late 17th or early 18th century. Handscroll; ink, colors, and gold on silk. H. 56.2 x L. 1,028.7 cm.
Museum purchase: Lawrence Archer Wachs Trust, 1995.1

The scroll opens with a scene outside the gates to the women's quarters of the imperial palace. Walking along the stone path and balustrade beside a lake, several servants accompany a man in informal robe and cap; perhaps he represents the emperor. He approaches the stairs to the gate; another servant gestures from the top of the stairs. A man wearing a dark green informal robe, who seems to be a tutor, grasps the sleeve of a young boy, likely an imperial prince, and looks toward the gate. Beyond the gate, the top of a pavilion and the tiled edges of the walls can be seen above dense mist. In the foreground three women gather on the veranda of a two-story pavilion. Several servants carrying various items walk toward another wall and inner doorway.

Inside this inner wall the number of women and their activities increases, as does the elaborateness of the garden setting. A young boy, riding in a goat-drawn canopied cart with an adult woman, presents a pair of double rings to a small girl who wears a red imperial wedding robe. She is held in the arms of a lady-in-waiting. In front of this cart an imperial wife or concubine rides in another goat-drawn cart; she has turned around to approvingly observe the children's betrothal. In the distance, other palace women can be seen in their residences.

The composition proceeds to a large courtyard lush with flowering trees, shrubs, and large fantastic garden rocks. In the foreground, carts move toward the central pavilion. In the background, numerous servants, female members of the imperial household, and young boys are engaged in various activities such as adjusting blinds, preparing gifts, and gathering together as they prepare for a celebration. All the bustle is intended in honor of the empress, who sits regally on a *kang* in the central throne room and watches a group of female dancers. From two hexagonal pavilions in the courtyard, female musicians accompany the dancers. More carts arrive from the left-hand side of the scroll. In a pushcart bearing a canopy decorated with flowers, a small boy offers an artemisia leaf to his tiny female companion and he places his other hand around her shoulder. A princess or secondary wife arrives in a stag-drawn chariot. On the covered walkway in the background are two servants, each holding a cat. A two-story pavilion is seen next; there one woman holds a tray of pomegranates while another dangles an open fruit, its seeds exposed, toward a child's outstretched hand. Under a fabric canopy, several women construct a lion from flower blossoms; in the foreground, women are gathering more blossoms. A maid assists a young boy as he crosses the threshold of the moon gate in another wall.

Beyond the wall, a balustraded walkway follows the perimeter of a lake. Two women on the veranda throw rocks at a pair of mandarin ducks, who scoot away in agitation. In a far pavilion, three women are engaged in a game of chess. Two women in a foreground tower look out over the water at women in dragon boats. On the island in the lake, a woman in a pavilion plays the *qin*. Beyond, two women hit butterflies with their fans, one woman pushes another on a swing, and several women with children are gathered around a young woman who is having her fortune told. A woman leans on the balustrade and lifts her skirt to show her foot to two young children. Nine herons surround a willow tree and fantastic garden rock. Other women cross a stone bridge capped with a small pavilion. In the last scene, two elaborate carts carrying young women attended by numerous servants proceed toward the right. In the background, five cranes are seen along the rocky shoreline beside a stand of bamboo.

The subject of this painting, springtime activities in the women's quarters of the imperial palace during the Han dynasty (206 B.C.–220 A.D.), represents a type of *shinü hua*, "paintings of beautiful women." The painting stems from the tradition of Tang-dynasty handscroll paintings that depict female members of the imperial household at their toilet, caring for children, or engaged in refined pursuits such as painting or music. The theme of "Spring Morning in the Han Palace" (*Hangong chunxiao tu*) purportedly originated in the Song dynasty with a now-lost painting by the artist Li Gonglin (1049–1106). The Ming-dynasty master Qiu Ying (ca. 1494–ca. 1552) produced the greatest extant version of this theme, a handscroll in the National Palace Museum, Taipei.[1] The "Spring Morning" subject gained particular popularity in the Qing dynasty; several versions were executed by imperial court artists in the eighteenth century, including Leng Mei's copy of Li Gonglin's original and a collaboration by Jin Kun, Lu Zhan, Chen Zhidao, and Wu Gui (now in the National Palace Museum, Taipei).[2] Particularly suited to less formal commissions by the imperial court, the subject allowed for relative artistic freedom in its execution. In 1714, for example, the eunuch Mao Tuan received an imperial order to take a handscroll of "Spring Morning in the Han Palace" to the court painter Shen Yuan to copy in color. "If there are features to be added or omitted he may make the required changes."[3] The imaginary nature of this theme thus gave artists an opportunity to produce an elaborate *tour de force* that would demonstrate their creative talents.

The preferred style for such paintings is known as *gongbi zhongcai* (fine line, heavy color), in which the forms are outlined in fine lines, filled in with brilliant, jewel-like colors, and finished with embellishments of gold. Under the patronage of the emperors Kangxi, Yongzheng, and Qianlong the most refined Qing paintings in the *shinü hua* genre were produced by well-known court painters such as Jiao Bingzhen, Leng Mei (see entry 41), Ding Guanpeng, Jin Tingbiao, and Chen Mei, and by many anonymous painters.[4]

The Museum's painting cannot be identified with a known artist or collector; the pair of tiny seals appearing at each end of the painting have so far defied identification. Without this information it cannot be determined with certainty whether the painting is the work of an artist associated with the imperial court or of a professional painter working in Suzhou. Arguing for possible court production are the size of the Museum's scroll, the employment of lavish materials in its production and mounting. The absence of imperial collection seals does not preclude the possibility of atelier work, because court painters were known to take private commissions.[5] However, the subject, style, and highly accomplished execution of the painting were common to both court painters and professional painters working in Suzhou. The subject was especially popular among Suzhou artists, who produced works in the tradition of Qiu Ying's famous painting of this theme.[6] Artists working outside the imperial household sometimes were commissioned by the emperor to produce work for the court, some artists worked intermittently in the imperial workshops, and artists hoping for appointments in the imperial atelier presented their work for the emperor's review, thus blurring the distinctions between court-commissioned art produced at the imperial atelier and work produced by independent professionals outside the court.[7]

According to Confucian ethics, women and men were to spend most of their time apart. In the *Book of Rites* it is stated that a strict demarcation should be observed between the inner quarters, where the women dwell, and the outer quarters, where the men live. This separation is analogous to the differentiation of gender roles: The men concerned themselves with community affairs, while the women were responsible for managing the household.[8] The Museum's painting conveys the separation of sexes with a clear distinction between inner and outer; the only men in the painting are shown outside the gate to the women's quarters.

In their mist-enshrouded complex of pavilions, lakes, and lush gardens, the women pursue elegant activities associated with spring, such as swinging under willow trees, chasing butterflies, gathering flowers, and playing chess.[9] In an elaborate pavilion in the center of the scroll the empress sits on her throne, attired in formal regalia; dancers and musicians entertain her. Many of the palace women come to her with gifts symbolizing wishes for long life and happiness. Some approach on foot; others arrive in fanciful carts that progress toward the central pavilion from both ends of the scroll. Blossoming trees and shrubs appear in profusion throughout the painting; these, and the focus on activities related to gathering and using flowers, are reminiscent of customs associated with the Festival of the Hundred Flowers, a spring fertility rite observed by women during the second month of the lunar year. Motifs throughout express concerns for fertility, emphasizing the roles of women in the imperial household and the expectation that they will provide the emperor with a potential heir to the throne.

The classic "Spring Morning" theme has erotic overtones as well. Such pictures were often produced for the idle male gaze, offering a view into the most private area of the Forbidden City during the spring, when *yang*, the male element, is ascendant and when nature becomes fertile. Paired animals and birds such as cats, dogs, cranes, egrets, and mandarin ducks appear throughout in further reference to fertility and sexuality.[10] The sensuous performance of sleeve dancers in the central scene is a convention that stems from Han dynasty ritual dances performed by shamanesses to dispel evil, to insure fertility, and as bearers of the elixir of immortality.[11]

Two separate vignettes illustrate the betrothal of young children. In one of these a woman holding a small girl dressed in a red wedding robe approaches a canopied cart; there another woman holds a small boy, who offers a pair of jade rings to the future bride. In another cart, adorned with peonies, a young boy and girl are seated together. The boy tenderly places his arm around his companion's shoulder and presents her with an artemisia leaf, a plant known for its healing properties and as a shield against poison. These scenes coincide with an increased emphasis on companionate marriage in the seventeenth century.

The Han Palace is a reference both to the Han dynasty, a past golden age, and to the ethnic, or Han, Chinese. The Manchu rulers'

commissioning of pictures of the Han Palace was meant to show their respect for, and assimilation of, Confucian values. At the Qing imperial court, however, women were required to wear Manchu dress; Han Chinese clothing was strictly prohibited. Yet most Qing *shinü* paintings depict women in Han costume which enhances their romantic and elegant appeal.[12] In this painting the dress is entirely appropriate to the subject. Another distinction between Manchu and Han ideals of female beauty was the practice of footbinding; beginning in the Song dynasty, Han girls bound their feet to form the tiny (two- to four-inch) "lotus," which men found highly erotic. The Museum's scroll includes an unusual scene of a woman showing her foot to a small child, who points at what remains discreetly hidden from the viewer. In addition to its erotic aspect, the showing of her foot may represent pride in this symbol of Han women's culture, identity and ideal of feminine beauty.[13]

The overall interpretation depends on the identity of the artist and/or the patron who commissioned it. If the painting is a work of the imperial atelier, as suggested by its size and mounting, it may be an expression of purely sensual fantasy. If the artist was a female member of the imperial household, the inclusion of nonsubmissive actions, such as the two women throwing rocks at mandarin ducks, may express the frustrations of sharing the emperor's affections or of being trapped in a noncompanionate marriage. If the painting was created by an artist outside the imperial court, such as a painter in Suzhou or Yangzhou, its meaning may have broader political implications. For example, the scenes of female rebelliousness toward male dominance, as in the depiction of women hitting butterflies, may be a veiled expression of southern Chinese resistance to the Manchu conquest of Southern China.[14]

Seals:
  Two seals, undeciphered.

Published:
  Archives of Asian Art, 49(1996), p. 114.
  Moss, *Scrolling Images*, pp. 79–82.

Exhibited:
  "Scrolling Images," Sydney L. Moss. Ltd., London, 1991, no. 9.

Notes:
  1. Illustrated in Fong and Watt, *Possessing the Past*, pp. 400–01.
  2. Moss, *Scrolling Images*, p. 80.
  3. Yang, "The Ch'ien-lung Painting Academy," p. 348.
  4. Shan, "Gentlewoman Paintings," pp. 56–57.
  5. Rogers, "Court Painting under the Qianlong Emperor," pp. 304–05.
  6. She Cheng, National Palace Museum, Taipei, and Yang Boda, Palace Museum, Beijing, suggested that the CAM scroll was by a Suzhou painter, see Moss, *Scrolling Images*, p. 81; Richard Barnhart concurred with these opinions, see correspondence, CAM curatorial files.
  7. She, "Painting Academy," pp. 320–21; Rogers, "Court Painting," pp. 305–06.
  8. Ebrey, *Inner Quarters*, pp. 23–24.
  9. A twelve-leaf album titled "The Pursuit of Pleasure in the Course of the Seasons," by the imperial court painter Chen Mei (died 1745), depicts pastimes of the imperial concubines in the inner quarters of the palace. The activities for the second and third months are illustrated respectively as swinging beneath willow trees and playing chess in a pleasure garden (*A Cidade Proibida*, pp. 154–57).
  10. Cahill, "The Three Zhangs," pp. 59–61.
  11. Erickson, "Twirling their Long Sleeves."

12. See Shan, "Gentlewomen Paintings," pp. 58–59.

13. For further discussion of footbinding in the seventeenth century, see Ko, *Teachers of the Inner Chambers*, pp. 147–51 and pp. 166–71.

14. Cahill suggests the Manchu-Han political relationship as similar to male dominance and female submission in "The Three Zhangs," pp. 67–68.

41. A Picture of Perfect Felicity (*Quan qing tu*)

Leng Mei (active ca. 1703–1742). Qing dynasty, circa 1723–1735.
Hanging scroll; ink and colors on silk. H. 150 x W. 99 cm.
Signed by the artist: jinmen huashi Leng Mei [Leng Mei, Master Painter of the Golden Gate].
Gift of Mrs. James L. Magrish, 1953.149

In the garden courtyard of their elegant compound, an upper-class family celebrates the Lantern Festival, culmination of the fifteen-day observance of the New Year. Presiding over the festivities is the family patriarch, seated on a couch with a small child at his side; accompanying him in the pavilion are his wife and three more children. In the garden, two women, presumably secondary wives or concubines, watch eight children playing.

New Year's customs center on the hope that the new year will bring prosperity and good fortune to the household. A typical Chinese practice is the hanging of *nian hua* (New Year's pictures) throughout the home. Whether elegant, refined paintings such as this one, or inexpensive and brightly colored popular woodblock prints (see entry 43), *nian hua* serve both decorative and amuletic functions: They contribute to a festive atmosphere, and their inherent symbolism anticipates blessings.

Leng Mei, from Jiaozhou, Shandong, studied under the respected Shandong painter Jiao Bingzhen (active ca. 1680–1720), who served in the imperial painting academy and may have helped to arrange Leng's imperial appointment. Leng was already a respected painter in the court of Kangxi (r. 1662–1722) before 1703. His imperial commissions included a copy of Qiu Ying's *Spring Morning in the Han Palace* (see entry 41) and the pictures in honor of Kangxi's sixtieth birthday. There is no record of Leng's presence in the imperial atelier under the emperor Yongzheng (r. 1723–1735), but by 1736 he was active as a court painter under the emperor Qianlong (r. 1736–1795).[1]

During his time away from the court, Leng Mei probably supported himself as a professional painter. *A Picture of Perfect Felicity* might have been painted during this absence from imperial service, for the artist signed his name "Leng Mei, Master Painter of the Golden Gate." This title indicated his status as a court painter but did not include *chen* ("your servitor"), the epithet of an imperial commission.[2]

Leng's use of mathematical perspective to define spatial depth stems from the influence of Jesuit painters who served the emperor Kangxi. The subject matter and style of this painting reflect the tastes of the upper-class patrons who would have supported Leng as a professional painter.[3]

The Museum's painting is rich with motifs expressing wishes for the New Year. Large blossoming plum trees, representing renewal and the coming of spring, enclose the pavilion. Four of the children surround a large lantern containing five red bats, a visual pun for "enormous blessing": The words for "red bat" (*hong fu*) sound like the words for "enormous good fortune" (*hong fu*). Five bats in captivity together signify attainment of the five blessings: long life, riches, health, a love of virtue, and a natural death. One child bears a branch of *lingzhi* fungus, symbol of longevity. The word for fish (*yu*) is homophonic with the word for abundance (*yu*); thus the boy who holds the fish-shaped lantern represents the desire for numerous sons to bring abundant wealth. A family's best hope for wealth and status was for its sons to achieve high rank in the government by passing difficult civil service examinations. The two children at the left enact the celebrations of a successful civil service candidate: One blows a horn, the other carries a branch of blooming osmanthus (*gui guan*), an emblem of victory or distinction. Two family members carry wish-granting scepters called *ruyi*; these express the sentiment "May all your wishes come true."

The typical upper-class Qing-dynasty household comprised several generations of multiple conjugal relationships and numerous offspring; such a complex family structure was prone to jealousy and conflict. The New Year provided an opportunity to discard past ill fortune and celebrate the hope of renewal. Much is done during the season to invite the positive *yang* forces to dominate. Thus *nian hua* typically capture the festive spirit of the celebration by presenting an idealized vision of family to encourage harmony, prosperity, and joy within the household.

Artists's seals:
Leng Mei zhi yin; jinmenhuashi

Recent provenance:
Mr. and Mrs. James L. Magrish

Published:
Hai-wai yi-chen Painting 2, p. 195.
Keppel, *China in 1700*, no. 31.

Exhibited:
Springfield Art Center, 1956.
"China in 1700: Kangxi Porcelains at the Taft Museum," Taft Museum, Cincinnati, 1988.

Notes:
1. Yang Boda, "Leng Mei ji qi *Bishu Shanzhuang Tu*."
2. See Barnhart, *Painters of the Great Ming*, p. 2; also Hucker, *Dictionary of Official Titles*, no. 2814.
3. Another painting by Leng Mei from this period is in the Roy and Marilyn Papp collection, Phoenix. See *Heritage of the Brush*, no. 24.

42. The Meeting of Cranes and Peacocks

Qing dynasty, dated 1839. Woodblock print. H. 32.4 x W. 57.1 cm.
Gift of Rosemarie E. Megrue in memory of her husband, Robert B. Megrue, 1993.173

On a garden terrace two children riding cranes approach two children riding peacocks. Each rider holds a flywhisk and carries a vase of blossoming peonies on his back. Flagbearers with their colorful banners accompany each pair of riders; the tops of two flags are also seen in the foreground. The peacock rider second from the left holds a wrapped bundle in the air, while a dancing child in the foreground carries a spray of peony and a branch of osmanthus. To the right, another small boy carries a box of books. Above the scene is this inscription:

> The meeting of cranes and peacocks is a tradition from ancient times;
> Currently they are playing everywhere.
> Several children gather together in a group,
> Singing in praise of a peaceful year.
> Ji-hai year [1899]. Inscribed by Qinyu Zhuren.[1]

Woodblock printing has a long tradition in China, dating back to religious prints of the Tang and Five Dynasties periods (see entry 26). During the Qing dynasty (1644–1911), colored woodcuts whose subject matter was associated with celebration of the lunar New Year gained popularity in all classes of Chinese society. Known as *nian hua*, ("New Year's pictures"), these prints were purchased annually and were used to decorate the household during China's most festive season (also see entry 41). Many printmaking centers flourished and produced images in distinctive regional styles. Among the most elegant are the prints from Yangliuqing, near Tianjin, whose figural style followed that of imperial court painting. The Museum's print was most likely produced by one of the Yangliuqing printing houses.

Subjects symbolizing good wishes dominate the iconography of *nian hua*. The visual vocabulary, based on popular tales, household deities, and homophonic puns, was widely understood throughout Chinese society. Children, usually boys, figure prominently among the main characters of *nianhua* because they are equated with good fortune. Engaged in activities charged with meaning, they embody happiness; their playful energy represents the spirit of celebration.

The iconography of this print concerns families' aspirations to produce male offspring who will become scholar-officials in China's government bureaucracy, thereby bringing fame and prosperity to the clan. To attain the status of a high-ranking official, one had to pass difficult civil service examinations. The meeting of cranes, symbols of longevity and wisdom, with peacocks, emblems of high rank, refers to the wish that the candidates will pass the examinations at the highest level.

Each boy rider wears a costume associated with a government official, and the procession imitates the celebrations of successful civil service candidates. One rider holds aloft a wrapped bundle containing a hat, the word for which, *guan*, sounds like the word for "official" (*guan*). Flywhisks, symbolic of authority, and peonies, emblems of wealth and distinction, are carried by each rider. In the foreground one small boy holds a spray of peony and a branch of osmanthus, *guihua*: "To pluck an osmanthus twig from the

Moon Palace" means "to pass the state examinations." Osmanthus is also a rebus for "noble" (*gui*); thus the term "osmanthus sons" refers to those who will gain high rank in the civil service. The flag finial in the shape of a halberd (*ji*) is a rebus for "good luck" (*ji*) and for "level or grade" (*ji*); thus it expresses the wish for the good fortune to attain a high-level position in the bureaucracy. The fan (*shan*) symbolizes an official's rank and is a rebus for "good" (*shan*).

Note:
1. Trans. Nora Ling-yün Shih.

43. Twin Pines and Level Distance (*Shuangsong pingyuan*)

Tracing copy after Zhao Mengfu (1254–1322). Shanghai, 1940s.
Handscroll; ink on paper.
Museum purchase, 1950.78

Throughout the history of Chinese painting and calligraphy, copying works of the past has been a respectable pursuit, both as a training exercise and for preserving great masterpieces. In addition to bona fide copying, China has a long history of forging works of art expressly for deception. Whatever the motivation, two general methods were employed for replicating directly from an existing work of art: freehand copying (*lin*) and tracing (*mo*). The Museum's painting, after the Yuan-dynasty master painter and calligrapher Zhao Mengfu, is a modern forgery produced through a tracing technique known as *xiangta*, "tracing by illumination."

In a letter to a friend, the Song-dynasty calligrapher Huang Tingjian (1045–1105) described the use of a special table outfitted with a drawer in which a lamp could be placed. Backlighting aided the copyist in capturing every nuance of the original.[1] A close variation on this centuries-old method was employed in the 1940s by a group of talented artists invited by the Shanghai collector Tan Jing to reproduce about two dozen paintings from the Yuan, Ming, and Qing periods in his personal collection, including all inscriptions, seals, and colophons. The replicas represented the collaborative work of specialists in imitating calligraphy, painting, seals, and mountings. A lamp was set below a table with a glass surface to illuminate the original, over which the blank paper or silk for the copy was placed. Fong published a list of eight pairs of paintings and their models known to have been produced in this way, including the Museum's handscroll and the handscroll from which it was copied, which is now in the Metropolitan Museum of Art.[2]

When the Museum purchased this handscroll, its mate had not surfaced; later the Cincinnati version was confirmed as the copy when studied together with its model.[3] The minor flaws of the copyist's hand, exposed through direct comparison with the original, might otherwise have gone undetected, for the Cincinnati painting is a masterwork of the forger's art. Upon initial examination the two paintings appear startlingly similar and the Cincinnati painting is very convincing. The extreme pliability of the Chinese brush, however, betrays even the slightest flaw, so that close stroke by stroke comparison revealed evidence of hesitations and slipups that are bound to occur in the process of slow tracing.

The copyist made numerous mistakes in the calligraphy of the artist's inscription in an attempt to reproduce the connections between individual strokes that occur spontaneously in cursive script. Evidence of the deliberateness of copying is especially apparent in these connections; sometimes they are a single hair's width when they occur naturally in the original, but they appear blotchy and forced in the copy, thus exposing their implausibility as having flowed from the brush of a master calligrapher such as Zhao Mengfu.[4]

When viewed alone, the Cincinnati painting appears to be an excellent work, but when compared with the Metropolitan Museum painting, its relative lack of freshness and vitality becomes readily apparent. Strokes are generally weaker than in the original and the copyist has not captured the depth and variety of textures in the rocks and trees. Nor has he achieved the same subtle colors of ink as did the painter of the Metropolitan Museum's scroll.[5]

Artist's inscription and signature:

Ever since my youth, after practicing calligraphy I have toyed with some small paintings, but landscape is one subject that I have not been able to master. This is because one cannot see even one or two masterpieces by Wang Yucheng [Wei], the great and small generals Li [Sixun and Zhaodao], and Zhang Guangwen [Qian] of the Tang period. As for the works of the Five Dynasties masters, such as Jing [Hao], Guan [Tong], Dong [Yuan], and Fan [Kuan], who succeeded one another [as leading masters], the brush idea of all of them is absolutely different from the style of recent paintings.

As for my own work, while I dare not compare it with the ancients, when I look at what painters have done in recent times, I daresay mine is a bit different.

Since [Dong] Yeyun has asked me for a painting, I will write this at the end of it. [Signed] Mengfu.[6]

Artist's seals:

Zhao Zi-ang shi; Zhao Mengfu

Colophons and seals:

Yang Zai (1271–1323), three seals; Tong Xuan (1425–98), three seals.

Collectors' seals:

Descendants of Mu Ying (1345–92); Qian Ning (d. ca. 1522); Yan Zun (active second half of 14th century); Lian Qingbian (1620–91); Lian Yong; An Qi (1683–1744); Qianlong (r. 1736–95); Ding Huikang (1869–1909); Kuai Guangdian (1857–1910), Zai Zhi (20th century), Tan Jing (20th century)

Recent provenance:

C. T. Loo

Published:

Cahill, *Index,* p. 254.
Edwards, "Sophistications of Chinese Art," p. 89.
Fong, "The Problem of Forgeries," p. 110, n. 63.
Fu, *Traces of the Brush,* no. 14.
Ho and Kohara, *Bunjinga Suihen* 3: pp. 60–61, 171.
Munsterberg, "Collection of Chinese Paintings," fig. 4.
Suzuki, *Chugoku Kaigashi,* 1, no. 15.
Suzuki, *Comprehensive Illustrated Catalog,* no. A24–002.

Exhibited:

"Masterpieces of Chinese Art," Virginia Museum of Fine Arts, 1954–1955.
"Traces of the Brush," Yale University Art Gallery; University Art Museum, University of California, Berkeley, 1977.

Notes:

1. Fu, *Traces,* pp. 3, 14.
2. Fong, "The Problem of Forgeries," p. 110, n. 63.
3. The two scrolls were the subject of a master's thesis by Mary Jane Clark, "Twin Pines and Level Distance," and were included together in "Traces of the Brush," an exhibition at Yale University Art Gallery that thoroughly examined original works of calligraphy with their copies. Fu, *Traces,* pp. 14–15, 250–51.
4. See Fu, *Traces,* pp. 14–15, for discussion of the calligraphy and for enlarged details of both scrolls, illustrating the differences.
5. For comparison, see details of the Metropolitan Museum of Art painting published in Fong, *Beyond Representation,* pp. 440–42.
6. trans. Fu, *Traces,* p. 250.

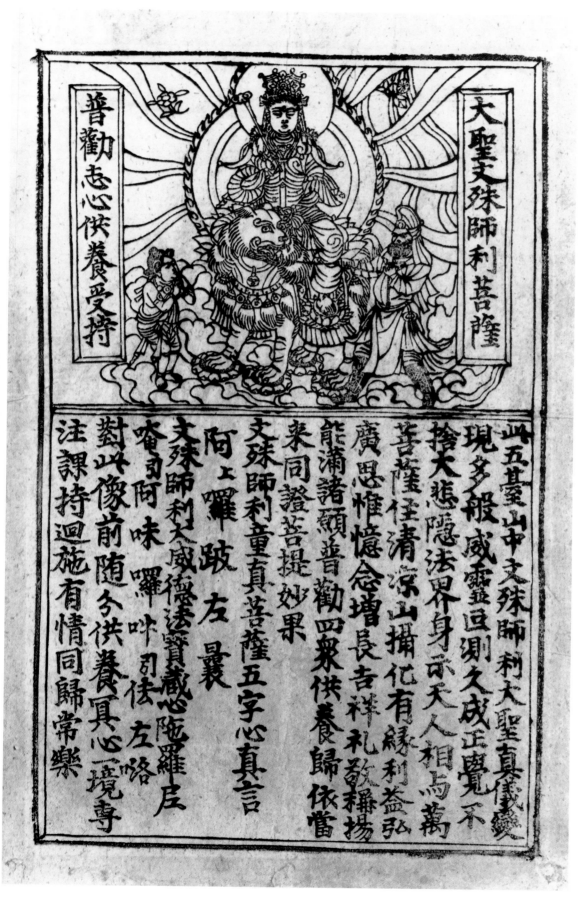

普勸志心供養受持　大聖文殊師利菩薩

此五臺山中文殊師利大聖真儀變現
多般威靈叵測久成正覺不
捨大悲隱法界身示天人相為萬
菩薩往清涼山播化有緣利益弘
廣思惟憶念增長吉祥礼敬稱揚
能浦諸頂普勸四眾供養歸依當
来同證菩提妙果

文殊師利童真菩薩五字心真言
阿ェ囉跋 左 曩
文殊師利大威德法寶藏心陀羅尼
唵司阿味 囉咪司伱左 洛
對此像前隨分供養真心一境專
注課持迴施有情同歸常樂

26. Prayer Sheet
Five Dynasties, circa A.D. 950

83

27. Ma Yuan, *The Four Sages of Shangshan*
Southern Song dynasty, circa 1225.

27d. Poem by Ni Zan, 1371   27c. Poem by Wang Feng, 1370 or 1371

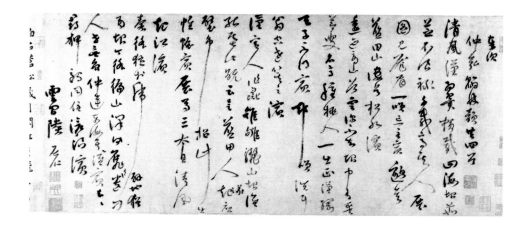

27b. Four poems by Lu Juren, circa 1370

27a. Poem by Yang Weizhen, circa 1370

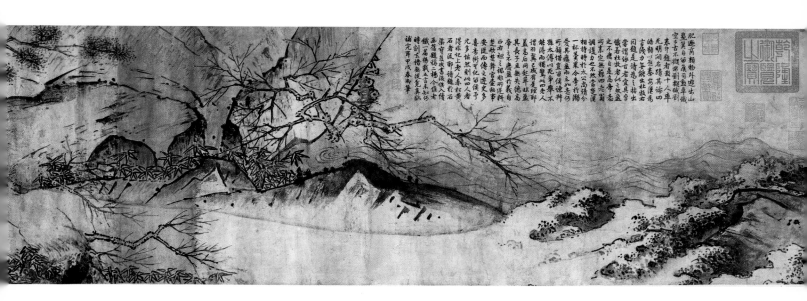

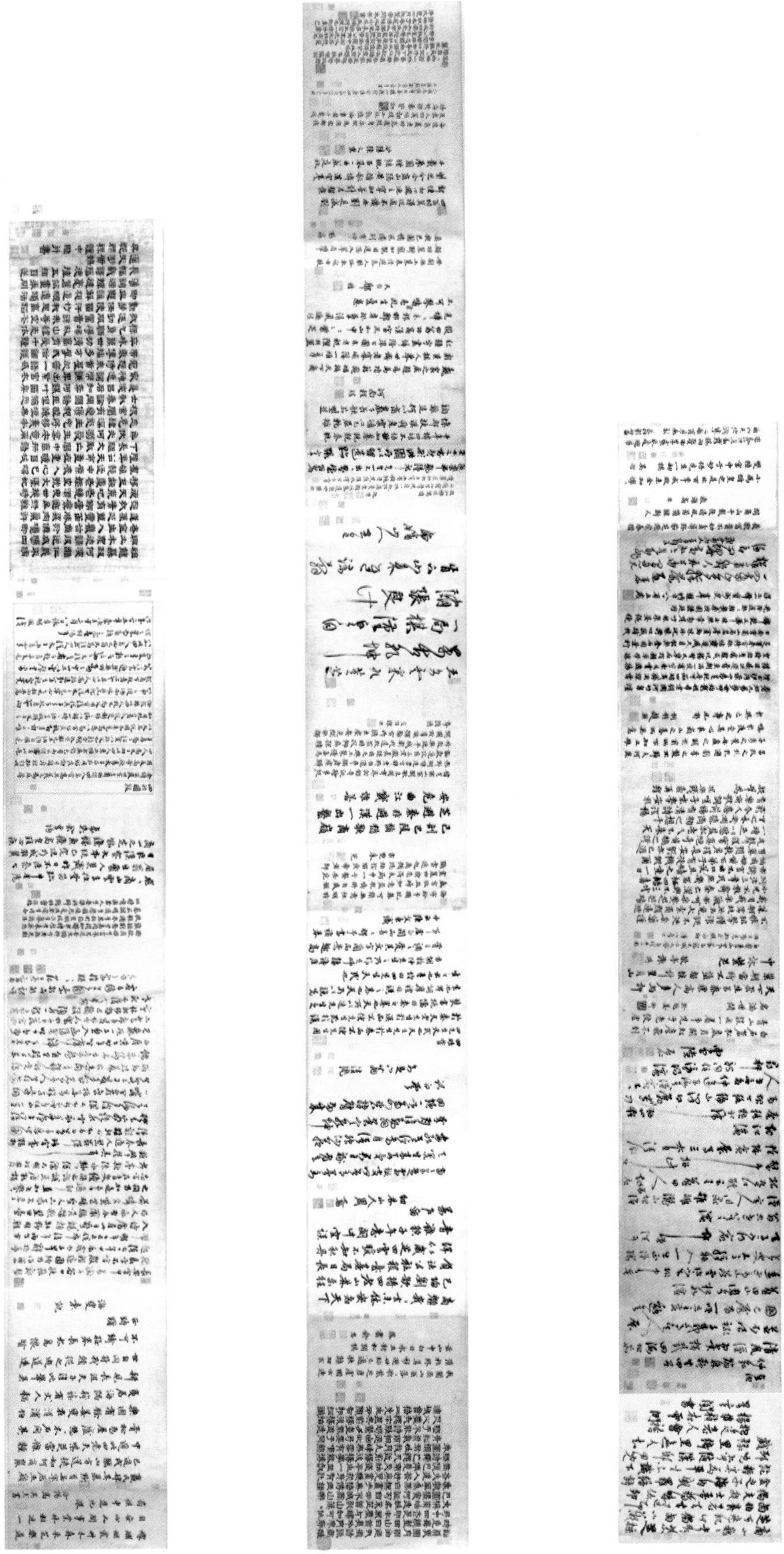

27. Colophons, *The Four Sages of Shangshan*

28. Liu Yuan, *Sima Yu's Dream of the Courtesan Su Xiaoxiao*
Jin dynasty, early 13th century

Detail

29. Qian Xuan, *Doves and Pear Blossoms after Rain*
Yuan dynasty, late 13th century

Detail

29c. Poem by Qian Liangyu, circa 1332–44   29b. Poem by Bao Xun, circa 1332–40   29a. Poem by Ke Jiusi, circa 1332

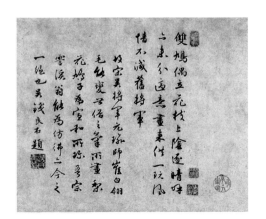

30. Colophon by Su Changling, 1354

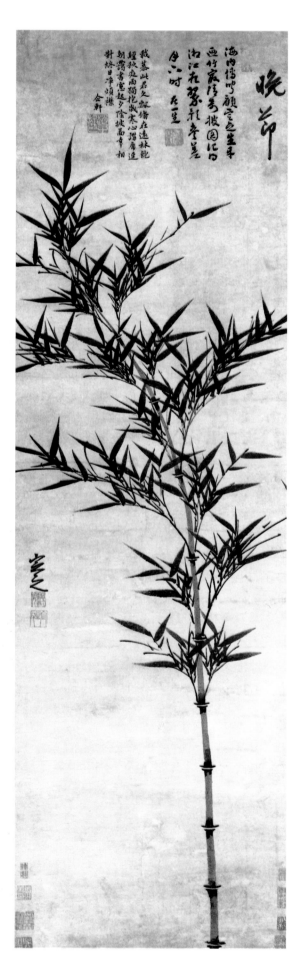

31. Gu An, *Bamboo*
Yuan dynasty, 14th century

Left
32. *Wenshu, Bodhisattva of Wisdom, at a Writing Table*
Yuan dynasty, dated 1354

33. *Lotus*
Yuan dynasty, 14th century

34. Wang Zhao, *Wild Geese Descending to a Sandbar*
Ming dynasty, late 15th or early 16th century

35. Attr. Wen Zhengming,
A Quiet River at the Foot of Misty Mountains
Ming dynasty, circa 1500–1512

36. Zhang Hong, *Birds by a Stream*
Qing dynasty, dated 1648

Detail

37. Wang Jian, *The Scenery of Mount Yu*
Qing dynasty, dated 1662

96

黄子久酷愛庚度
山水畫卧其下
畫具烟雲變幻
後乙子寧欲墊
之月悒筆腴拈
澁不怗典之
事長莊卷
顯用具高
未識覽者山
為何山平
壬寅夏月舟次
庚山畫并記
王鑑

Detail

38. Bada Shanren, *Birds and Lotus Pond*
Qing dynasty, dated 1690

Detail

40. *Spring Morning in the Han Palace* (details)
Qing dynasty, late 17th or early 18th century

40. *Spring Morning in the Han Palace*
Qing dynasty, late 17th or early 18th century

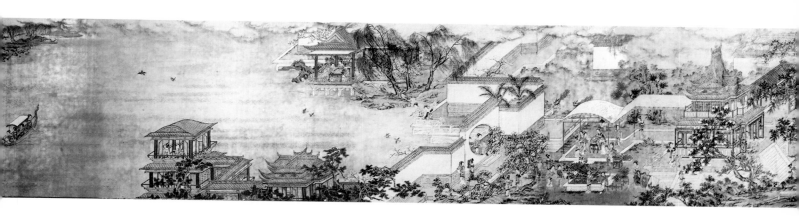

全慶圖

金門畫史冷枚

Left
41. Leng Mei, *A Picture of Perfect Felicity*
Qing dynasty, circa 1723–1735

42. *The Meeting of Cranes and Peacocks*
Qing dynasty, dated 1839

43. After Zhao Mengfu (1254–1322), *Twin Pines and Level Distance*, 1940s

Detail

44. Jar, Banshan Type

Gansu province, Neolithic Yangshao culture, Banshan phase, circa 2500 B.C. Earthenware with painted decoration. H. 28.5 cm.
Museum purchase, 1950.41

The wide-shouldered jar of reddish clay has a short, slightly everted mouth and two lug handles. The body of the vessel tapers to a narrow, flat base. Decoration on the shoulder consists of four repeating whirlpool designs painted in alternating black and purple stripes; the black stripes have sawtooth edges. The exterior of the neck is painted with repeating simple Xs in black, and the mouth has a painted design of black and purple swags along the interior rim.

Red pottery with painted geometric designs forms a significant portion of the surviving artistic achievements of Neolithic China. By about 5000 B.C., the largest agrarian culture in China was the Yangshao. Early Yangshao sites were concentrated in the river valleys of southwestern Shanxi, northwestern Henan, Shaanxi, and eastern Gansu provinces. Yangshao culture, named after a small village in Henan province where excavations first yielded a distinctive red pottery painted with black designs, spread radially from there over a wide geographic area encompassing large portions of Shaanxi, Shanxi, Hebei, Henan, Gansu, and Qinghai provinces. Discovery and excavation of numerous sites over the last seven decades have enabled archaeologists to define a chronology and regional phases associated with this Neolithic culture.[1]

The Museum's jar is a typical example from the Banshan phase, the intermediate phase of later (3000–1500 B.C.) Yangshao culture. Banshan-type jars are characterized by broad-shouldered shapes with lug handles, narrow flat bases, and either short, wide, everted mouths or tall necks with narrow mouths. Decoration is confined to the shoulder of the vessel and consists of boldly painted linear designs, usually in two colors: black, and red or purple. The whirlpool spiral of alternating purple stripes and black bands accented with sawtooth edges on the Museum's jar is a frequently occurring Banshan motif. Like other designs painted masterfully by Gansu potters, it conveys a rhythmic energy that complements the robust form of the vessel.

Although the potter's wheel had been in use in China as early as the fourth millennium B.C., Yangshao ceramics were built up by hand with clay coils. Then, when partially dry, they were beaten with paddle and anvil to thin and strengthen the vessel walls.[2] The Gansu potters employed a construction method well suited to the rigidity of their material, a relatively unweathered loess with low clay content that does not readily absorb water.[3]

Most of the excavated Banshan phase ceramics have come from simple single or double burial pits consisting of a wooden casket that held the remains of the deceased along with painted pottery vessels.[4] A jar similar to the Museum's was excavated in 1973 from Tomb M26 at Dibaping, Guanghe county, Gansu province.[5]

Provenance:
    C.T. Loo

Published:
    Cincinnati Art Museum Handbook, p.58.
    Masterpieces from the Cincinnati Art Museum, p.55.
    Avril, "Highlights of Chinese Art," p.73.
Notes:
    1. For a thorough discussion of Yangshao culture, see Chang, *Archaeology of Ancient China*, pp.108–56.
    2. The exterior surfaces of Yangshao pottery have been carefully smoothed so that only slip decoration, wipe marks, or scrape marks might appear, but xeroradiographs have revealed the diamond-shaped pattern of paddle and anvil impressions. Xeroradiographs also show that the bodies are relatively porous. See Vandiver, "Technical Studies," pp.119–21.
    3. Vainker, *Chinese Pottery and Porcelain*, p.19. Throwing requires greater plasticity, thus necessitating the use of clays that can absorb sufficient water. Also see Wood, "Recent Researches," note 12.
    4. Chang, *Archaeology of Ancient China*, p.146.
    5. Published in *Gansu Caitao*, no.78.

45. Goblets

Shandong province, Neolithic Longshan culture, circa 2700–2100 B.C. Burnished earthenware. H. 23.5 and 19.6 cm.
Museum purchase with funds provided by the Oliver Charitable Lead Trust, 1996.449a,b

Each goblet is thinly potted of black earthenware that has been burnished to a satiny sheen. The goblets are not identical. The cup of the taller goblet is flared widely at the rim, then tapers sharply to straight sides and an angled base. The exterior has a surface decoration of three thin, horizontal raised lines. The smaller goblet has a flared rim that tapers in a gentle curve to the angled base of the cup. Its surface shows continuous horizontal scoring beginning just below the rim and ending near the base. Below the base, each goblet has a solid, narrow stem above and below a wide, hollow bulb that is pierced with vertical incisions. The taller goblet is supported by a hollow, straight-sided circular foot; the shorter goblet rests on a hollow circular foot with flared sides.

In northeast China during the third millennium B.C., the Longshan Neolithic culture thrived simultaneously with the Yangshao culture (see entry 44) of the northwest. Longshan culture was named after the town near which excavations in 1930–1931 first revealed the black ceramics that represent its potters' highest achievement.

Made of a fine-grained clay turned on a potter's wheel, Longshan black vessels are characterized by extremely thin walls (generally 1 to 3 mm thick) and unusual boldness of silhouette. Each goblet in the Museum's set is composed of separately thrown parts luted together to form the hollow bulb in the stem. These ceramics are distinguished by minimal surface decoration and by the rich black color achieved through reduction firing. The burnished surface presents a handsome metallic sheen.

The Longshan black goblets are an outgrowth of earlier Dawenkou black goblets. The context in which the latter were found helps us understand the significance of the Longshan ceramics. The richest Dawenkou burials included numerous stemmed goblets placed alongside the corpse; this suggests that they were made for rituals in which drink was shared with ancestral spirits.[1] Excavated examples of comparable Longshan black ware have also been found at burial rather than residential sites, and then only in the richest tombs. The delicate black pottery was placed beside the arms of the deceased, along with jade ritual items. Ordinary pottery was also buried with the dead but was deliberately separated from the ritual items in these tombs. For these reasons and because of the ceramic's extreme fragility and impracticality for everyday use, Chinese archaeologists categorize the Longshan black vessels as ritual paraphernalia.[2]

Longshan artists, whether producing pottery or jade ritual items, strained their materials by pursuing thinness to its limits. Through extraordinary technical skill and enthusiastic exploration of new shapes, these artists emphasized artistry at the expense of practicality. The later *Book of Rites* confirms this distinction between ritual objects and utilitarian items: "The ritual vessels may be of use but are never made for people's convenience. The idea is that those which serve to communicate with spirits should not be identical with those for rest and pleasure."[3]

Published:
   Stephen Solovy Fine Art, *Splendors of Chinese Art*, no. 1.
Notes:
   1. Tomb M17, Dazhujia, Ju county, Shandong province, a fourth millenium B.C. Dawenkou burial, contained numerous stemmed goblets placed alongside the corpse (reported in *Kaogu xuebao*, 1991, no. 2, 167–206). A line drawing of the burial is published in Rawson, *Mysteries*, p. 251.
   2. Wu Ruozuo identified these characteristics of Longshan black vessels as indicating that they were ritual items. See Wu, *Monumentality*, p. 27.
   3. See Wu, *Monumentality*, pp. 43–44 and the quote from the *Book of Rites*, p. 27.

46. *Li* Tripod

Probably Henan province, Shang dynasty, 13th to 11th century B.C. Earthenware with cord-impressed designs. H. 15.9, W. 18.4 cm.
Museum purchase, 1950.42

The squat grey earthenware vessel has a wide mouth with everted rim and a body formed by the joining of three wide lobate legs. Surface decoration consists of vertical and horizontal cord markings that follow the contours of the vessel.

Hand-built grey earthenware vessels impressed with a simple decoration of markings made by a beater wrapped in cord originated in the Neolithic period. The primary functional ceramic type of ancient China, cord-marked wares have been found in all regional Neolithic cultures and enjoyed a long history, remaining in use through the Zhou dynasty.

Numerically, grey cord-marked earthenware vessels are the most common Shang dynasty ceramics, representing about 90% of the excavated finds from Anyang.[1] Shang-period *li* tripods differ from their Henan Longshan Neolithic prototypes in that the earlier

wares have three high lobate legs joined near the neck of the vessel, whereas the later shape is a more fully integrated form whose lobes join closer to the base.[2] The wide mouth with splayed rim is another feature that appears on Shang examples. *Li* tripods functioned primarily as cooking vessels used for boiling and simmer-stewing.[3] The museum's *li* resembles those unearthed at Xiaotun and at Miaopubeidi, Anyang.[4]

Provenance:
   C. T. Loo
Published:
   Edwards, "Sophistications of Chinese Art," p. 83, fig. 1.
Notes:
   1. Li, *Anyang*, pp. 202–03.
   2. Compare a Henan Lungshanoid *li* in the Asian Art Museum of San Francisco with a Shang period *li* in the Buffalo Museum of Science; published in Shangraw, *Origins of Chinese Ceramics*, nos. 11 and 12, respectively.
   3. Chang, *Food in Chinese Culture*, p. 34.
   4. Chang, *Archaeology of Ancient China*, fig. 285, p. 332. Also see Chang, *Shang Civilization*, pp. 105–107 for a comparable illustrated vessel unearthed from Miaopubeidi M105, Period IV.

47. Jar

Eastern Zhou dynasty, Warring States period, 5th or 4th century B.C. Stoneware with impressed design. H. 27.5 cm.
Museum purchase, 1950.43

The grey-beige jar of bulbous form has a wide mouth, a minimal straight neck, and a wide shoulder tapering to a flat base. Surface decoration consists of a combed band of wavy lines around the rim, an impressed checkerboard pattern of squares filled in with diagonal lines in alternating directions on the shoulder, and a plain-weave fabric-impressed pattern overall from shoulder to base.

Unglazed ceramics with impressed geometric and textile designs appear in southeastern China from the Shang dynasty into the Han dynasty, in contrast to the glazed wares that were produced in the north beginning in the late Shang dynasty. During the Eastern Zhou period many of these unglazed ceramics combine several impressed patterns on a single vessel, as on this jar.[1] The jar has an uneven shape because it was handbuilt by the coiling method rather than thrown on the potter's wheel.

Described as *ying tao*, literally "hard pottery," this type of ceramic was made of a dense clay with strong adhesive properties. Southern potters fired these vessels at higher temperatures than northern potters fired their grey wares (see entry 46). This created ceramics of harder paste.[2]

Provenance:
   C. T. Loo
Published:
   Mathes, *Treasures of American Museums*, p. 80.

Notes:

1. A 1978 conference on impressed-design pottery produced south of the Yangtze River was published as an entire issue of *Wenwu Jikan* 3 (1981).

2. Han dynasty tombs in Changsha and Shaoxing have yielded jars of this type. See Wang, *Han Civilization*, p. 143, figs. 188-91.

48. Tomb Figure of a Kneeling Woman

Western Han dynasty, 2nd or 1st century B.C. Earthenware and lead or pewter, painted with unfired pigments. H. 46.3 cm.
Museum purchase: Gift of Mr. and Mrs. Leonard Minster, by exchange, 1989.100

The grey pottery figure is in the form of a kneeling woman whose left hand rests on her left knee. A hole remains in the right sleeve where the right hand, now missing, was once attached. The figure wears a simple oversized robe with padded white collar and red lapels; the tunic is gathered around the feet in back. The head, with simple hairstyle parted in the middle, retains a molded metal hair ornament attached above the right side of the face. The S-shaped ornament has long fingerlike projections which cascade down the forehead, partially obscuring the eyes. Overall applied red, white, light brown, and black pigments remain, partially obscured by incrustations of earth.

According to beliefs prevalent during the Han dynasty, the human soul would separate, upon death, into two distinct entities: the *hun*, which would ascend to heaven and the *po*, which (if adequately supplied) would dwell for eternity in the tomb. Han tomb furnishings, called *mingqi* (literally "spirit objects") served the needs of both elements by providing earthly comfort for the *po* and cosmic imagery to guide the *hun* successfully to heaven.

Early Han ceramic tomb figurines were made of unglazed earthenware painted with unfired pigments. On larger figures, such as the Museum's, head and body were formed separately and then assembled with a wooden dowel inserted in the neck to support the head. Often both hands of such figures were also made of wood. This figure, which is unusual for having one ceramic hand, is missing its wooden right hand, which probably held an offering of some sort.

The figure's serene expression imparts a quiet beauty and appropriately reflects her function as an eternal companion to the *po* of the deceased. The woman's otherwise restrained elegance is punctuated by the *buyao* ("swaying step") hair ornament, a special type of hairpin constructed such that its stringed beads would gently sway and jingle as she moved.[1] This feature rarely survives; on most extant ceramic figures of Han court women, tiny slots in the hairline are the only remaining evidence of the original adornment.[2] The ornament on the Museum's figure is only one of the original pair. Rather than projecting forward, as was intended, the ornament is pressed against the forehead because the head toppled accidentally when its wood support disintegrated.

Published:

Archives of Asian Art, 44 (1991), p. 108.
Avril, "Highlights of Chinese Art," p. 74.

Notes:

1. I am indebted to James C. Y. Watt for this information. The famous portrait on the second-century-B.C. painted banner from Mawangdui shows Lady Dai wearing *buyao* hair ornaments. See Tsao, "From Hair to Ear," p. 79.

2. A kneeling figure of a court lady with both hair ornaments intact was formerly in the Hardy collection and was sold at Sotheby's New York, on September 21, 1995, lot 47. Similar examples of this kneeling woman type, but missing the hair ornaments, include a figure in the Freer Gallery of Art, publ. *Oriental Ceramics: The World's Great Collections*, vol. 9, black and white illus. 9; and a figure of a woman in the Osaka Municipal Museum of Art, *Masterpieces*, no. 232.

49. *Hu*

Eastern Han dynasty, 1st or 2nd century A.D. Earthenware with molded decoration under lead glaze. H. 52.1 cm.
Museum purchase, 1950.45

The reddish earthenware pear-shaped vase has a tall, slightly flaring neck. Its bulbous lower body tapers to a high, straight base like a ringfoot but the base has a flat bottom. The vessel is covered overall in a green lead glaze which has deteriorated to a silvery iridescence. Surface decoration consists of a simple collar below the rim, three raised ropelike bands at the shoulder and around the widest part of the vessel, framing a pair of mask-and-ring-handle motifs, and a single raised band where the vessel meets the foot.

Stoneware was the earliest glazed ceramic in China because the high melting point of the glaze required firing temperatures above 1200 degrees centigrade. For this reason, glazed wares were fairly expensive to produce. During the Han dynasty, however, potters began to add lead oxide as a flux; this lowered the melting temperature of silica glazes sufficiently to allow earthenware to be glazed. This significant technical breakthrough resulted in a proliferation of relatively inexpensive mortuary ceramics in imitation of more expensive materials such as bronze. The clay body of Han lead-glazed ceramics was made of the same loess as was used in earlier earthenware, but it appears bright red (rather than grey) as a result of oxidation firing. The change in firing technique was necessitated by the tendency of lead glazes to blacken and blister in reduction firing.[1]

This *hu* is strongly indebted to bronze tradition in its shape and surface decoration; probably it was meant as an affordable substitute for bronze. Prolonged exposure to moisture has caused the once-brilliant green glaze to corrode to a silvery iridescence. This phenomenon occurs frequently with Han lead glazes and gives the vessel an attractive, though unintentional, patina.

Provenance:

C. T. Loo

Notes:

1. Wood, "Recent Researches," pp. 144–45.

50. *Hu*

Shaanxi province, Han dynasty (206 B.C.–A.D. 220). Earthenware with relief decoration under lead glaze. H. 33 cm.
W. W. Taylor Fund, 1939.51

The pear-shaped vase with a slightly flaring neck has a wide bulbous body tapering to a flat-bottomed base. Covered in a dark olive-green glaze, the vessel is decorated with a simple collar around the rim, a single raised ropelike band around the base of the neck, and a wide band of relief decoration bordered in ropelike bands around the shoulder. The relief band includes a hunting scene of riders on horseback and a pair of mask-and-ring-handle motifs.

This jar is one of a large group acquired in China by Berthold Laufer on behalf of the Field Museum of Natural History during the Blackstone Expedition of 1908–1910. The Cincinnati Art Museum purchased this jar from Chicago's Field Museum in 1939. Surface decoration is confined to a frieze in relief around the shoulder of the vessel, which shows a scene of men hunting on horseback in a wilderness of animals.

Hunting scenes appear on Eastern Zhou bronzes; they refer to the ritual hunts annually performed by the Zhou king to exorcise evil spirits from the intermediate realm between heaven and earth, thereby maintaining unobstructed communication with heaven and the ancestral spirits.[1] This exorcistic theme remained important in Han cosmology. Archers on horseback who turn back to shoot at leaping animals, often felines, appear on many hill jars and on *hu* jars similar to the Museum's. The horsemen symbolically rid the mountain realm of evil spirits that otherwise might prevent the *hun* soul from reaching its heavenly destination.[2]

Provenance:
Collected in Xi'an, Shaanxi province by Berthold Laufer; Field Museum of Natural History, Chicago

Notes:
1. Munakata, *Sacred Mountains*, pp. 20–24.
2. Munakata, *Sacred Mountains*, p. 84.

51. *Wenjiuzun*

Han dynasty (206 B.C.–A.D. 220). Earthenware with relief decoration under lead glaze. H. 23.5 cm.
Museum purchase: Deaccession funds, 1989.45

The cylindrical vessel is supported on three feet in the form of crouching bears. The reddish earthenware is covered inside and out with a brilliant green lead glaze that has deteriorated in some areas to a silvery iridescence. Surface decoration on the vessel consists of a band of rhombic pattern in low relief below the rim; in high relief is the main frieze of spirited figures and animals that include monkeys, wild boars, tigers, dragons, bears, birds, archers on horseback, humans and mock mask-and-ring handles. The conical lid is in the shape of mountain peaks. It has animals and figures in relief and a rhombic pattern border in high relief

along the edge. Three spur marks are located below the flat rim of the lid; these precisely match the three spur marks on the rim of the vessel body.

Among the most engaging Han-dynasty ceramic mortuary vessels is a type commonly known as the "hill jar" because of its distinctive lid in the form of a range of mountain peaks. Such vessels were produced for the tomb as affordable substitutes for luxury items of bronze or lacquer. Formerly thought to relate to tripod cosmetic boxes (*lian*), vessels of this shape actually functioned as wine warmers (*wenjiuzun*). The archaeological evidence is based on gilt bronze vessels inscribed *wenjiuzun* unearthed in Shanxi province from a site of the first century B.C.[1] The cylindrical form of the vessel, the use of animals in relief as decoration, and the tripod feet in the form of crouching bears relate the bronze *wenjiuzun* to the earthenware hill jars.[2] Lead-glazed earthenware hill jars were a common type among Han tomb furnishings, and numerous examples survive today in public and private collections.[3]

Mountains have been an important subject for artists in China since the late Zhou dynasty. According to Daoist belief, they are a place for seeking spiritual enlightenment and traditionally are associated with the realm of the immortals. In Confucian thought, they provide refuge from corrupt society. Mountains were worshiped in Zhou court rituals to ensure prosperity: Because they were believed to be the source of clouds and rain, they were viewed as embodying the earth's power. Considered sacred in Han ideology, mountains were regarded as cosmic pillars connecting heaven's canopy with the world of mortals.[4]

Prevailing Han beliefs about the afterlife maintained that upon death the *po* soul would remain in the tomb, but the *hun* soul would embark on a journey through a fantastic mountain wilderness in its ascent to heaven. This wilderness was inhabited by all kinds of creatures, both good and evil. Some hill jars, in the main frieze around the vessel, show scenes of confrontation between animals, referring to the dangers of the journey. Others, such as the Museum's jar, display more agreeable scenes alluding to the safe arrival of the *hun* at its destination, as indicated by a figure mounted on a dragon approaching a winged man. This interaction may represent the *hun* soul of the deceased, carried by its dragon mount, being greeted by an official of heaven.[5] The various animals that inhabit the mountainous wilderness appear on the lid and in the frieze around the body. The crouching bear, such as forms the feet of this vessel, is an auspicious omen.[6]

For efficient loading in the kiln, the *wenjiuzun* were stacked with their lids inverted and resting on the rim of the vessel. Three spurs placed along the rim kept the glazed lid and vessel from fusing together. The spur marks on the lid and body of this vessel match perfectly, indicating that the two parts were fired together.

Published:
Avril, "Highlights of Chinese Art," p. 74.

Notes:
1. Sun-Bailey, "What Is the 'Hill Jar'?" Also illustrated in *The Chinese Exhibition*, no. 205.

2. Because bronze *wenjiuzun* do not have the mountain-form lids, perhaps the hill jar is a composite derivative of two common metal forms, the *wenjiuzun* vessel and the hilly lid of the *bo shan* censer. A bronze *wenjiuzun* in the Freer Gallery, missing its lid, is stylistically even closer to ceramic hill jars. Its surface decoration consists of hilly landscapes crowded with various animal and humanoid creatures in two bands of high relief. See Freer Gallery of Art, *Masterpieces*, p. 22; also Pope, et al., *Freer Chinese Bronzes*, vol. 1, pl. 115.

3. Sun-Bailey, "What Is the 'Hill Jar'?"; *Oriental Ceramics: The World's Great Collections*, vol. 9, black and white illus. 6 and vol. 5, black and white illus. 7; Ayers, *Far Eastern Ceramics*, black and white illus. 14; Monroe, *Chinese Ceramics*, no. 7; Schloss, *Art of the Han*, no. 61; Munakata, *Sacred Mountains*, nos. 33–35.

4. Munakata, *Sacred Mountains*, pp. 2–12.

5. See Munakata's interpretation of the decorative scheme seen on three hill jars similar to the museum's, *Sacred Mountains*, pp. 88–89, nos. 33, 34 and 35. These are contrasted with the depiction of animals in confrontive poses on other hill jars, *Sacred Mountains*, pp. 86–87, nos. 31 and 32.

6. See Wu, *Wu Liang Shrine*, pp. 76–77, for a discussion of human figures and animals as auspicious omens that inhabit sacred mountains. Also, see Wu, "A Sanpan Shan Chariot Ornament," pp. 38–59.

52. Tomb Figure of an Official

Northern Wei dynasty, early 6th century A.D. Earthenware with unfired pigments. H. 36.6 cm.
Bequest of Mrs. J. Louis Ransohoff, 1965.173

The grey earthenware figure represents a standing man dressed in a military costume consisting of a red long-sleeved tunic and cuirass worn over loosely fitting trousers, which are gathered at the knees with red bands and then flare toward the ground, where they conceal all but the toes of the shoes. The slender, frontal figure wears a small cap and gazes forward with slight smile; his clenched right hand is held in front of the abdomen, and the left hand is concealed beneath the long sleeve. The head is modeled fully in the round; the reverse of the body is flat and only roughly finished.

Ceramic tomb figures of the Northern Wei dynasty display many of the same stylistic traits as Buddhist stone sculptures of the period (see entries 15, 17, 18). These features include attenuated bodies, rhythmic linear drapery, and elongated squarish faces with slender, pointed noses and slight smiles.

Tombs of the Six Dynasties period excavated in northern China have yielded large quantities of military figures, suggesting that the political turmoil of the times led many aristocrats to employ personal armies.[1] The museum's figure wears military attire typical of the early sixth century; this is distinguished by its *liangdangkai*, an iron or leather cuirass composed of a breastplate and a backplate tied together with shoulder straps.[2] The figure wears a civilian official's cap rather than combat headgear. This feature, combined with the obeisant stance and gesture (the left hand concealed beneath the long sleeve and right hand resting close to the chest and clenched to hold what may have been a ceremonial object), suggests that he is a court official wearing ceremonial rather than battle garb.

Two figures in the Schloss collection apparently were made from the same molds as this figure. They have been identified as representing cavalry officers, on the basis of contemporary painted images depicting mounted soldiers dressed in similar body armor and billowing trousers.[3]

Provenance:
Mathias Komor; Mrs. J. Louis Ransohoff
Notes:
1. Wang, "General Comments on Chinese Funerary Sculpture," p. 52.
2. See Dien, "Study of Early Chinese Armor," pp. 26–30.
3. See Lewis, *Into the Afterlife*, no. 44, pp. 100–01.

53. *Hu*

Northern China, Six Dynasties, first half of 6th century A.D.
Glazed stoneware. H. 29.9 cm.
Museum purchase, 1950.46

The pear-shaped vase with a tall, tapering neck is encircled at the middle with two raised ridges. The wide, dished mouth has a slightly everted straight rim. Four trapezoidal lugs are attached around the shoulder; the bulbous body tapers downward to a low foot and concave base. The vase is covered overall with olive green transparent glaze, which has accumulated in glassy pools around the neck ridges and lug handles, and has formed uneven streaks over the body ending in thick drips just short of the base.

Although the earliest glazed stonewares in China were produced at northern kilns during the Shang dynasty, relatively few were made in the north until the sixth century A.D. Eastern and southern kilns, especially those of Zhejiang province, instead dominated production of high-fired ceramics. The Museum's *hu* vase with transparent olive-green glaze represents the resumed production of glazed stonewares in northern China during the Six Dynasties period. Northern wares show indebtedness to the southern stonewares in their shapes and in the adoption of features such as the wide, dished mouth and the placement of square lugs on the shoulder. The northern glazes differ, however, in their inclination to olive green rather than grey green color and in their tendency to streak and accumulate in glassy pools around surface details.

A similar *hu* was excavated at Xiaomachang, Hebei province, from an Eastern Wei tomb dated to the sixth century.[1] Another vessel of similar shape but with black glaze is in the Shanghai Museum.[2]

Provenance:
Low-Beer collection; C. T. Loo
Published:
Avril, "Highlights of Chinese Art," pp. 74–75.
Mino and Tsiang, *Ice and Green Clouds*, no. 37, pp. 106–07.
Exhibited:
"Ice and Green Clouds: Traditions of Chinese Celadon," Indianapolis Museum of Art, Minneapolis Institute of Arts, The Asia Society Galleries, Kimbell Art Museum, The Art Institute of Chicago, 1986–88.
Notes:
1. Both illustrated in Mino and Tsiang, *Ice and Green Clouds*, p. 106, fig. 37a.
2. *Zhongguo Taoci*, no. 108.

54. Tray, Gongxian Ware

Henan province, Sui or early Tang dynasty, 7th century A.D. Stoneware with white slip and transparent glaze. H. 6.9 cm., dia. 29.8 cm.
Museum purchase, 1950.47

Supported by three radially placed ring feet, the round, white-bodied shallow plate has curved sides, inverted lip, and slightly convex interior. The tray is coated with a transparent, finely crackled glaze that displays a greenish tinge where it has pooled in the interior of the plate and where droplets have formed on the base of each ring foot. The center of the underside is unglazed, exposing the cream-colored clay body.

This tray, simple and understated in its elegance, is an example of the high-fired white-bodied ceramics considered to be the world's first porcelain. Historical records suggest that such white wares were sent as tribute to the Sui and Tang imperial courts and evidently were prized as highly as jade, silk, lacquer and metalwork.[1]

White-bodied wares made of low-fired kaolinic clays, with carved surface decoration resembling that of ritual bronzes, were produced in Henan province during the late Shang dynasty.[2] Beginning in the sixth century A.D., these kaolinic clays were used to produce high-fired stonewares. The Museum's tray, with its clear, greenish-tinged glaze, represents the porcelain produced at the Gongxian kilns, near Luoyang, whose potters supplied porcelain to the imperial court at both Changan and Luoyang.

A whiteware tray of comparatively crude form with four ring feet was unearthed in 1959 in Anyang, Henan province from a tomb dated 584.[3] More elegantly shaped Gongxian-ware trays, such as the Museum's, have been excavated from early seventh century sites.[4] Such trays apparently were used for serving wine, as evidenced by known sets complete with their stemmed cups.[5] A tray nearly identical to this piece, also lacking cups, is in the Meiyintang collection.[6]

Provenance:
    J. T. Tai; C. T. Loo
Published:
    Edwards, "Sophistications," p. 83, fig. 2.
    Mathes, *Treasures of American Museums*, p. 99.
Notes:
    1. Vainker, *Chinese Pottery and Porcelain*, pp. 64–68.
    2. The most widely published example is in the Freer Gallery; see Valenstein, *Handbook of Chinese Ceramics*, fig. 17. A jar excavated at Anyang and now in the collection of the Palace Museum, Beijing, is illustrated in *Zhongguo taoci*, no. 51.
    3. *Zhongguo taoci*, no. 123.
    4. Kamer Aga-Oglu, file correspondence, noted a similar dish in the Academia Sinica, Taipei, found in an Anyang tomb dated 603 A.D.
    5. See Mino, *Pre-Sung Dynasty Chinese Stonewares*, pl. 36.
    6. Krahl, *Meiyintang Collection*, vol. 1, no. 201.

55a. Woman Holding a Vase

Tang dynasty, first half of 8th century A.D. Earthenware painted with unfired pigments. H. 31.5 cm.
The William T. and Louise Taft Semple Collection, 1962.410

The buff-colored clay figurine is in the form of a slender woman who holds a vase in her hands and gazes forward. Her hair is parted in the center and piled in two high chignons. She wears a high-waisted long-sleeved dress of floor length, which conceals all but the tips of her shoes. A long shawl is wrapped around her shoulders and draped over her garment, falling below the knees. Only traces of original pigment remain.

55b. Standing Woman

Tang dynasty, first half of 8th century A.D. Earthenware painted with unfired pigments. H. 30.4 cm.
The William T. and Louise Taft Semple Collection, 1962.409

The buff-colored clay figurine is in the form of a standing woman with her head slightly lowered, looking downward. She clasps her hands, which are concealed beneath long sleeves. A hood over her head covers her piled-up hair; the sides of the hood drape over the sides of her head and rest on her shoulders. She wears a high-waisted floor-length dress and an overshawl that is tucked beneath her bodice, wraps around her shoulders, falls over her right arm, and rests at knee length.

Economic prosperity and increased wealth in the merchant class in the early Tang dynasty prompted the regulation of funerary rituals and furnishings on the basis of social class. Sumptuary laws were designed primarily to reserve the most elaborate burial displays for the ruling elite. Aristocratic tombs were furnished with hundreds of *mingqi* representing all kinds of guardians, warriors, court dignitaries, beauties, entertainers, and servants. Such figures played an important role in funerary rituals. First displayed on carts as part of the procession to the burial site, the sculptures then were lined up outside the tomb to form a spirit path for the coffin. After the deceased was interred, the figures and furnishings were placed in specially made niches within the tomb, where they would provide for the needs of the deceased and enhance his or her social status in the afterlife.

Through their stances and gestures, the Museum's *mingqi* exhibit their funerary purpose: One woman carries an offering for the deceased, while the other looks downward, her covered head and concealed hands expressing deep respect.[1] The appearance of these court women reflects a standard of elegance prevalent from the late sixth into the eighth centuries. The foreign-style dresses with high-waisted full skirt, tight-fitting bodice and shawl wrap emphasize the women's slenderness, as do their piled chignons. By the mid-eighth century, fashions had changed; ideal beauty was associated with corpulence, upswept hair framing the face, and loose, gauzy clothing.

Tomb figures were made of the same kaolinic clays as Tang high-fired wares (see entry 54), but were fired at much lower temperatures, which accounts for their softness.[2] Because of the market for enormous quantities of tomb furnishings, potters had to work as efficiently as possible. Molds were widely used for producing standardized parts and appliqués. These were then assembled by luting, in which the parts were joined with a dilute mixture of clay known as slip. After a biscuit firing, the figures and vessels either were coated with lead-based glazes and subjected to a second firing, or were painted with unfired pigments and occasionally embellished with gold.

Provenance:
William T. and Louise Taft Semple
Notes:
1. An identical figure is in the Schloss collection. See Baker, *Seeking Immortality*, p. 33.
2. Wood, "Recent Researches," p. 146.

56. Military Official on a Horse

Tang dynasty, late 7th or early 8th century A.D. Earthenware with *sancai* lead glazes and traces of unfired pigments. H. 40.0 cm. The William T. and Louise Taft Semple Collection, 1962.415

The figure portrays an official seated astride a large horse. The rider's arms are bent, and his hands are clenched into fists as if to hold the now-missing reins. Both horse and rider are modeled of buff-colored clay and coated with white slip. Amber and green glazes flow in streaks over the man's garments and the horse's head and body. The man's head is unglazed; only traces of unfired pigments remain. His hair is pulled up into a chignon concealed by a wedge-shaped cap.

This rider wears the distinctive cap, tunic and loose trousers of a Tang military official and was once part of an entourage of ceremonial mounted riders for a high ranking individual's tomb. Ceremonial attendants were only one type among the various ceramic figures required for a fully furnished tomb of the Sui and Tang periods (see entries 55 and 57).

The official's mount is a horse of Arab stock. From the beginning of the Tang period to the middle of the seventh century, the government increased the number and quality of horses in its care from 5,000 to more than 700,000 by importing breeders from Samarkand that they believed were descendants of the "heavenly horses" of Ferghana (see entry 57). Superior to the native ponies of China, these horses were key to the military strength of the state and to the protection of Tang China from nomadic peoples of northern and central Asia.[1]

The prosperity and worldliness of Tang society are expressed boldly in its celebrated *sancai* ceramics, characterized by an exuberant use of colorful lead-glazes. *Sancai*, literally "three-color," refers to the dominant colorants: iron oxide for golden yellows and amber browns, copper oxide for green, and imported cobalt for blue.

The use of a white slip on the clay surface under the glazes enhances the brilliance of the colors. The tendency of lead glazes to run during firing was exploited so that the colors would mingle and flow over surfaces to create a variety of attractive effects.

The light-firing "earthenware" clays of the Tang dynasty, according to scientific analysis, are actually underfired clays of the same type used in northern stoneware and porcelain (see entry 54). For *mingqi* the potentially weak structure of underfired stoneware was not a concern. In fact, *sancai* wares may have been biscuit-fired first to give strength, and then fired a second time at a lower temperature to mature the glazes.[2]

Provenance:
C. H. Mori; William T. and Louise Taft Semple
Notes:
1. Schafer, *Golden Peaches*, pp. 58–64.
2. Wood, "Recent Researches," p. 145.

57. Horse

Tang dynasty, 8th century A.D. Earthenware with *sancai* lead glazes. H. 52.1 cm.
Museum purchase, 1950.49

A richly caparisoned horse, with mane closely cropped except for a long tuft of hair over the withers, stands on a flat rectangular stand. Its head tilts slightly to the left, and its tail is decoratively tied and bundled. The buff-colored clay is covered overall in white slip and lead glazes of amber and blue, which drip downward over the head, neck, withers, and haunches. Adorned with a saddle and with decorative trappings on the bridle, around the neck, and over the rump, the horse is riderless.

Tang dynasty China's passion for horses was manifested in the widespread practice of equestrian sports, such as polo, among the aristocracy. Government edicts attempted to preserve the high social status associated with horsemanship by restricting the lower classes, namely merchants and artisans, from riding. Thus the presence of magnificent horses among burial furnishings contributed significantly to the display of the deceased person's wealth and status in life and the afterlife.

Horses bred from Arab stock, descendants of the "heavenly horses" of Ferghana, were highly prized in China (see entry 56). Identified with divine horses of antiquity, they were believed to be the precursors of dragons and to sweat blood; their swiftness and strength were legendary. Surely any high-ranking tomb occupant would be poorly-supplied without a dragon-steed to carry the soul off to heaven.

The large size of the Museum's horse and the predominance of blue glaze suggest further that the figure was made for the tomb of a high-ranking official or member of the aristocracy. Blue is the rarest of *sancai* glazes because it relied on expensive, imported cobalt for its color; generally it was reserved for use on smaller items. The Museum's horse is remarkable as one of the largest blue-glazed horses known.[1]

Captivating in its dignified stance, its elegant golden trappings, and the dramatic streaks of rich color emphasizing its full, taut musculature, this horse recalls the Tang poet Li Bo's (701–762) description of prized foreign steeds:

The Horses of Heaven come out of the dens of the Kushanas,
Backs formed with tiger markings, bones made for dragon wings.[2]

Provenance:
    J. T. Tai; C. T. Loo
Published:
    Avril, "Highlights of Chinese Art," pp. 74–75.
    Cincinnati Art Museum Handbook, p. 62.
    Edwards, "Sophistications," p. 85.
    Masterpieces from the Cincinnati Art Museum, p. 76.
    Mathes, *Treasures of American Museums*, p. 14.
Notes:
    1. A larger horse of the same type (H. 61 cm.) is in the Matsuoka Museum of Art, Tokyo. See Figgess, "Chinese Ceramics in the Matsuoka Museum," *TOCS* (1986–87), p. 10 and cover illus.
    2. Schafer, *Golden Peaches*, p. 60.

58. Tripod Tray

Tang dynasty, late 7th or 8th century A.D. Earthenware with *sancai* lead glazes. Diam. 29 cm.
Museum purchase, 1950.48

The shallow round plate with everted rim is supported by three cabriole legs. The interior is decorated with an incised design of alternating lotus blossoms and lingzhi fungus, which surrounds a central roundel containing a flying goose among clouds. The tray of buff-colored clay is covered in white slip and lead glazes of amber, green, and blue. Three spur marks are visible in the interior.

Extensive and prosperous trade with the cultures of Central and Western Asia fueled Tang China's seemingly insatiable demands for the exotic. To satisfy their patron's cosmopolitan tastes, Chinese artists infused their creations with motifs and styles of foreign origin, including many borrowed from Buddhist art (see entry 11). This tripod tray, with its design of a flying goose within a rosette composed of lotus flowers and palmettes, exemplifies the kind of Chinese assimilation of foreign motifs that characterized this extraordinarily creative period.

Such trays were used to present food offerings to Buddhist temples or ancestral shrines, or as part of the funerary rites. The configuration of the design into a rosette and the individual motifs composing the design are Buddhist in derivation and meaning. Geese among clouds represent the souls of the faithful, who after death could visit the earth in the form of birds during the annual migrations.[1] Lotus flowers refer to rebirth in a Buddhist paradise, where souls emerge as infants from the unfurled blossoms. Here the form of the stylized palmettes that alternate with the lotus blos-

soms is reminiscent of *lingzhi* fungus, a Chinese symbol of longevity and immortality.

Incising not only delineates the design but also effectively confined the lead glazes, which tended to run during firing, to precise color fields.

Provenance:
    J. T. Tai; C. T. Loo
Published:
    Avril, "Highlights of Chinese Art," pp. 74–76.
Note:
    1. Bivar, "Trade between China and the Near East," p. 4.

59. Rhyton in the Form of a Goose

Tang dynasty, probably Henan province, 8th century A.D. Earthenware with *sancai* lead glazes. H. 8.4, L. 13.5 cm.
Museum purchase: Deaccession funds, 1989.46

The curved, horn-shaped vessel with goose-head terminal and oval opening has molded relief decoration in floral and nipple patterns. It is coated with an amber-colored lead glaze on the exterior and a green lead glaze on the interior.

Direct connections between the Chinese and Sasanian courts furnished Tang potters with new metalwork shapes and decorative elements to enrich their indigenous ceramic tradition.[1] One shape borrowed from Sasanian metalwork is the animal-head rhyton, which first appeared in China in the early seventh century.[2] By the eighth century the Chinese had adapted the form so that the animal head turned back to face the opening of the vessel. Such vessels apparently were used in two ways: as rhytons[3] or, with the addition of an oil tray, as lamps.[4]

The Museum's rhyton was made in a two-part mold, its surface decorated sensitively in a pattern of floral and nipple motifs against a matted ground. The decoration also was inspired by metalwork; the matted ground imitates ring matting in silver. The rhyton is stylistically related to wares assigned to Henan production in the second half of the eighth century and anticipates the decorative vocabulary of the Liao dynasty (947–1125).[5]

Provenance:
    Ip Che; J. J. Lally
Published:
    Anthology of Chinese Art, p. 313.
    Avril, "Highlights of Chinese Art," pp. 75–76.
Exhibited:
    "Min Chiu Society Silver Jubilee Exhibition," Hong Kong Museum of Art, October 25, 1985–January 15, 1986, no. 114.
Notes:
    1. Watson, *T'ang and Liao Ceramics*, pp. 12–13.
    2. See Medley, *Tang Pottery and Porcelain*, London, 1981, p. 20, figs. 4 and 5, for an example in the British Museum. An ox-head rhyton in the Royal Ontario Museum is illustrated in Vollmer et al., *Silk Roads-China Ships*, p. 71. For a fourth-

century example of the Sasanian silver prototype, see Lawton et al., *Asian Art in the Arthur M. Sackler Gallery-The Inaugural Gift*, no. 20.

    3. Watson, *T'ang and Liao Ceramics*, p. 13, fig. 2.

    4. Lamps exist in the St. Louis Art Museum, illustrated in Medley, *T'ang Pottery and Porcelain*, p. 30, fig. 15, and in the Metropolitan Museum of Art, illustrated in Valenstein, *Handbook of Chinese Ceramics*, p. 48, fig. 20.

    5. Watson, *T'ang and Liao Ceramics*, figs. 2, 134.

60. Bowl, Ding Ware

Hebei province, Northern Song dynasty, 11th or 12th century. Porcelain with incised design under white glaze. H. 7 cm, diam. 18.9 cm.
Museum purchase, 1950.55

The ivory-colored bowl has a six-lobed rim and deep, slightly curved sides that taper to the foot. Decoration is limited to the interior of the bowl and consists of freely incised lotus and sagittaria with foliage. A band of copper alloy binds the rim. Accumulations of the transparent glaze appear as brownish streaks on the underside. The short, straight foot is completely glazed.

In the Song dynasty, the demands of the imperial court, a growing scholar-aesthete class, and wealthy merchants all contributed to the need for ever greater quantity and variety in high-quality ceramics. Whereas Tang ceramic styles exhibit strong foreign influence, a decline in overland trade with the Middle East slowed the influx of foreign goods in this dynasty. Thus, Song ceramics reflect a period of cultural introspection. The intellectual tastes of China's scholar elite were at the forefront in the evolution of a new indigenous aesthetic.

According to later connoisseurs, the five greatest ceramic wares of the Song dynasty are Ding, Ru (see entry 63), Jun (see entry 64), Guan, and Ge. Ding porcelains, distinguished by a warm, ivory-colored glaze, were made at kilns in the northern province of Hebei from the Tang to the Yuan dynasties. The name derives from a geographic designation: the former Ding prefecture, the area near modern Quyangxian, Hebei province. Dingzhou was an ideal location for producing ceramics because of its proximity to sources of clay and glaze materials, coal mines for fuel, and rivers providing transport to the coast. By the eleventh century, the products of these kilns were sent as tribute to the imperial court, but they were not made exclusively for court use. Excavations of tenth-century Buddhist sites yielded numerous Ding vessels, many with some form of lotus decoration.[1]

Ding kilns were simple single-chamber downdraft types commonly called *mantou*, after the steamed bread whose shape they resemble. Sophisticated potting techniques were employed to produce the thin-walled Ding wares. Bowls were fired on their rims in stepped saggars; this process allowed even heating and the efficient firing of numerous vessels in a relatively small space. Because the thin-walled bowls were more stable when resting on their rims, they were less likely to slump during firing. To prevent the bowls from adhering to the saggar, the potters left the rims unglazed; later

this raw edge was bound with silver or with a copper alloy. Another distinguishing characteristic of Ding glaze is the appearance of brownish glaze drips, known as "tear drops," that resulted from dipping the vessels in the glaze. Firing in a slightly oxidizing atmosphere accounts for the warm ivory color of the glaze.

The quality of Ding at its zenith is exemplified in the Museum's delicate, thinly potted bowl with elegant, incised decoration. The lobed shape derives from Tang and Song dynasty silver, as does the extreme thinness of the body. Decoration on the interior of this bowl consists of a lotus plant with mature blossom, its fully open petals revealing the seed pod, in combination with the water plant sagittaria, identified by its distinctive tripartite leaves. The lotus, symbol of Buddhist purity, also possessed secular meaning as an emblem of Confucian integrity. When shown with its seed pod, as here, it also serves as a symbol of fertility.[2]

Provenance:
    J. T. Tai; C. T. Loo
Published:
    Edwards, "Sophistications," p. 83, fig. 3.
Notes:
    1. Vainker, *Chinese Pottery and Porcelain*, pp. 94–95.
    2. Wirgin, *Sung Ceramic Designs*, pp. 170–71.

61. Plate, Ding Ware

Hebei province, Jin dynasty, 13th century. Porcelain with mold-impressed design under white glaze; Ding ware. H. 6.4 cm, diam. 29.8 cm.
Museum purchase, 1950.54

The wide-mouthed deep plate has curved sides tapering to a short, straight foot and a flat, recessed base. Glaze coats the entire vessel except for the rim, which is bound with copper. Interior decoration consists of molded floral designs in shallow relief: The central roundel with keyfret border contains lotus, sagittaria, smartweed, and mallow. Surrounding this is a frieze of dense, scrolling peony blossoms, leaves, and stems contained within raised linear borders.

Beginning in the eleventh century, the Ding potters added molding as a decorative technique. By pressing the soft clay against a dome-shaped mold into which designs already had been carved, a potter could simultaneously form and decorate the bowl, thus eliminating the laborious step of incising each piece individually (see entry 58). Moreover, this method permitted the efficient production of complex designs.

A densely packed and precisely executed panoply of botanical motifs, arranged so as to suggest an urban garden, fills the interior of the Museum's plate. The central medallion represents a lotus pond; its blossoming lotus and other water plants are surrounded by a keyfret-patterned balustrade or short fence that separates it from the peony bed forming the outer decorative frieze. The peony was the most popular floral motif in Song decorative arts. Symbolic of wealth and rank, the showy flower first became prominent in the imperial and private gardens of Changan. During the Northern Song dynasty it was immensely popular in Luoyang and Yangzhou, both famous for the cultivation of numerous peony varieties.

Hangzhou, the southern Song capital, was especially famous for its gardens.[1] The particular attention given to naturalistic details on this plate surely would have delighted a Southern Song connoisseur of plant varieties. Gardens signified a level of prosperity, social status, and leisure inherent in the Song ideal of the good life, and were an important component of every elite residence. They also served as places of retreat, where Confucian virtues could be cultivated in scholarly leisure-time activities such as painting and composing poetry.

A plate produced from the same mold as this is in the Indianapolis Museum of Art.[2] A slightly larger plate with similar molded decoration was excavated from the early fourteenth-century Sinan shipwreck.[3]

Provenance:
 C. T. Loo
Published:
 Keppel, *China in 1700*, p. 5, not illus.
Exhibited:
 "China in 1700: Kangxi Porcelains at the Taft Museum," Taft Museum, Cincinnati; Flint Institute of Arts; Art Gallery, Ball State University, 1988–89.
Notes:
 1. See a description of the gardens of Hangzhou from the 1235 "Duzheng jisheng," translated by Clara Yu, in Ebrey, *Chinese Civilization*, p. 183.
 2. The Indianapolis bowl was also acquired from C. T. Loo; see Mino and Robinson, *Beauty and Tranquility*, pl. 82, pp. 216–17. According to records in the Loo archive, New York University, both bowls were obtained in China in 1947.
 3. *Relics Salvaged*, 1, pl. 85, no. 122, pp. 97, 320–21.

62. Bowl, Yaozhou Ware

Shaanxi province, Northern Song or Jin dynasty, 12th or 13th century. Stoneware with olive-green glaze. H. 7 cm, diam. 17 cm. Museum purchase: Phyllis H. Thayer Purchase Fund, 1996.13

The conical bowl has a wide mouth with everted rim; the rounded sides taper to a small, slightly splayed ringfoot. Glazed overall with a translucent olive green glaze, the bowl has exterior decoration of incised vertical fluting and interior molded decoration of peonies and leaves. The clay body is brownish grey where exposed on the foot.

Influenced by the fine green-glazed Yue wares of southern China sent as tribute to the north during the late Tang and Five Dynasties period, the Yaozhou kilns of Shaanxi province continued the green-glazed stoneware tradition of northern China (see entry 53). The primary kilns were located in Tongquan county at Huangbaozhen, near Xi'an, but Yaozhou-type wares also were made in Henan province, at Qingliangsi and Linru.

This thinly potted bowl has the characteristic Yaozhou olive green color, which derives from a small amount of iron oxide in the glaze fired in a reduction atmosphere. During the firing process, the nearly transparent glaze pools in the carved or molded recesses of the vessel surface, creating a darker tone that accentuates the carved or molded decoration. The glaze also exhibits a tiny pattern of crazing, which contributes to its luminous depth.

Floral motifs, especially peony and lotus, abound on Yaozhou ceramics. The peony, which symbolizes wealth and rank, was the most popular cultivated flower in Song-dynasty China, and its praise is recorded in treatises of the period.[1] In addition, the herbaceous peony (*shaoyao*), mentioned in the ninth-century *Book of Odes*, sometimes served as a farewell gift and token of love.[2] The Museum's bowl is decorated with a finely executed molded motif of intertwined pairs of herbaceous peony blossoms, repeated three times on the interior.

Several other examples of this relatively rare molded design are known.[3]

Notes:
 1. Wirgin, *Sung Ceramic Designs*, p. 167
 2. Bartholomew, *Hundred Flowers*, no. 8b.
 3. Krahl, *Chinese Ceramics from the Meiyintang Collection*, vol. 1, no. 431; Christie's Swire, 1–3 May 1994, lot 609; Wirgin, *Sung Ceramic Designs*, pl. 4f.

63. Tripod Vessel *Zun*, Ru Ware

Northern Song dynasty, late 11th or early 12th century. Porcelaneous ware with blue-green glaze. H. 13.3, diam. 19.0 cm. Museum purchase, 1950.60.

The straight-sided cylindrical vessel is supported by three short cabriole legs. Exterior surface decoration consists of three groups of horizontal raised bands: two just below the rim, three around the center, and two just above the base. The vessel is covered with a finely crackled glaze that varies in color from brownish green to grayish blue-green. Six sesame-seed spur marks appear on the glazed base.

By the early twelfth century, Ding wares (see entries 60 and 61) had fallen out of favor with the imperial court.[1] For about 40 years in the late Northern Song dynasty, Ru ware, characterized by a thick, unctuous pale blue or blue-green glaze whose texture resembles jade, was made exclusively for imperial use. Regarded as the epitome of Song ceramics, Ru is also the rarest of Chinese ceramic types. According to contemporary writings, only pieces rejected by the court could be sold.[2]

Ru ware vessels are generally small, simple, and unadorned, reflecting the abstemious and subtle artistic taste of the Emperor Huizong (reigned 1100–1125). Thinly potted of a buff- or ash-colored clay, Ru wares were completely coated with glaze; tiny "sesame-seed" spurs supported the vessels during firing. With a small amount of iron in the glaze and strict control of the reduction atmosphere, Ru potters created a celebrated sky-blue color. The opaque, semi-gloss glaze with warm undertone is further distinguished by its fine network of pale or colorless crackle.[3]

The difficulty of creating the intended sky-blue color can be appreciated by considering the Museum's vessel, whose glaze exhibits the crackle pattern unique to Ru ware, but whose color shows evidence of problems in the firing process. One side is a fine blue-green color; the other side appears brownish because of an influx of oxygen. More successful examples of Ru ware *zun* vessels are in the Palace Museum, Beijing and at the Percival David Foundation, London.[4]

Until the Ru kiln was discovered by Shanghai Museum archaeologists in 1986, only about thirty examples of this ware were known worldwide. All forty-three of the blue-glazed sherds unearthed with the kiln showed the fine crackled surfaces associated with Ru ware. They were either glazed overall and fired on sesame-seed spurs or were fired on a setter with the footring left free of glaze. In addition, the firing tools discovered, such as spur setters and a temperature tester, confirmed a kiln site.

In 1989 a hoard of forty-seven intact Ru ware vessels was unearthed near Qingliangsi.[5] It is not known whether the recently excavated Ru kiln site was the only one that produced these official wares; some Southern Song writings suggest that an official kiln was set up in Kaifeng, the capitol, and operated there during the Zhenghe (1111–1118) and Xuanhe (1119–1125) periods, until the Song capitol moved to Hangzhou in 1127.[6]

Provenance:
    C. T. Loo
Published:
    Edwards, "Sophistications," p. 83, fig. 4.
    Avril, "Highlights," pp. 75–76.
Notes:
    1. Ding wares were rejected, according to contemporary writings, because they had *mang,* a word variously interpreted as referring to the unglazed rims, the teardrop effect, or the ware's having become as commonplace as grain. See M. Rogers, "Mechanics," p. 68.
    2. Vainker, *Chinese Pottery and Porcelain*, p. 100.
    3. On the basis of its crackle pattern, the Museum's vessel is undoubtedly Chinese Ru ware, although numerous curatorial file comments identified the CAM censer as Korean. See Mowry, "Koryu Celadons," for a study and comparison that distinguishes between Korean celadons and Chinese Ru ware. For a discussion of the connections between Koryo celadons and Ru ware, see M. Rogers, "Mechanics," pp. 64–66.
    4. Wang, *Discovery of Ru Kiln*, pl. 59 and 66.
    5. Zhao, "Jinshi nianlai Henan taoci kaogu de xin shouhua."
    6. See Fan Dongqing and Zhou Lili, "The Investigation of the Ru Kiln Site," in Wang, *Discovery of Ru Kiln*, pp. 101–02. Another interpretation of the evidence is offered by Li, "Song Guan Wares: Song Official Wares," pp. 28–30.

64. Bowl, Jun Ware

Jin dynasty, 12th or 13th century. Stoneware with splashed blue glaze. H. 8.9, diam. 19.4 cm.
Museum purchase, 1950.64

The wide-mouthed bowl has rounded sides tapering to a slightly splayed ringfoot. The dark grey-brown body is exposed where the glaze stops just short of the base. The glaze is light blue; a tear-shaped purple splash on the interior extends down from the rim.

Jun ware, a rather heavily potted ceramic characterized by a dark body and a frosty blue glaze with purple splashes, was also produced for the Northern Song court (see entry 63). Although the kiln at Juntai was abandoned as an official kiln when the Song capital moved south to Linan [Hangzhou],[1] the Jun potters continued to produce their distinctive ceramics under the Jin and the Ming dynasties. In fact, the name Jun came to be associated with these wares only in the Ming dynasty, after the geographic designation Junzhou (modern Yuxian) in Henan province. Jun wares were produced at numerous kiln sites in Henan, notably in the area of Linru.

Jun glaze has an iron content similar to that of Ru and Yaozhou, and the ware is also fired in a reduction atmosphere. Its distinctive opalescent, sugary appearance, however, results from a unique crystalline structure that is formed in phase separation during cooling. The effect is optical rather than compositional because the microstructure of the glaze causes light to be reflected toward the blue end of the spectrum.[2]

By applying copper oxide onto the glaze, the Jun potters achieved a stunning visual effect of purple splashes against lavender blue that has been likened to "floating clouds" or "the sky at dusk."[3] Watt suggests that the appreciation of Jun ware may reflect the late Northern Song court's fascination with Daoism; the purple splashes would have recalled the purple mist associated with Daoist immortals.[4]

A slightly smaller Jun bowl waster in the Henan Provincial Museum, still attached to its sagger, is similar to the Museum's bowl in shape and decoration.[5]

Provenance:
    C. T. Loo
Notes:
    1. Li, "Song Guan Wares." pp. 30–31.
    2. See *Iron in the Fire*, p. 13. Blue Jun glazes are higher in silica (the glass-forming oxide) and lower in alumina (the stiffener that prevents the glaze from running off the pot during firing). During cooling this composition seems to cause the unmixing of the glass spheres in the glaze base. The diameters of these spheres reflect light toward the blue end of the spectrum. Also see Vandiver, "Technical Studies," pp. 126–28.
    3. Feng, "Chinese Celadons," p. 41.
    4. Watt, "Antiquarianism and Naturalism," p. 242.
    5. Thorp, *Son of Heaven*, p. 153, no. 84.

65. Teabowl, Jian Ware

Shuiji kilns, Jianyang, Fujian province, Southern Song dynasty, 12th or 13th century. Glazed stoneware with silver rim. H. 7.1, diam. 12 cm.
Gift of Olga Dobrogorski-Platz in memory of Louis A. Platz, 1982.270

The bowl has an indented, vertical lip and pitched walls that taper to a short, straight foot. The rim is bound with silver. On the interior of the bowl the glaze is thin at the rim, displaying a russet brown color. In the bottom of the bowl it has accumulated in a lustrous bluish black pool. On the exterior the thick glaze covers about two-thirds of the surface and also exhibits a russet brown color around the rim. The glaze stops unevenly about one-third of the way from the base of the bowl except in a few places where a stream of glaze runs nearly to the top of the foot. The unglazed clay body is coarse in texture; its color is light brown on the surface and purple-black in pitted areas.

Tea drinking, introduced by southern Chinese living in the Tang capital, had become widespread throughout northern China by the eighth century. Its popularity was increased by the dissemination of writings such as Lu Yu's *Classic of Tea (Chajing)*, which meticulously described techniques for the proper preparation, serving, and consumption of tea. The habit had reached nearly a cult status by the Song dynasty; many kilns responded to tea connoisseurs' needs with a variety of wares specially designed to enhance the tea-drinking experience.

Ever more elaborate methods for processing and preparing tea were practiced during the Song period, when powdered white tea from Fujian gained preference over red-leaf teas. The process of making white tea involved steaming the leaves, squeezing them until all the juice was extracted, and then laboriously using mortar and pestle to grind them into a fine paste. The paste was pressed into a mold to form a tea cake; powdered tea was made by drying the tea cake in a pan, grinding it, and forcing it through a sieve. This powder became a drink when boiling water was added in a warmed bowl and the mixture was whipped to form a silvery froth. According to Emperor Huizong's *Daguan chalun* [*Discourses on Tea in the Daguan Era, 1107–1110*], only the finest possible powder, properly prepared, would form "a silver suspension reflecting the light, the peaks surging and the foam clinging to the walls of the bowl." This phenomenon, called "biting the bowl," was the object of tea contests; in order to win, the froth could not allow any water to be seen along the bowl's walls.[1] Black-glazed ceramics were considered best for showing off such foamy white tea.

The Museum's bowl has subtle silvery brown "hare's fur" streaks on its bluish-black glossy glazed interior and exterior. This decorative feature was created by first immersing the bowl in glaze, allowing it to dry, and then dipping only the rim in an iron-rich slip. During firing (when the bowl was placed upright in the kiln and supported by a small clay firing cushion) the slip ran, forming a pattern of fine vertical streaks. The color of the streaks could range from yellow to russet to brown or silvery brown, depending on the amount of iron in the slip and the atmosphere, the firing time, and the temperature in the kiln.[2]

Cai Xiang wrote in *Chalu*, "The most practical tea bowls are those made in Jian'an with streaks resembling hare's fur in their black glaze, as their thicker body can retain the heat for a longer time." The preference for Jian wares was further confirmed by the poet Su Zhe (1039–1112):

Water with bubbles like crabs' eyes retains the youthful zest
Bowls with hare's fur glaze show the color at its best.[3]

Notes:
1. *Ancient Chinese Tea Wares*, pp. 29–31.
2. Mowry, *Hare's Fur*, p. 219.
3. Both quoted in *Ancient Chinese Tea Wares*, p. 31.

66. Tea Bowl, Cizhou-Type Ware

Northern China, Henan province, Southern Song dynasty, 11th or 12th century. Porcelain with black glaze. H. 5.2, diam. 13.7 cm. Museum purchase, 1950.57

The bowl has a slightly everted lip and flaring sides that taper to the short, straight-walled footring. The recessed base and well-defined footring are unglazed, exposing the light-gray clay body. Some kiln sand has adhered to the surface of the footring. The interior and exterior are coated with a dark brown glaze that appears black where it is thick. Markings with a metallic luster are scattered throughout the interior and on the exterior just below the rim.

Cizhou is the broadly applied term for popular ceramics made in northern China from the Northern Song to the Ming period. This is the old geographic designation of the area known today as Ci Xian, encompassing southern Hebei and northern Henan provinces, where the greatest concentration of kilns producing these popular ceramics was located. Archaeological evidence shows that the widely distributed Cizhou wares were produced in other provinces as well, from Shandong to Ningxia.[1] The most common form of decoration on Cizhou wares involves various painted and/or incised techniques over a coating of white slip. Cizhou kilns in Henan and Shandong provinces also produced dark-glazed ceramics with characteristics similar to those of southern dark-glazed wares made in Fujian province. These black wares met market demands for dark-glazed tea ceramics in the Northern Song period that would show off the newly popular Fujian white-leaf tea (see entry 65).

Decoration on both northern and southern black wares was created by applying iron oxide slip over the glaze to form surface patterns of russet brown reminiscent of "partridge feathers" or "hare's fur" (see entry 65). This bowl is decorated in the *zhegu ban*, or partridge-feather mottling technique. The tiny markings were either splashed or brushed onto the surface over the unfired glaze. As the fired vessel cooled, hematite crystals formed on the surface where the iron-rich slip was applied, producing a metallic sheen that defined the mottling.[2]

Provenance:
J. T. Tai; C. T. Loo

Notes:
1. Valenstein, *Handbook*, pp. 93, 120, n. 8
2. Mowry, *Hare's Fur*, pp. 32, 135–37.

67. Bottle, Cizhou Ware

Yuan Dynasty, 13th or early 14th century. Glazed stoneware.
H. 28.6 cm.
Museum purchase, 1950.56

The pear-shaped bottle has a narrow neck flaring to an everted rim. The bulbous body tapers to a splayed foot. Covered in a thick brown-black glaze, the bottle exhibits russet-brown painted decoration of abstract bird forms.

This type of *changjing ping*, or long-necked bottle, was used for serving wine in the Jin and Yuan dynasties. It represents a distinctive type of black-glazed ware made by Cizhou kilns (see entry 66 for another type) from the twelfth to the fourteenth century. The lustrous black color was achieved by thickly applying an iron oxide glaze enriched with 5–6% iron. Another glaze with even higher iron content (above 6%) was then splashed or painted on the surface; during firing these additions burned to a rusty brown color. They also ran slightly, blurring the edges of the designs to create a furlike texture that contrasts with the black background.

The calligraphically executed designs, one on each side of the Museum's bottle, derive from bird motifs seen on earlier vessels of this type. Each bird is shown in descent: The head is formed of a single dot near the base of the bottle, the body feathers fan out above, and the tail is rendered in a single stroke extending upward to the base of the bottle's neck. The Museums bottle is typical of the Yuan-dynasty versions, in which the birds are painted so cursorily and so abstractly that they might be mistaken for stylized floral designs.[1]

Provenance:
  C. T. Loo
Notes:
  1. See an earlier bottle in the Sackler Museum, Harvard, on which the bird designs are more clearly defined; Mowry, *Hare's Fur*, no. 52. Two other bottles published in Mowry, nos. 53 and 54, also exhibit bird designs. Mowry relates these designs to northern Song paintings of pheasants and magpies, and to painted birds on other Cizhou-type wares.

68. *Zun* Vase, Cizhou Ware

Hebei province, possibly from Guantaizhen, Jin dynasty, 12th century. Stoneware with white slip and transparent glaze, painted and incised in iron brown under lead glaze. H. 30.8 cm.
Museum purchase, 1950.51

The thickly potted tall-necked vase of zun shape has a trumpet mouth with everted rim. The ovoid body tapers to a wide flaring foot and flat, recessed base. The reddish buff stoneware body is covered with white slip and an iron-brown painted design of scrolling peonies, incised in the sgraffito technique. The vase is covered with a transparent green lead glaze that shows areas of iridescent degradation.

Cizhou ceramics reflect popular rather than imperial taste; Cizhou wares are not mentioned in Song dynasty writings, and there is no evidence that they were presented as tribute to the court.[1] They served primarily as household and kitchen wares for merchants and commoners of north China; Cizhou kilns supplied wine manufacturers with a variety of containers.[2] Inexpensive and readily available, these stonewares possess a sturdiness that made them especially well suited for everyday use.

Characterized by robust shapes and informal design, most Cizhou wares were decorated with a variety of techniques based on painting and/or incising designs over white slip. The surface decoration of the Museum's vase, with its silhouette tree-peony design, represents the sgraffito technique so frequently employed in decorating Cizhou wares. A coating of white slip was first applied over the entire vessel, followed by an iron-rich slip painted directly over the white slip. This darker layer then was carved away to expose the white layer beneath and create the bold silhouette of the plant; incising further defined petals and leaves. A transparent lead glaze, whose green color derives from copper oxide, was applied over the slip decoration, and the vase was fired a second time at a lower temperature to mature the lead glaze.[3] The sgraffito peony design on a *zun* vase in the Tokyo National Museum is identical to that on this vase; it consists of peony blossoms on the shoulder, surrounded by scrolling leaves that vine horizontally across the lower portion of the base to the right around the blossom, then sweep upward, and terminate at the base of the trumpet rim.[4] A sherd excavated at Guantaizhen shows similar peony designs.[5]

Considered the "King of Flowers," the peony is the floral motif that occurs most frequently on ceramics, beginning in the Song dynasty. The tree peony (*mudan*), cultivated by the Sui and Tang imperial courts, became immensely popular during the Northern Song dynasty, when Luoyang gained fame as the great center of cultivation for numerous varieties of the plant. Symbol of wealth and rank, the *mudan* was also a favorite theme in literature and the subject of scholarly treatises in the eleventh and twelfth centuries.[6]

Provenance:
  C. T. Loo
Published:
  Masterpieces from the Cincinnati Art Museum, p. 55.
Notes:
  1. Vainker, *Chinese Pottery*, p. 116.
  2. Mino, *Freedom*, p. 13.
  3. See *Iron In the Fire*, no. 32, for a similar example of the type, but with clear rather than lead glaze, in the collection of the City of Bristol Museum and Art Gallery, Or. N2445.
  4. See Mino, *Freedom*, p. 108, fig. 106.
  5. Mino, *Freedom*, p. 102, fig. 96.
  6. See Bartholomew, *Hundred Flowers*, no. 13. Also Wirgin, *Sung Ceramic Designs*, pp. 166–70.

69. Bottle, Cizhou Ware

Jin dynasty, late 12th or 13th century. Stoneware with incised decoration, painted in iron brown under lead glazes. H. 28.9 cm.
Museum purchase, 1950.50

The thickly potted pear-shaped vase has a slender neck flaring to the everted rim. The short, flared foot has a flat, recessed base. Decoration consists of a band of incised and painted upright lotus petals bordered by simple horizontal bands of yellow on the shoulder and a large frieze of scrolling lotus blossoms and leaves around the widest girth of the vessel.

The use of three-color lead glazes and incised designs represents the Cizhou potters' continuation of the decorative traditions of the Tang and Liao dynasties. The lotus-petal border and the main frieze of scrolling lotus were defined by incising outlines in the soft clay; areas then were colored in with green and yellow lead glazes. Iron oxide slip was brushed on the tips of the lotus blossoms, creating bold russet-colored accents. A clear glaze coats the entire decorated portion of the bottle. A similar bottle is in the Indianapolis Museum of Art.[1]

Provenance:
> C.T. Loo
Published:
> Mino, *Freedom*, p. 226.
> Hai-wai Yi-chen Pottery and Porcelain 2, p. 92
Notes:
> 1. See Mino, *Freedom*, pl. 101; also Mino and Robinson, *Beauty*, pl. 70.

70. *Meiping*, Cizhou Ware

Jin dynasty, 12th or 13th century. Stoneware with white slip, painted in iron brown under transparent glaze. H. 38.1 cm.
Museum purchase, 1950.52

The tall, thickly potted vase of meiping shape with rounded shoulder tapers slightly to the flat, recessed base. The buff-colored stoneware body is covered with white slip and an underglaze iron-brown painted decoration of peonies and moths. The conical mouth is restored.

The *meiping*' literally "plum blossom vase," a tall vessel featuring a wide shoulder and a short neck, was a new shape in the Song dynasty. The fluid grace of the painted peony on this *meiping* contrasts with the rather stiff treatment of peonies in the sgraffito technique (see entry 64). Through a successful combination of thick strokes making up petals and leaves with stems so delicate as to seem almost unable to support their load, the decorator wielded the brush with a confidence reminiscent of the ink painting of that period.[1]

The plant represented here is the herbaceous peony (*shaoyao*), which blooms later than the tree peony. The stem consists of soft plant tissue, which distinguishes it from its woody relative. *Shaoyao* is mentioned in the *Book of Odes*; by the Song dynasty,

cultivation of *shaoyao* was centered in Yangzhou. A favorite love token or farewell gift, *shaoyao* ranked below the tree peony as the "Prime Minister of Flowers."[2]

Provenance:
> C.T. Loo
Published:
> Mathes, *Treasures of American Museums*, p. 34.
Notes:
> 1. See Mino, *Freedom*, pp. 164–65, for similar examples.
> 2. See Bartholomew, *Hundred Flowers*; also Wirgin, *Sung Ceramic Designs*, p. 167.

71. Pillow, Cizhou Ware

Hebei Province, Yuan dynasty, late 13th or 14th century. Stoneware with white slip, painted in iron brown under transparent glaze.
L. 43.5 cm.
Museum purchase, 1950.53

The rectangular pillow has a slightly concave top that slopes forward and overhangs the nearly vertical sides. Underglaze iron-brown painted decoration on the top, sides, front, and back consists of ogival panels surrounded by dense floral and scroll designs. The central ogival panel of the top surface displays a scene of a kneeling man and a man bending forward, showing respect to a man standing in front of a pavilion inside a walled compound. A fourth male, outfitted with bow and quiver, looks on. To the right the pavilion is partially obscured by clouds; to the left a garden rock stands among banana plants within a fenced area beside a balustrade. The front panel of the pillow displays blossoming hibiscus; the back panel shows a blossoming spray of peony; each side panel is decorated with a single lotus blossom. A small airhole was drilled in the back panel. The unglazed bottom has an impressed seal in the form of a bell, with a four-character mark that reads: "Wang shi Shouming."

Hard pillows made of stone, wood, or bronze have been unearthed from Han-dynasty tombs, but ceramic pillows did not come into use until the seventh century. Their popularity, whether for daily use or as tomb furnishings, reached its peak during the Song period. Produced by all the major kilns that supplied vessels, pillows were embellished with a broad variety of decorative techniques. The Museum's example is one of the Cizhou kilns' distinctive rectangular pillows painted in underglaze iron with scenes from popular literature and drama. In the Yuan dynasty, variety plays and vernacular stories were first disseminated through woodblock prints; their widespread popularity then was reflected in Cizhou ceramic pillows.

An unusual feature of some Cizhou pillows is the presence of signatures and seals, a departure from the usual anonymity of Chinese potters and decorators. The Museum's pillow includes a signature of the painter located to the left of the main scene: *Zhangbin yiren zhi*, "made by the hermit who has retired to the banks of the Zhang [River]," an artist's studio name. (The Zhang River is located near the Cizhou kilns.) The bottom of the pillow displays the impressed mark of the potter, Wang Shouming. Other pillows with this signature and impressed mark, but different painted scenes, are known.[1]

Decorative elements on the Museum's pillow have various origins. The ogival panels reflect foreign influence through Mongol sources, and the brocadelike decoration probably imitates textiles of the period.[2] The scene depicted may come from the *Hanshu* [Han Documents], which extol the efforts of loyal ministers to follow Confucian moral dictates, often at great personal risk.

The scene on the Museum's pillow is reminiscent of a painting in the National Palace Museum, Taipei. That painting illustrates a story known as "Breaking the Balustrade," in which the official Zhu Yun remonstrated with the emperor about the corruption of high officials. When Zhu requested a sword to behead one of the corrupt as an example, the emperor asked him to identify the official he would behead. Zhu named Zhang Yu, marquis of Anchang. Enraged at Zhu's insubordination, the emperor ordered Zhu Yu to be taken away and executed. Zhu clung to the balustrade until it broke, saying that he would gladly join the other virtuous officials who were executed for admonishing the emperor. Xin Qingji, a virtuous general, intervened on Zhu's behalf, offering his own life instead. Impressed by their courage, the emperor let both go free and ordered the balustrade to remain broken as a reminder.[3]

Provenance:
    C. T. Loo
Published:
Hai-wai Yi-chen Pottery and Porcelain, 2, p. 129
Notes:
    1. British Museum, OA1936.10–12.219, illustrated in Medley, "Patterns," p. 69; two others, one in the Mr. and Mrs. Yeung Wing Tak collection and the other an excavated example in the Handan City Museum, Hebei, were both published in Museum of the Western Han Tomb of the Nanyue King, *Chinese Ceramic Pillows*, no. 111 and p. 471 respectively.
    2. Medley, *Patterns*, p. 68.
    3. See Cahill, "Imperial Painting Academy," pl. 82 and p. 177.

72. *Guan* Jar, Cizhou Ware

Northern China, Yuan dynasty, 14th century. Stoneware with white slip and iron-brown painted decoration under clear glaze. H. 28.5 cm. Gift of Mrs. Robert McKay, 1957.477

The bulbous jar has a short neck and wide shoulders tapering to a narrow, recessed base. The exterior is painted in underglaze iron brown over white slip, with designs of chrysanthemum sprays in cloud-collar panels. The interior is coated in iron brown.

The brown-black painting on fourteenth-century Cizhou ceramics has a richness and sheen reminiscent of lacquer and represents some of the most powerful brushwork achieved by the Cizhou potters. The decoration on the Museum's large jar closely resembles the chrysanthemum designs on a Cizhou pillow dated 1336 in the Boston Museum of Fine Arts.[1] The flower of autumn, the chrysanthemum is also a symbol of retirement from public office and thus represents a life of ease.

Provenance:
    Alexandra Emery Moore McKay
Notes:
    1. Mino, *Freedom*, pp. 136–37.

73. Bowl, Longquan Ware

Zhejiang province, Southern Song dynasty, 12th or 13th century. Porcelaneous ware with blue-green glaze. H. 7.6, diam. 20.1 cm. Museum purchase, 1950.65

The wide bowl with gently curving sides tapers to a small footring. It is covered with a bluish grey-green translucent glaze that pools in a darker ring on the interior of the bowl. The glaze stops just short of the base of the footring; where unglazed, the body is light grey with a halo of burnt iron along the edge of the glaze. Scattered salting of the glaze appears along the interior and exterior of rim, on the footring, and as individual white specks scattered throughout the glaze. The interior is undecorated; the exterior is decorated with carved rows of overlapping long and short petals.

The Longquan kilns of southern Zhejiang province were making green-glazed wares as early as the fifth and sixth centuries, but the establishment of the Southern Song capitol at Linan (modern Hangzhou) encouraged the kilns to expand and flourish as never before. Hundreds of dragon kilns of enormous length, each capable of firing tens of thousands of ceramics at a time, made Longquan county one of the most productive pottery-making areas in China. Demands for the celebrated Longquan green-glazed ceramics continued well into the Ming period (1368–1644).

Southern Song Longquan ware is characterized by its blue-green color, jadelike translucency, and semigloss sheen. Longquan of this period also exhibits tiny white specks near the glaze surface that accumulate along the rims and bases to form a saltlike frosting. These precipitates are anorthite and wollanstonite crystals formed by coarse mixing of the viscous glaze and by a tendency to underfiring. Tiny entrapped air bubbles also contribute to the milky translucence of the glaze.[1]

Bowls with carved lotus petals on the exterior, though relatively rare in the Southern Song period, eventually became one of the most popular everyday wares; by the Yuan dynasty, lotus bowls were being made in large quantities for distribution to a large domestic market and for export. Longquan lotus bowls have been excavated from sites throughout China, and have been found in Mongolia, Japan, southeast Asia, and Africa.[2]

Provenance:
    C. T. Loo

Exhibited:
    Douanes Expositions, Paris.
Notes:
    1. Vandiver and Kingery, "Celadons," pp. 219–20.
    2. For references to numerous excavated examples see discussion of a similar

bowl from the Indianapolis Museum of Art in Mino and Tsiang, *Ice and Green Clouds*, no. 76. Another Southern Song example is in the Meiyintang collection; see Krahl, *Chinese Ceramics*, vol. 1, no. 539. Longquan lotus bowls were found in the Sinan shipwreck, *Relics Salvaged*, vol. 1, pl. 15, no. 18.

74. Bowl, Longquan Guan-Type Ware

Zhejiang province, Southern Song dynasty, 12th or 13th century. Stoneware with crackled green glaze. H. 4.4, diam. 16.8 cm.
Museum purchase, 1950.59

The shallow bowl has rounded sides tapering to a small unglazed foot-ring that exposes the light grey clay body with its slight reddish tone. The bowl is thickly glazed inside and out with an opaque blue-green glaze of semigloss sheen and an overall crackle pattern in yellow-brown. Decoration consists of carved lotus petals around the exterior.

Among the ceramics used by the Southern Song imperial court was a green-glazed ware with crackle pattern known as Guan ("official") ware. Produced by kilns established just outside Linan, the capitol, Guan ware is a legacy of the Ru ware tradition of the Northern Song period. These pieces are characterized by thin potting and thick glazes applied in so many layers that the glaze is often much thicker than the vessel itself. Typically they display an overall light brown or brown-black crackle caused by differences in cooling rates between body and glaze. The crackle patterns follow the stress lines of shapes thrown on the potter's wheel. At first they appeared accidentally, but they came to be widely appreciated and the effect then was induced deliberately.

To meet the demand for Guan-type ceramics that the official kilns alone could not meet, the Longquan kilns also produced unctuous, jadelike ceramics wares of the Guan type. The shape and the overlapping carved petals on the exterior of the Museum's bowl are characteristic of Guan-type bowls produced at Longquan. Similar bowls are in the Percival David Foundation[1] and the National Palace Museum.[2]

Provenance:
    Matthias Komor; C. T. Loo
Notes:
    1. Scott, "Guan or Ge Ware?" p. 18, pls. 12–13.
    2. National Palace Museum, *Sung Dynasty Guan Ware*, no. 111.

75. Round Box, Longquan Ware

Zhejiang province, Southern Song dynasty, 12th or 13th century. Porcelaneous ware with green glaze. H. 4.4, diam. 10.5 cm.
Museum purchase, 1950.66

The round box has a light grey clay body that is burnt orange where exposed. The box is glazed inside and out in a translucent grey-green. Decoration consists of an incised pair of addorsed lotus blossoms on the lid. The interior of the lid exhibits a deep finger swirl.

Small, round lidded boxes such as this were probably made to hold cosmetics; the interiors of some are even equipped with small dishes![1] The Museum's box has elegant carved decoration of two lotus blossoms under a thick, translucent blue-green glaze that mimics the color and tactile quality of jade.[2]

Provenance:
    C. T. Loo
Exhibited:
    Detroit Institute of Arts, 1947–1948
Notes:
    1. See the Longquan cosmetic box with interior dishes in the Victoria and Albert Museum, publ. Kerr, *Chinese Art and Design*, p. 142.
    2. Two similar Longquan round boxes are illustrated in Wirgin, *Sung Ceramic Design*, pls. 39d, 39f.

76. Vase, Longquan Ware

Zhejiang province, Yuan dynasty (1279–1368). Porcelaneous stoneware with olive-green glaze. H. 28 cm.
Museum purchase, 1950.67

The pear-shaped bottle has a slender neck and a flared, slightly everted rim. The globular body tapers to a high footring. The vase is undecorated except for the coating of olive-green glaze that stops just short of the exposed foot. The light grey clay body has oxidized to a reddish color.

Longquan wares remained popular well into the Ming dynasty. While the glazes of Song-dynasty Longquan wares tend toward an opaque bluish green because of underfiring, Longquan products of the Yuan (1279–1368) and Ming (1368–1644) dynasties typically are a luminous olive color, the result of improvements in kiln technology. The Museum's elegantly proportioned vase shows off its brilliant olive-green color to handsome effect.

Provenance:
    C. T. Loo

77. Daoist Shrine, Longquan Ware

Zhejiang province, Longquan kilns. Ming dynasty, early 15th century. Porcelaneous stoneware with green glaze and traces of lacquer and gilding. H. 27.9 cm.
Gift of Dr. Robert A. Kemper, 1991.163

The green-glazed shrine has the form of a two-story pavilion consisting of deep niches under a roof decorated with cloud and floral designs. Each niche is framed by a pair of dragons with gaping mouths and outstretched claws, whose bodies descend from the eaves and then turn upward from the low balustrade to face the opening of the niche. Inside the niche of the upper story are unglazed figures of a seated female deity flanked by boy and girl acolytes. Inside the lower niche an unglazed seated figure of a male deity is flanked by male attendants. On the ground before the deity are a tortoise and a snake. The sides and back of the shrine are glazed but undecorated; the back contains two firing holes. The unglazed, hollow base exposes the reddish clay body.

The Longquan potters, in addition to making vessels, created small architectural models and portable shrines. Several Daoist shrines produced by the Longquan kilns are known in public collections. One of these, a shrine in the British Museum, is significant not only for its impressive size and elaborate construction, but also for the inscription on its back which dates it to 1406 A.D., the fourth year of Yongle's reign. Similar Longquan shrines can be dated in this way to the early fifteenth century.[1]

In the upper tier of the Museum's two-storied tower Xiwangmu, Queen Mother of the West, sits flanked by her child acolytes: Jintongzi, the Golden Boy, who gestures his devotion, and Yunu, the Jade Girl, who holds a tray of peaches. The lower tier houses a male seated figure wearing a loose robe over a military costume. This is Zhenwu, Lord of the Northern Quadrant; before him a snake and a tortoise are copulating. Zhenwu is flanked by two male attendants.

A tenth-century hagiography of Xiwangmu, *Yongcheng jixian lu [Record of the Assembled Immortals of the Heavenly Walled City]*, written by Du Guangting (850–933), describes the goddess's residence:

> *The palaces and towers where she resides are located on Pestle Mountain in the Tortoise Mountain Range, in the splendid parks of Mount Kunlun with its hanging gardens and lofty atmosphere. Here there is a golden city a thousand levels high, with twelve-storied jade buildings and towers of jasper essence. There are halls of radiant lucid jade, nine-storied mysterious terraces, and purple kingfisher cinnabar chambers.*[2]

The many practices of Daoist adepts included visualizations of transcendence to communicate with gods and immortals; if these were executed correctly, one could bring the gods into the body to achieve blessings such as immortality.[3] Perhaps such shrines were used to aid in these visualizations, because Daoists believed not only that Xiwangmu's jade palace was a dwelling place for the soul in the afterlife, but also that her residence served as a cosmic pillar through which gods and humans could communicate.[4]

The shrine's luminous green glaze resembles jade, and its surface is adorned with numerous symbols of its divine location. Vapors rise from the roof; stylized flowers, perhaps meant to be peach blossoms, refer to the peaches of immortality that ripen only once in three thousand years; the dragons entwining the pillars refer to the dragons that serve as vehicles to Mount Kunlun.

The surfaces of the figures were left unglazed and later were covered with gold lacquer; only traces of this remain. Gold had special significance for Daoists because it was an important ingredient in elixirs. A similar Longquan Daoist shrine, also in the form of a two-tiered tower, is in the Royal Ontario Museum.[5]

Provenance:
  Robert A. Kemper
Exhibited:
  "Cincinnati Collects Oriental Art," Cincinnati Art Museum, March 7–April 28, 1985.

Published:
  Archives of Asian Art, 46(1993), p.112.
  Cincinnati Collects Oriental Art, no. 97.
  Durrell, *A Selection of New Acquisitions*, pp.12–13.
Notes:
  1. Vainker, *Chinese Pottery and Porcelain*, pp.160–61.
  2. Kohn, *Taoist Experience*, pp.57–59.
  3. S. Cahill, *Transcendence*, pp.35–36.
  4. S. Cahill, *Transcendence*, p.73.
  5. Royal Ontario Museum, George Crofts collection, 922.20.236.

78. Bowl, *Qingbai* Ware

Jiangxi province, Jingdezhen, Southern Song dynasty, 12th or 13th century. Porcelain with bluish glaze. H.5.1 cm, diam. 14.0 cm. Museum purchase, 1950.70

The thin-bodied bowl is conical in shape with a solid, cylindrical base and recessed foot. The white porcelain body is covered overall with a transparent glaze that is blue where it pools. The unglazed, recessed foot shows burnt iron. The interior has an incised and combed decoration of floral scrolls.

Qingbai (literally "blue white") wares, also sometimes called *yingqing* ("shadow blue"), were produced in the vicinity of Jingdezhen, Jiangxi province, beginning in the Southern Song dynasty. The ware owes its color to a small amount of iron in the glaze, fired in a reduction atmosphere.[1] Where the glaze pools, it is a clear icy blue; in contrast, the thin glaze on the body is white and thus enhances the incised decoration beneath. The bodies of these porcelain wares have a unique granular texture, often likened to refined sugar, because they were produced by using only crushed porcelain stone (*baidunzi*) without the addition of china clay (*gaolin*). The glaze also was composed of crushed porcelain stone, to which burned limestone was added as a flux.

This bowl is typical of *qingbai* wares produced in the vicinity of Jingdezhen during the Southern Song dynasty. The geology of that region provided abundant raw materials for porcelain: china stone (*baidunze*) and china clay (*gaolin*), named after its source, the Gaoling Hill near Jingdezhen. Beginning in the Southern Song dynasty, Jingdezhen was China's foremost porcelain-making center; during the Ming and Qing dynasties Jingdezhen supplied the imperial court with ceramic wares of the highest quality.

The wide conical bowl of eggshell thinness has a very narrow but solid cylindrical base that provides sufficient weight to stabilize the bowl and prevent it from tipping over when filled with liquid. Decoration consists of delicate, freely drawn floral designs, identified by Wirgin as the "bud-tendril" motif; this is characterized by triangular flowers and conventionalized leaves, many of which resemble buds, against a hatched background.[2] Other bowls of this type are in the collections of the Museum of Far Eastern Antiquities, Stockholm,[3] and the Royal Ontario Museum, Toronto.[4]

Provenance:
    J. T. Tai; C. T. Loo
Notes:
    1. See Wood's discussion of Chinese high-fired glazes in
Iron in the Fire, pp. 11–13.
    2. Wirgin, *Sung Ceramic Designs*, p. 51, fig. 4b and pl. 13a.
    3. Gyllensvärd and Pope, *Chinese Art from the Collection of H. M. King Gustav VI Adolph*, no. 99. *Oriental Ceramics: The World's Great Collections*, vol. 8, color plate 34.
    4. ROM acc. no. 982.179.1

79. Jar, *Qingbai* Ware

Jiangxi province, Jingdezhen, Northern Song dynasty, 11th or 12th century. Porcelain with bluish glaze. H. 13.0 cm.
Museum purchase, 1950.69

The jar is globular with a wavy, everted rim and a curved, splayed foot. Exterior decoration consists of a regular pattern of carved overlapping petals on the body; the interior is adorned with simple vertical ribs. The vessel is glazed inside and out with a transparent bluish glaze.

Both the shape and the decoration of this jar were inspired by silver vessels. Wavy rims, seen on Tang silver vessels and lids,[1] continued to be employed in Five-Dynasties and Song-dynasty ceramic types such as Yue, Yaozhou, Ding and *qingbai*; often they emulated the graceful leaf of the lotus. A silver lid in the form of a lotus leaf was found in the Tang hoard of gold and silver excavated in 1982 near the Dingmao bridge, Dantu county, Jiangsu province.[2]

The Museum's jar is an exceptionally fine example of the Song-dynasty Jingdezhen potters' command of porcelain art. The vessel is potted so thinly as to be translucent; its fluid shape, carved decoration of overlapping petals, and ribbed undulating rim fuse perfectly with the luminous blue glaze to create a fully integrated object of extraordinary grace.

Provenance:
    J. T. Tai; C. T. Loo
Published:
    Keppel, *China in 1700*, pp. 4, 22, no. 1.
Exhibited:
    "China in 1700: Kangxi Porcelains at the Taft Museum," The Taft Museum, September 8–October 23, 1988; Flint Institute of Arts, April 15–June 10, 1989; Ball State University, July 16–September 17, 1989.
Notes:
    1. Gyllensvärd, *Chinese Gold, Silver and Porcelain*, no. 47.
    2. Thorp, *Son of Heaven*, no. 77.

80. Bowl, *Qingbai*-Type Ware

Jiangxi province, Nanfeng kilns, Southern Song dynasty, 13th century. Porcelain with painted slip and incised decoration under a bluish glaze. H. 4.2, diam. 11.0 cm.
Gift of Dr. Robert A. Kemper, 1991.164

The bowl is conical with a vertical mouth that is slightly indented just below the rim. The pitched sides taper to the countersunk base. The interior and the upper portion of the exterior are covered with a translucent, light bluish green glaze. Interior decoration consists of an incised prunus spray and a crescent moon with painted iron-oxide accents and iron oxide applied over the glaze to the rim. The clay body is light grey.

By the thirteenth century, the kilns of Jingdezhen were the leading production center for *qingbai* wares. The popularity of these wares among the literati of the Southern Song dynasty (1127–1279) led to the production of *qingbai*-type wares at other kilns in Jiangxi province. The Baishe kilns, near Nanfeng, made a distinctive ware with *qingbai* glaze over white slip, which featured incised decoration and painted iron-oxide accents.[1] The painted rims of these Nanfeng bowls probably imitated gold or silver bands, such as those added to Ding, *qingbai*, or Jian ware bowls to cover their unglazed edges.[2]

In the Song dynasty, the flowering plum was a favorite source of metaphors in poetry and painting. The plum tree which brings forth its blossoms in late winter, symbolizes the fortitude of the rustic recluse. Its delicate blossoms, which last only briefly and easily fall prey to harsh weather, are a metaphor for transient beauty. The flowering plum evolved as an important symbol for the Southern Song court: a sad reminder of the former glory of the Northern Song capital, yet a symbol of survival of the government in exile.

The city of Linan (modern Hangzhou), capital of the Southern Song, was famous for the plum trees that flourished along the West Lake. A place of legendary beauty, Linan was also a bustling city of more than a million people, the largest city in the world at that time. The scholar-officials who worked and lived there built private gardens as retreats from the noise and pressures of the capital. There they engaged in various scholarly pursuits, including the appreciation of the revered plum blossom. During the Song dynasty, poetry praising the qualities of the plum was elevated to its own genre. In the wake of this literary veneration, a special category of painting known as *momei* (literally "ink-plum") took root in the late Song and flourished in the subsequent Yuan and Ming dynasties. The plum motif eventually found its way from the scholar-official class into the general decorative vocabulary, and in the twelfth and thirteenth centuries appeared often on ceramics and other decorative art forms purchased by citizens of all classes.

Gazing at plum blossoms by moonlight was a favorite activity of the refined Southern Song scholars, who often alluded to it in plum poetry and depicted it in painting. Thus, it is not surprising that the combination of plum and moon was employed as decoration on small bowls of the Ding, Longquan, or *qingbai* type, all of which were favored by the literati.[3]

An identical Nanfeng bowl is in the collection of the Museum of East Asian Art, Bath.[4] In addition to bowls with *qingbai* glazes, the Baishe kilns produced prunus-decorated bowls with brown glaze.[5]

Provenance:
    S. Marchant and Son; Robert A. Kemper

Published:

    Art on the Market, no. 143.

    Avril, "Highlights of Chinese Art," p. 76.

Exhibited:

    "Art on the Market: Selections of Antiquities and Oriental Art," Cincinnati Art Museum, 1988, no. 143.

Notes:

    1. See *Kaogu* no. 12 (1963) pp. 686–89, for excavation report of the Nanfeng kiln site. A sherd from the Nanfeng kiln was exhibited in "Exhibition of Ceramic Finds from Ancient Kilns in China," Hong Kong, Fung Ping Shan Museum, 1981.

    2. Tregear, *Song Ceramics*, pp. 154–56.

    3. For a discussion of plum and moon motifs on decorative arts of the twelfth and thirteenth centuries, see Neill, "Flowering Plum" pp. 196–98. Illustrated examples include a twelfth-century lobed silver dish in the Nanjing Museum excavated from a tomb dated 1199, a thirteenth- or fourteenth-century lobed Longquan plate in the British Museum, and a circular lacquer box formerly in the Sedgwick collection, London. Also see Wirgin, *Sung Ceramic Design*, p. 176: A small Longquan conical bowl with incised decoration of prunus and moon is illustrated as pl. 38b; another Longquan bowl with this design is shown in pl. 39b; Ding-type bowls with the prunus and moon include pl. 84i.

    4. Museum of East Asian Art, *Inaugural Exhibition*, 1, no. 121. Another Nanfeng bowl with prunus and crescent moon decoration was sold at Sotheby's London on December 10, 1991, lot 128.

    5. See Mowry, *Hare's Fur*, no. 111.

81. Vase, *Qingbai* Ware

Yuan dynasty, 13th or 14th century. Porcelain with relief decoration under bluish glaze. H. 29.2 cm.
Museum purchase, 1950.68.

The pear-shaped vase has a slender neck, flaring mouth and slightly splayed foot. Surface decoration consists of a pair of appliqué designs of flying ducks who carry reeds in their mouths. The bottle is covered overall with a satiny, pale blue glaze that stops just short of the base.

Yuan dynasty *qingbai* differs from that of the Song in a tendency to thicker potting and translucent, rather than clear, bluish glazes (compare entries 78 and 79). Molding and appliqué gradually replaced incising as the preferred decorative techniques. The pear-shaped bottle with flaring lip known as *yuhuchun ping*, literally "spring in a jade jar," is a typical Yuan shape made at the Jingdezhen kilns and was also favored for underglaze blue and underglaze copper decoration. In fact, many of the Yuan *qingbai* design schemes anticipate early underglaze painted decoration.

This vase has appliqué decoration of ducks carrying reeds in their mouths, a rebus for "May you achieve first place in the [civil service] examinations."[1] The same motif appears on a pair of *qingbai* vases with stands in the Asian Art Museum of San Francisco[2] and on the interior of a blue-glazed spouted bowl in the Victoria and Albert Museum.[3] A *qingbai* vase identical to the Museum's is in the Tsui Museum of Art, Hong Kong.[4]

Provenance:

    Mrs. Weaver Greenwich; C. T. Loo

Published:

    Avril, *Highlights of Chinese Art*, pp. 75–76.

    Lee and Ho, *Chinese Art Under the Mongols*, no. 112.

    Medley, *Yüan Porcelain and Stoneware*, p. 20, pl. 6A.

Exhibited:

    "Chinese Art Under the Mongols: The Yuan Dynasty (1279–1368)," Cleveland Museum of Art, October 2–November 24, 1968.

Notes:

    1. Gao, ed., *A Chinese-English Glossary And Illustrations of Antique* [sic], p. 382; also Eberhard, *Chinese Symbols*, p. 87.

    2. Medley, *Yüan Porcelain and Stoneware*, pl. 9.

    3. Medley, *Yüan Porcelain and Stoneware*, pl. 57.

    4. *The Tsui Museum of Art*, no. 53.

82. Bowl, *Shufu* Ware

Jiangxi province, Jingdezhen, Yuan dynasty, early 14th century. Porcelain with relief decoration under bluish glaze. H. 4.6, diam. 12 cm.
Gift of Dorothy Christian Pipkin in memory of Edward L. Pipkin, 1990.1347

The small bowl has slightly flaring straight sides angled sharply to the base, which is supported on a proportionately small, unglazed footring. Molded decoration on the interior consists of a band of scrolling chrysanthemums on the sides and dragons on the bottom. The bowl is covered in a thick, opaque bluish glaze that displays a fine pattern of crazing.

Shufu is a distinctive type of porcelain ware related to *qingbai* (see entries 78–81), which also was produced in and near Jingdezhen in the late thirteenth and fourteenth centuries. Named for the two-character inscription that appears on some examples of the type, *shufu* is characterized by a thick, semiglossy opaque glaze described as *luanbai*, or "eggwhite." Technical differences between *qingbai* and *shufu* wares exist in the composition of the bodies; *shufu* wares also required a higher firing temperature. The relatively unplastic nature of both wares' body material limited the size of the vessels that could be produced successfully.

The term *shufu*, generally translated as "privy council," may refer to the Shumiyuan, a ministry of the government that dealt with military and civil affairs and also commissioned these ceramics for ceremonial use.[1] The ware was not made exclusively for official use, however, as evidenced by the large quantities excavated from the 1323 Sinan shipwreck off the coast of Korea.[2]

This bowl exhibits a subtle molded decoration of chrysanthemum scrolls on its interior walls and dragons on the interior bottom; the thick glaze all but obscures the decoration, making it difficult to discern unless held against a strong light. The same design is more highly visible on a dish in the Ashmolean Museum.[3] A bowl with lotus scroll decoration in the Percival David Foundation is identical to this specimen in shape and size.[4]

Published:

    Cincinnati Collects Oriental Art, no. 99.

Exhibited:
    "Cincinnati Collects Oriental Art," Cincinnati Art Museum,
March 7–April 28, 1985
Notes:
    1. Scott, *Percival David Foundation of Chinese Art*, p. 65.
    2. *Relics Salvaged*, pls. 87 and 197.
    3. Medley, *Yüan Porcelain and Stoneware*, pl. 16A, B.
    4. *Imperial Taste*, no. 25; Scott, *Percival David Foundation of Chinese Art*, p. 65,
no. 53; also Medley, *Yüan Porcelain*, pl. 19A, B. Another bowl of this shape is illustrated in Lee and Ho, *Chinese Art under the Mongols*, no. 120.

83. *Guan* Jar

Jiangxi province, Jingdezhen, made for the Near Eastern market,
Ming dynasty, circa 1400–1410. Porcelain painted in underglaze
blue. H. 21.0 cm.
Museum purchase: John J. Emery Endowment and George M. Toe-
Water Endowment, 1987.147.

*The globular jar has a short, slightly tapered neck and beaded rim. The
wide shoulders slope gently to a recessed base. The clay body is white
porcelain with iron impurities that have oxidized to burnt orange on the
unglazed base. Decoration painted in underglaze blue consists of the following
horizontal bands (from top to bottom): a classic scroll on the neck,
four sprays of fruiting and blossoming plants on the shoulder, scrolling
peonies around the widest girth of the vessel, and lappets containing lotus
blossoms along the base. The clear glaze has a bluish tinge that is especially
apparent in areas of dripping or pooling.*

Cobalt was imported from the Near East in the Tang dynasty, and
its use as a colorant in lead glazes applied to low-fired earthenware
ceramics (see entries 57 and 58) is well known. The use of cobalt
for underglaze painted decoration may have begun in the eighth century,
as suggested by the discovery of stoneware fragments with underglaze
blue unearthed in 1975 and 1983 from Tang-dynasty
strata in Yangzhou.[1] Archaeological evidence has also revealed examples
of underglaze cobalt on Song-period ceramics, though
these are relatively rare. Porcelain with underglaze cobalt decoration
was not produced in quantity until the early fourteenth century.
This phenomenon is generally attributed to the demands of Middle
Eastern merchants living in China and to the encouragement
of international trade by the Mongol government. Many Yuan- and
early Ming-dynasty porcelains with underglaze cobalt decoration
were exported to the Near East because the new aesthetic was more
pleasing to foreign than to domestic markets.

The Museum's jar is one of a large group of Chinese blue-and-
white porcelains discovered in the markets of Damascus, Aleppo,
and Douma during the 1960s. As these Syrian cities modernized,
Chinese porcelains, which had survived in private hands since
they were exported from China in the fourteenth and fifteenth centuries,
began to appear in market stalls, where they had been
bartered for goods, services, or money.[2] This jar was one of only
three early fifteenth-century porcelains among the approximately
800 found in this way; the group also contained about a dozen

pieces dating from the fourteenth century, but the great majority
were produced in the second half of the fifteenth century or later.[3]

About 60% of the porcelains found in Syria had been broken and
then reassembled with metal rivets; this was a common method
of repair in the Near East and India, where Chinese porcelains were
highly prized. After pairs of small holes were drilled, one on each
side of the break, heated U-shaped brass rivets were inserted. When
the rivets cooled and shrank, the two pieces were drawn tightly
together.[4] Rivet repairs in the Museum's jar existed until recently, but
they were removed and the jar was reassembled to better conceal
breaks on the exterior. Remnants of the rivet holes are still visible on
the interior.

Painted decoration on the Museum's jar combines elements of
clearly Western origin, such as the scrolling vine, with Chinese motifs
such as tree peony blossoms.[5] The skeletal version of the
scrolling vine around the neck, called "classic scroll," carries over a
favorite fourteenth-century motif. Delicate fruiting sprays of
grapes, lychees, loquats, and pomegranates on the shoulder of the
jar are based on Chinese pharmaceutical illustrations.[6] A rare design
element is the band of lappets containing lotus blossoms growing
out of pairs of addorsed leaves, which encircles the base of the
jar. This motif is known on only one other jar, a *guan* in the Ardebil
Shrine, Teheran, whose entire design echoes that of the Cincinnati
vessel.[7] Other underglaze blue-decorated vessels that were
clearly painted by the same workshop are in the collections of
the Topkapi Saray and the Iran Bastan Museum.[8]

In 1988, Chinese archaeologists excavating the site of the Ming
imperial factory at Jingdezhen unearthed a group of blue-and-
white porcelains of the type exported to the Near East. These included
a jar of the same shape as the Museum's, with identically
executed sprays of scrolling peonies. The jar was found in the stratum
dated to the early years of the Yongle emperor's reign
(1402–1424).[9]

Provenance:
    Found in Damascus, Syria; Theo Larsson; Sotheby's London, 10 June 1986,
lot 218; Eskenazi Limited, London
Published:
    Archives of Asian Art, 42 (1989): pp. 94–95.
    Avril, "Highlights of Chinese Art," pp. 76–77.
    Carswell, "China and the Near East," p. 22, pl. 6e.
    Salmon, "Report from London," p. 72, illus.
    Sotheby's London, 10 June 1986, lot 218.
Notes:
    1. Wu and Leidy, "Recent Archaeological Contributions," pp. 97–99.
    2. John Carswell discovered this source of Chinese porcelains while conducting
research in Syria. See Carswell, "China and the Near East," p. 20.
    3. The other two early fifteenth-century porcelains found in this group are
a shallow dish in a private collection and a porcelain imitation of a Mamluk metalwork
stand, in the British Museum. See Carswell, "China and the Near East,"
p. 22, pls. 6c and 7c; the latter also is published in Carswell, "An Early Ming Porcelain
Stand," pp. 176–182.
    4. Carswell, *Blue and White*, p. 22.
    5. Rawson, *Chinese Ornament*, pp. 75–88.
    6. Krahl, "Plant Motifs, Part I," 52–65.
    7. Pope, *Chinese Porcelains from the Ardebil Shrine*, plate 56.

8. Krahl, *Chinese Ceramics in the Topkapi Saray*, vol. 2, illus. pp. 414–430; *Oriental Ceramics: The World's Great Collections*, vol. 4, color plates 53–58.
    9. Liu, "Imperial Porcelain," pp. 62–63.

84. Double-Gourd Vase, *Fahua* Ware

Ming dynasty, late 15th or early 16th century. Porcelain with enamel glazes applied to biscuit. H. 39.5 cm.
Museum purchase: Gift of Mr. and Mrs. Leonard Minster, by exchange, and gift of the William T. and Louise Taft Semple Collection, by exchange, 1989.102.

The large vase is gourd-shaped with slightly tapered neck and flat base. Surface decoration consists of motifs outlined in slip trails, organized in horizontal registers encircling the body: from the top, beaded ropes and precious pendants along the rim; a lotus pond with blossoming lotus plants and a flying heron on the upper bulb; lotus plants alternating with herons standing in water on the lower bulb; and upright lotus panels along the base. The vase is glazed overall in turquoise and transparent glazes against a cobalt blue background; the interior and base are glazed in a brilliant green.

During the Ming dynasty, porcelains decorated in polychrome enamels, often applied over the glaze, became widespread. Also typical of the Ming period is a group whose enamels were applied directly to the biscuit (the fired, unglazed porcelain body) and whose decoration is defined by raised outlines in trailed slip. Known as *fahua* ("designs within borders"), this ware is generally associated with cloisonné enamels, which were known in the early Ming dynasty. The colors employed on these wares include turquoise, aubergine, yellow, dark purple-blue, and green. The purple-blue probably comes from the use of native Chinese cobalt, whose high manganese content accounts for the purple tone. Turquoise and green are produced primarily by copper oxide with varying traces of iron, tin, and manganese. The slightly pink colorless glaze contains a tiny amount of iron oxide. Unlike the colorful Han and Tang wares, which owed their brilliance to lead glazes, *fahua* wares employed alkaline glazes rich in potassia as a flux.[1] Because *fahua* wares were produced at both northern and southern kilns, variations in body shape and glaze composition are common.

Although the designs chosen to adorn Chinese decorative objects may reflect mere aesthetic considerations, motifs were employed largely to communicate meaning through symbolism or puns. The double gourd or bottle gourd is a popular vessel type, not only for its appealing shape but also because of its associations. As a vessel the bottle gourd represents abundance and good luck; it is also an attribute of the Taoist immortal Li Tieguai.[2] Also seen on this vase are precious pendants that include *lingzhi* fungus, representing longevity; stone chimes, which stand for celebration and joy; and pearls, symbols of purity. The main decoration shows herons among lotus, a rebus or pun meaning "May your path be always upward": The Chinese words for *heron (lu)* and *lotus (lian)* are homonyms for *path (lu)* and *always (lian)*. This motif refers to a wish for numerous promotions in civil service.

A *fahua* vase in the Nelson-Atkins Museum[3] has decorations nearly identical to the Museum's and apparently was produced at the same kiln. Lotus and heron motifs dominate the decoration of a *fahua* jar in the Freer Gallery, although in that specimen the ropes with precious pendants alternate with cloud collars containing floral sprays.[4]

Provenance:
    Chrysler Museum; Michael Weisbrod
Published:
    Lee and Weisbrod, *Chinese Ceramic Art*, pp. 94–95.
    Avril, "Highlights of Chinese Art," p. 77.
Exhibited:
    "Chinese Ceramic Art: Innovation and Imitation," New York, Michael B. Weisbrod, Inc., November 30–December 20, 1988, cat. no. 42.
Notes:
    1. Wood, et al., "An Examination," pp. 172–82.
    2. Bartholomew, *Hundred Flowers*, no. 35.
    3. Lion-Goldschmidt, *Ming Porcelain*, p. 124, fig. 98.
    4. Lion-Goldschmidt, *Ming Porcelain*, p. 126, fig. 100.

85. Bowl

Ming dynasty, Jiajing period (1522–1566), porcelain with overglaze enamels. H. 9.0, W. 17.3 cm.
Gift of Paul Ashbrook Barker, 1995.43

The square bowl has a short square foot; the sides flare evenly to a wide mouth. Painted decoration on the interior and exterior in iron-red and brown enamels over the glaze create designs in reserve on the white ground. Interior decoration includes a border of peaches on vines along the rim and a design of a peony and longevity graph in the bottom. Exterior decoration consists of rocks, lingzhi *fungus, and Eight Treasures* (ba bao) *motifs among waves. The base bears a six character mark of Jiajing in underglaze blue.*

Among the porcelains produced at Jingdezhen during the reign of Jiajing (1522–1566) were "two-color" wares, a relatively rare type characterized by the application of two enamel colors over the glaze after the first firing. Usually the painted designs were applied only to a small repertoire of vessel shapes such as dishes and square bowls, small lidded jars, double-gourd vases, and square boxes. The designs were executed in brown outlines on a yellow, green, or white ground. Then red enamel was applied as a background color so that the design motifs appeared in reserve.

This bowl is an unusual example of the type because the designs have been created in reserve against a white ground, without the intermediate step of applying a colored enamel layer overall. Instead the white of the glazed porcelain serves as the second color. This bowl exhibits many of the designs typical of Jiajing-period porcelains; longevity motifs (longevity graph, peaches, and *lingzhi* fungus) predominate. The Eight Treasures (cash, horn cups, artemisia leaf, single and double lozenges, painting, books, jade chime, and mirror) appear in pairs among waves on the exterior and represent auspicious themes such as wealth, happiness, healing, victory, culture, and learning.

Many of these motifs reflect the Daoist interests of the Jiajing emperor, who neglected affairs of state in a fervent search for the elixir of immortality. The political decline is reflected as well in the overall quality of ceramics produced during the late Ming. Jiajing's demand for massive quantities of porcelains, coupled with ever-increasing production for export, taxed the Jingdezhen potters. As a result, the precision and refinement characteristic of earlier Ming porcelains was replaced by a coarseness and slight carelessness that nevertheless have their own vigor and charm.

Provenance:
  Robert Ashbrook; Paul Ashbrook Barker

86. Jar

Ming dynasty, late 16th century. Porcelain with underglaze blue decoration. H. 37.5 cm.
Gift of Mrs. Audrey Emery, 1954.486

The globular jar with rounded shoulders tapers slightly to the recessed base. The neck is short and straight, with a slightly everted rim. Decoration painted in underglaze cobalt consists of scrolling lotus around the neck, with cloud collars along the shoulder. The main decoration is composed of tree peony, bamboo, osmanthus, rocks and magpies, and a qilin *on ling-zhi* fungus. *The base is unglazed, with no mark.*

In the sixteenth century, enormous demands from the imperial court for Jingdezhen porcelains led to a decline in quality as potters were pushed to the limits of their production capacity. Decoration evolved to include more popular designs that would appeal widely to domestic and export markets. Robust designs were drawn freely in dark outlines and then were filled in with two or more lighter shades of blue.

Decoration on the Museum's jar consists of a garden filled with botanical, bird, and animal symbols that express wishes for prosperity, longevity, happiness, and success. The peony, symbol of wealth and rank, grows from behind a fantastic garden rock along with osmanthus (*guihua*), a symbol of success in the civil service examinations. Bamboo, symbol of integrity and resilience, also grows in this garden. Magpies, bringers of joy and good news, are often associated with marital happiness. The higher in the trees the birds appear, the greater the degree of joy they represent. *Lingzhi* mushrooms, emblem of longevity, grow along the ground line. A band of *ruyi* heads along the shoulder of the jar are a rebus for "as you wish."

87. *Huqqa* (Water Pipe) Bases

Qing dynasty, Kangxi period (1662–1722), made for the Indian market. Porcelain with underglaze blue decoration and brown glaze. H. (including ring base and tobacco bowl) 26 cm.
Gift of Drs. Martin and Carol Macht, 1991.276 a–f

Each huqqa base consists of three separate parts: the globular vessel body with rounded bottom and tall straight neck with horizontal flanges; a shallow ring support; and a tobacco bowl with a deep semicircular top pierced with small holes, a straight neck with one horizontal flange, and long hollow foot. The tobacco bowls and necks have brown glaze overall. The vessel has brown glaze overall except four reserve roundels on the globular vessel body; each of these contains scrolling plant motifs painted in underglaze blue. The shoulder carries a reserve band of scrolling floral motif against a dotted background, also painted in underglaze blue.

According to written records of the Song, Yuan, and Ming dynasties, China's trade with India focused on the export of porcelain and silk by ship, to be traded for Indian spices, coconuts, wood, betel nuts, pearls, and gemstones, as well as frankincense, rosewater, and coral. Demand for Chinese ceramics in India varied according to religious beliefs. The Mughals, who practiced Islam, followed Persian tradition by ordering large quantities of Chinese ceramics. Hindu hygienic practices, on the other hand, restricted the use of ceramic vessels for eating and drinking. Buddhists and Jains, who tended to follow Hindu customs, also were not prodigious users of ceramics.[1] Thus, Chinese potters produced distinctively Indian shapes for the Indian market.

The base of the *huqqa* (water pipe), whose bulbous form derives from the Indian *kumbha* water pot, is the most engaging of the shapes made expressly for tobacco-smoking Mughal patrons. Tobacco was introduced to India in 1604, according to the memoirs of Asad Beg, an officer in Akbar's court.[2] Smoking became popular at the Mughal court, where a water pipe known as a *huqqa* served the habit. The smoker drew through a long cloth-covered tube attached to the huqqa base, a bulbous vessel filled with scented water for filtering and cooling the smoke. *Huqqa* bases typically were made of glass, metal, or ceramics. The Museum's porcelain *huqqa* consists of three separate parts: the globular vessel, a ring support, and the tobacco bowl. (The latter appear in the illustration as stoppers.)

A mid-eighteenth-century Indian painting in the Freer Gallery shows Mughal women smoking at a *huqqa* very much like these.[3] A similar porcelain *huqqa* base is in the Metropolitan Museum of Art.[4]

Provenance:
  Drs. Martin and Carol Macht

Exhibited:
  On loan to the Cincinnati Art Museum, 1984 to 1991.

Published:
  Avril, "Highlights of Chinese Art," p. 77.

Notes:
  1. Greensted and Hardie, *Chinese Ceramics*, p. 9.
  2. Stronge, "Huqqa," p. 124.
  3. Hardie, "China's Ceramic Trade with India," p. 27.
  4. Valenstein, *Handbook of Chinese Ceramics*, p. 224. The Met *huqqa* base is also published by Hardie, "China's Ceramic Trade with India," pp. 25–28.

88. Jar

Qing dynasty, Kangxi period, circa 1690–1710. Porcelain with underglaze blue decoration. H. 19.3 cm.
Gift of Mary and Edward O'Connell, 1995.157

The globular jar has a short, slightly tapered neck and recessed base. The neck and upper shoulder of the jar are unglazed; the body and the base are glazed. Painted decoration in underglaze blue depicts women watching boys at play in a garden. The upper shoulder has a dentil border, and the base displays a double ring in underglaze blue without nianhao.

This jar was made at the end of the Transitional period, spanning the end of the Ming and the early part of the Qing dynasty from about 1630 to the end of the seventeenth century. The political decline at the end of the Ming and the upheaval during the changeover to the Qing affected the Jingdezhen kilns dramatically. The loss of imperial orders for ceramics spurred changes in decoration to appeal to the interests of the educated urban elite, and to reflect aspects of popular culture.

The Museum's jar depicts the moon goddess Chang-E, who ate the herb of immortality that her husband obtained from Xiwangmu, Queen Mother of the West. Chang-E dwells in the Palace of Far-Reaching Cold and grants to any scholar who passes the civil service examinations a sprig of the celestial cassia tree. On this jar, Chang-E is shown with young men dressed in the robes and hats of successful candidates and with younger boys who represent future candidates. The goddess appears in four scenes: watching boys lighting firecrackers, observing a young man who teases a small boy with a whirligig, accompanying boys playing with a noisemaker, and observing two boys as they practice martial arts. An early transitional prototype for Kangxi depictions of Chang-E on porcelain is a tall vase dated 1638 in the Butler Family Collection.[1]

This jar, which is missing its lid, is of the classic ginger jar shape, a new vessel type invented during the Kangxi reign.[2] The shape of the jar and the dentil pattern around the shoulder resemble those of a mid-Kangxi period ginger jar in the Victoria and Albert Museum. A similar figural style, characterized by lively facial expressions and by animated hand and body gestures, can be seen on a blue-and-white Daoist temple vase in the Victoria and Albert Museum, dated 1708.[3]

Provenance:
Sandy Greeno; Edward and Mary O'Connell

Notes:
1. Curtis, *Chinese Porcelains*, no. 41.
2. Butler, et al., *Seventeenth Century Chinese Porcelain*, no. 131.
3. Kerr, *Chinese Ceramics*, pp. 58–61.

89. Arrow Vase

Qing dynasty, Kangxi period, circa 1683–1710. Porcelain with underglaze blue. H. 22.5 cm.
Gift of Alfred T. and Eugenia I. Goshorn, 1924.39

The vase has a tall, slightly flaring neck with two cylindrical attachments, sloping shoulders, and a rounded body tapering to a recessed base. The bottom bears a six-character mark of Kangxi in underglaze blue. Decoration painted in blue depicts the moon behind clouds and sprigs of bamboo on the neck and cylindrical attachments; the decoration on the body consists of a warrior on horseback holding his helmet in his right hand and a spear in his left hand. He is accompanied by an attendant carrying a banner. On the back of the vase is a bearded man holding a curved sword.

The kilns at Jingdezhen were razed during the civil war that erupted from the 1674 "Revolt of the Three Feudatories," in which southern Chinese rebelled against Manchu rule. Zang Yingxuan, from the imperial Board of Works, arrived at Jingdezhen in 1680 to oversee the resumption of imperial ceramic production. By 1683 the kilns again were supplying porcelain to the court. Zang's presence at Jingdezhen, and that of subsequent supervisors, contributed to the high quality that distinguishes Kangxi-period (1662–1722) porcelains, whether produced for imperial, domestic, or export markets. Greater refinement of clays and advances in kiln design and firing techniques during this period resulted in porcelains of purer whiteness, clearer and more luminous glaze, and more brilliant underglaze blue.

The decoration of porcelains during the Kangxi reign continues many of the literary subjects that became popular during the Transitional period. Although the figures on the Museum's vase — a mounted official with an attendant carrying a banner that reads *tai shi*, "Grand Astrologer,"[1] and a bearded rogue wielding a sword — have not been identified, they undoubtedly represent characters from a popular drama or novel such as *Romance of the Three Kingdoms (Sanguozhi yanyi)* or *The Water Margin (Shuihu zhuan)*. Jingdezhen porcelain decorators copied woodblock-printed cards and books, such as those issued in the 1640s and in 1657 and based on illustrations of *Shuihu zhuan* by the artist Chen Hongshou (1598–1652). In Chen's illustrations, the figures were set against a plain background without landscape setting or borders, as are the figures on the Museum's vase.[2]

Notes:
1. Hucker, *Dictionary*, p. 481, no. 6212.
2. Kerr, *Chinese Ceramics*, pp. 102–03.

90. Vase

Qing dynasty, reign of Kangxi, circa 1690–1720. Porcelain with *yingcai* overglaze enamels. H. 46.3 cm.
Gift of Mrs. Alfred Anson, 1952.395

The tall vase is cylindrical, with squarish shoulders and a straight neck with a raised horizontal band; the body tapers slightly to a recessed, flat, unmarked base. The mouth rim is everted and flattened. Decoration consists of a meander pattern along the sides of the mouth rim; the neck displays rectangular panels containing butterflies and flowers that alternate with offering vessels. On the shoulder is a pattern of prunus blossoms and cartouches with symbols of the four accomplishments of scholars.

129

The vessel's body has an overall pattern of multicolored blossoms and yellow dragons on a green stippled background, which surrounds three large panels bordered with cloud collars. Each panel contains a large basket of flowers.

In contrast to the austere, restrained shapes and decoration of imperial porcelains, ceramics made for the general domestic market and for export are vivacious in the execution and variety of designs. One of the most popular decorative techniques was painting with overglaze enamels known as *yingcai*, or "strong colors." Because the brilliance of these clear or translucent colors was enhanced when applied over a high-fired clear glaze, the technique required two firings: One at a high temperature for the glazed porcelain, and another firing at a lower temperature to mature the enamels after the painted decoration was applied. The *yingcai* decorated wares, highly sought after by European and American collectors, were categorized according to color families based on terms assigned by the French collector Albert Jacquemart. According to Jacquemart's terminology, porcelains with a *yingcai* palette dominated by greens, as on this vase, are called *famille verte*.

The shape of this vase, known as *rouleau* in the West, is called *bangchui ping* ("club-shaped vase") in Chinese, after a wooden club used to beat clothes during washing. Prominent among the extensive surface decorations are three large baskets, each of a distinct, fanciful design and overflowing with a variety of flowers. The floral basket symbolizes the Daoist immortal Lan Caihe, patron of gardeners, who is usually shown carrying such a basket. Lan was fond of collecting as many varieties of flowers as possible; according to one story, he obtained his magic basket of flowers upon entering a cave in which flowers of all four seasons grew simultaneously. The basket was bestowed on him by an old woman; in addition to blossoms, it contained seeds that could be used to perform magic.

The motif of Lan's basket filled with flowers — symbolizing wishes for harmony, progeny, wealth, rank, and longevity — would have been appropriate for any auspicious occasion such as New Year, a birthday, a betrothal or a wedding. Each basket is filled to overflowing; more blossoms are visible through openings in the sides. Each basket contains a different combination of flowers including (among others) lotus, peony, chrysanthemum, hydrangea, aster, pink and camellia, connoting the wish that all good things will occur in abundance. The motifs of the four accomplishments of scholars — a book, representing poetry; scrolls, to signify painting; a wrapped *qin*, emblem of music; and a chessboard with gaming pieces, to represent chess — symbolize the gentleman cultivated in the Confucian virtues.

91. Vase

Qing dynasty, Kangxi period, circa 1700. Porcelain with *yingcai* overglaze enamels and gold. H. 43.5 cm.
Gift of Edward Greeno Jr., 1971.771

The tall vase is cylindrical, with squarish shoulders, and a short, straight neck with a slightly raised horizontal band; the mouth rim is everted and flattened. The body swells slightly and tapers to a recessed, flat, unmarked base. The sides of the rim have a diaper pattern of hatched upright and inverted triangles in black against green. The neck has a painted decoration of a landscape with a pavilion and fisherman in a boat. Shoulder decoration consists of painted ogival panels with alternating chime against ribbon and artemesia leaf against ribbon; between these panels are begonia blossoms and leaves against a lingzhi-*and-spiral background. The main panel of decoration shows a group of scholars holding fans and looking at each other or toward a two-story pavilion. At the entrance of the pavilion a man in a green robe greets a man in an orange robe; the latter approaches the door to announce the arrival of a scholar in a light green robe, holding a fan. A woman on the balcony leans on her elbow and looks down at the young scholar. She is accompanied by an attendant holding a fan and a woman holding an embroidered ball.*

This vase illustrates the triumphant return of a scholar who has passed the civil service examinations and is returning to the hometown of his beloved. The scene is taken from the *Romance of the Western Chamber (Xixiangji)*, a novel that relates the love story of Zhang Junrui and Yingying. The story was immensely popular during the Kangxi period; woodblock-printed illustrations were copied by Jingdezhen decorators.[1]

The arrival of Zhang, shown outside the doorway surrounded by a crowd of congratulatory colleagues, is announced by an attendant to the man inside. At that moment Yingying leans over the balcony railing, and the lovers' eyes meet. Behind Yingying is her mother, who holds an embroidered ball, symbol of success in the examinations. She had forbidden the lovers to marry unless Zhang passed the examinations. Yingying's servant Hongniang, who was instrumental in assisting the secret courtship, stands next to Yingying and holds a fan. Appropriate to the emotions inherent in the story are the begonia blossoms depicted on the shoulder of the vase: According to popular legend, they are created by a woman's tears as she yearns for a distant lover.[2]

Provenance:
    Frank Caro; Mrs. Joseph Andrews; Edward Greeno Jr.
Notes:
    1. See a contemporary *yingcai* vase with multiple scenes from the *Xixiang ji* in the Taft Museum; Derham and Johnson, *Chinese Ceramics*, pp. 640–41.
    2. Bartholomew, *Hundred Flowers*, no. 43.

92. Vase

Qing dynasty, Kangxi period, circa 1700. Porcelain with *yingcai* overglaze enamels and gold. H. 45.5 cm.
Gift of Edward Greeno Jr., 1971.772

The tall vase is cylindrical, with sloping squarish shoulders and slightly swelling sides that are rounded toward the short, recessed, unmarked base. The short neck has straight sides except for the raised horizontal band and a slight flare upward toward the everted and flattened rim; the rim is thumb-indented on its exterior sides. The sides of the rim have a painted keyfret band in black against green. Painted decoration on the neck consists of a landscape with a pavilion and a fisherman in a boat. Decoration on the shoulders includes plum against a swastika diaper pattern and cloud-collar cartouches containing scholars' emblems: a book, two scrolls, wrapped qin, and a group consisting of a book, a pearl, a lozenge, a cup and a basket. The main decoration is a bearded man wearing a military uniform and a gold helmet, seated in a canopied boat along with female attendants holding fans, a female attendant holding a ewer, two trumpeters, a woman companion of the emperor, and a servant woman on the bow presenting pair of lotus blossoms. Three other boats, each with an oarsman and women gathering lotus from the lake, are filled with lotus. A willow tree and clouds are visible on rocky precipice.

The subject of this vase is unidentified but undoubtedly comes from one of the popular dramas or novels whose woodblock printed illustrations served as sources for porcelain decoration.

Provenance:
   Frank Caro; Mrs. Joseph Andrews; Edward Greeno Jr.

93. Reticulated Double Vase in Imitation of Guan Ware

Qing dynasty, Qianlong period, circa 1736–1756. Stoneware with crackled grayish blue-green glaze. H. 20.3 cm.
Museum purchase, 1950.63

The pear-shaped vase has a tall straight neck with everted rim, and sloping shoulders that contain a row of openwork inverted teardrops. The body of the vessel is double-walled; the glazed interior wall is visible through the openwork design of scrolling leafy vines that form the glazed outer wall. The body tapers gradually, abruptly then curves inward to the straight, recessed foot. The vase is covered in a thick, opaque grayish blue-green glaze that exhibits crackle and minute bubbles overall. The inside of the footring and base is also glazed; where the clay body is exposed, it is dark purple-brown. The base is unmarked.

During the latter part of Yongzheng's reign and the early years of Qianlong's reign, Tang Ying served as controller of imperial porcelain production at Jingdezhen. Under his direction, significant contributions to the development of ceramics were made in the mid-eighteenth century: New types of glazes were developed, and revered glazes of the Song dynasty were re-created.

Although the new versions of Guan and Ge wares in traditional Song shapes were sometimes difficult to distinguish from their predecessors, Song-style crackled glazes were also added to vessels of distinctly Qing type.[1] The double-walled construction and reticulated decoration of the Museum's vase are characteristic not of Song-period vessels, but of one of Tang Ying's innovations early in Qianlong's reign (1736–95), based on descriptions of openwork carved vases in the *Tao Ye Tou Shuo.*[2] Similar openwork pattern vases

were also decorated in overglaze enamels. The inner portions of some of the double-walled vases also could turn independently, though the Museum's was not constructed to do so. This vase reflects the Qing emperor's keen interest in the antique glazes of the Song dynasty combined with an appeal to the Qing taste for ornamentation and technical innovation.[3]

Provenance:
   C. T. Loo
Notes:
   1. See Wang Qingzheng, "Yongzheng Imitations," and Ts'ai Ho-pi, "Song Dynasty Guan Ware."
   2. Quoted by Bushell, *Oriental Ceramic Art*, p. 226. A similarly reticulated porcelain vase with overglaze enamel decoration, Qianlong period, is illustrated by Sullivan, *Arts of China*, p. 244.
   3. See Scott, "Archaism and Invention," pp. 80–82.

94. Pair of Bowls

Qing dynasty, mark and reign of Qianlong (1736–1795). Porcelain with *fencai* overglaze enamels. H. 6.3, diam. 13 cm.
Bequest of Katharine J. Appleton, 1949.123, 124

Each small bowl has an everted rim and gently curving sides that taper to a short, straight foot. The interior of each bowl is undecorated; the rims are painted gold. Exterior decoration consists of a dense pattern of scrolling peaches, peonies, lotus, swastika-shaped flowers, and endless knots painted in opaque pale colors on a white background. Six-character marks of Qianlong are painted in iron red on each base.

Porcelains with opaque overglaze enamels, known in China as *fencai* ("powdery colors") or *ruancai* ("soft colors"), traditionally have been known in Western publications by their European designation *famille rose*, because of the predominance of pink in the polychrome palette.[1] The pink comes from colloidal gold, a colorant introduced by Jesuits employed at the imperial enamel and glass-making workshops in Beijing. When mixed with white lead arsenate pigment, the gold produced a range of pinks and purples. The addition of white to the *yingcai* color palette resulted in new possibilities for opaque pastel as well as brilliant colors. Both the style of decoration and the use of *fencai* enamels show the influence of products of the imperial enameling workshop.[2]

   The Museum's bowls are decorated in an intricate pattern of scrolling, jewellike flowers, tendrils, and auspicious motifs that densely fill the exterior surface of the vessel and reflect an aesthetic like that of the intricately embroidered textiles of the period. Ceramics with similar designs form a subgroup of enameled porcelains of the Qianlong reign.[3] This brocade style was used both on altar vessels, usually with a predominance of Buddhist motifs, and on vessels for imperial court use. Here the auspicious emblems refer primarily to wishes for longevity. These include peaches, swastika-shaped tendrils, and a symbol for "ten thousand," as in "May you live ten thousand years," a form of addressing the emperor. The endless knot (*pan zhang*), one of the eight Buddhist symbols, signifies a long life uninterrupted by setbacks. Peonies are emblems of wealth and rank; the lotus represents purity and harmony.

Notes:
1. See Cort and Stuart, *Joined Colors*, pp. 28–29.
2. Kerr, *Chinese Ceramics*, p. 114.
3. National Palace Museum, *Ch'ing Dynasty Enamelled Porcelains*, pls. 117 and 118; also a pear-shaped vase with similar decoration but with Jiaqing seal mark and period was sold at Christie's Hong Kong, March 31, 1992, lot 664.

95. Double-Gourd Vase with "Tea-dust" Glaze

Qing dynasty, Jiaqing period (1796–1820). Glazed porcelain.
H. 28.6 cm.
Gift of Alfred T. Goshorn, 1897.88

The vase is shaped like a double gourd. The narrow, pear-shaped upper gourd is connected to the larger, globular lower gourd by a pinched waist in the form of bound lappets. Slender ear-shaped handles extend from the upper gourd to the shoulder of the lower, where they terminate in ruyi *heads. The foot is slightly flared, with a recessed base on which a six-character mark of Jiaqing is impressed in sealscript. The vase is covered inside and out with an olive-green glaze that exhibits an overall pattern of minute yellow specks.*

The olive-green speckled glazes known as *chayemo* ("tea-dust") were an invention of the Yongzheng period, and may have resulted from attempts to reproduce Song-style brown and black wares. The "tea-dust" wares belong to the high-fired group; that is, they were created in a single firing at high temperature. The distinctive olive color and speckled effect result from underfiring an iron-rich Jian-type glaze (see entry 65).[1]

This double-gourd shape with handles is called by the Chinese a *Da Ji* or "Great Auspiciousness" vase.[2] The type originated during the Qianlong period and continued to be produced in the subsequent Jiaqing period. The Museum's vase has an impressed seal of Jiaqing on its base.

Provenance:
Alfred T. Goshorn
Notes:
1. *Iron in the Fire*, p. 89.
2. Gao, *Chinese-English Glossary*, p. 5.

96. Vase with "Tea-dust" Glaze

Qing dynasty, late 18th or early 19th century. Glazed porcelain.
H. 33.7 cm.
Gift of Alfred T. Goshorn, 1897.100

The vase has a tall straight neck that flares slightly toward the rounded shoulders; the compressed, bulbous body is supported by a wide, splayed foot. The vessel is glazed inside and out in a dark olive green with a pattern of fine blue streaking overall; the glaze appears brown where it has pulled away from the mouth. The recessed base is glazed and has an impressed four-character mark of Chenghua. The exposed porcelain was painted with a dark brown wash. Minute pitting of the glaze appears overall.

The glaze color of this vase resembles bronze patination. It exhibits a pattern of minute dark-blue streaks over the olive-green glaze.

97. Vase with "Robin's Egg" Glaze

Qing dynasty, 18th or 19th century. Glazed porcelain. H. 34 cm.
Gift of Alfred T. Goshorn, 1897.103

The pear-shaped vase has a tall flaring neck with everted rim, and a short rounded body that tapers to a high, flared foot. It is glazed overall in mottled turquoise and blue, including the inside of the base. The clay body appears dark brown where exposed. There is no mark.

First appearing in the eighteenth century, the "robin's egg" glazes were among the various new low-fired glazes invented at Jingdezhen under Tang Ying's supervision.

After the first firing of the unglazed porcelain, the speckled effect was created by blowing a spray of opaque pale turquoise glaze on a coating of opaque deep blue glaze; during firing the turquoise, whose color derives from copper opacified with arsenic, ran slightly.[1] A similar glaze of different composition was used on stoneware at Yixing and at the Shiwan kilns, Canton.[2]

Notes:
1. Medley, *The Chinese Potter*, p. 256.
2. Kerr, *Chinese Ceramics*, p. 88.

45. Goblets
Neolithic Longshan culture, circa 2700–2100 B.C.

47. Jar
Warring States period, 5th or 4th century B.C.

46. *Li* tripod
Shang dynasty, 13th to 11th century B.C.

49. *Hu*
Eastern Han dynasty, 1st or 2nd century A.D.

Left
48. Tomb Figure of a Kneeling Woman
Western Han dynasty, 2nd or 1st century B.C.

50. *Hu*
Han dynasty (206 B.C.–A.D. 220)

51. *Wenjiuzun*
Han dynasty (206 B.C.–A.D. 220)

52. Tomb figure of an official
Northern Wei dynasty, early 6th century A.D.

53. *Hu* jar
Six dynasties period, first half of 6th century A.D.

54. Tray, Gongxian ware
Sui or early Tang dynasty, 7th century A.D.

56. Military Official on a Horse
Tang dynasty, late 7th or early 8th century A.D.

Right
57. Horse
Tang dynasty, 8th century A.D.

58. Tripod tray
Tang dynasty, late 7th or 8th century A.D.

59. Rhyton in the form of a goose
Tang dynasty, 8th century A.D.

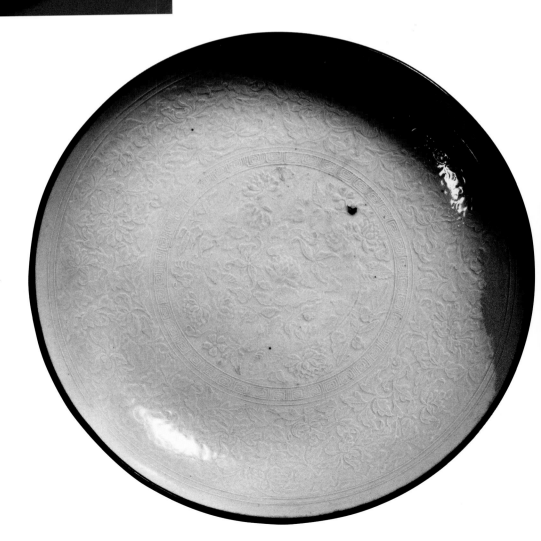

60. Bowl, Ding ware
Northern Song dynasty, 11th or 12th century

61. Plate, Ding ware
Jin dynasty, 13th century

62. Bowl, Yaozhou ware
Northern Song or Jin dynasty, 12th or 13th century

149

63. Tripod *Zun*, Ru ware
Northern Song dynasty, late 11th or early 12th century

65. Teabowl, Jian ware
Southern Song dynasty, 12th or 13th century

66. Teabowl, Cizhou-type ware
Southern Song dynasty, 11th or 12th century

67. Bottle, Cizhou ware
Yuan dynasty, 13th or early 14th century

68. *Zun* vase, Cizhou ware
Jin dynasty, 12th century

71. Pillow, Cizhou ware
Yuan dynasty, late 13th or 14th century

157

73. Bowl, Longquan ware
Southern Song dynasty, 12th or 13th century

74. Bowl, Longquan Guan-type ware
Southern Song dynasty, 12th or 13th century

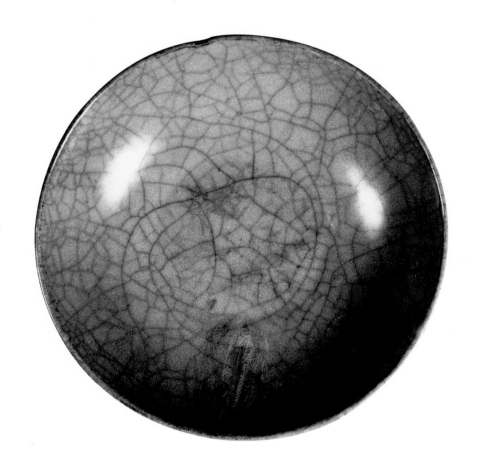

75. Round box, Longquan ware
Southern Song dynasty, 12th or 13th century

77. Daoist shrine, Longquan ware
Ming dynasty, early 15th century

78. Bowl, *Qingbai* ware
Southern Song dynasty, 12th or 13th century

79. Jar, *Qingbai* ware
Northern Song dynasty, 11th or 12th century

80. Bowl, *Qingbai*-type ware
Southern Song dynasty, 13th century

81. Vase, *Qingbai* ware
Yuan dynasty, 13th or 14th century

83. *Guan* jar
Ming dynasty, circa 1400–1410

84. Double Gourd Vase, *Fahua* ware
Ming dynasty, late 15th or early 16th century

85. Bowl
Ming dynasty, Jiajing period (1522–1566)

Detail

86. Jar
Ming dynasty, late 16th century

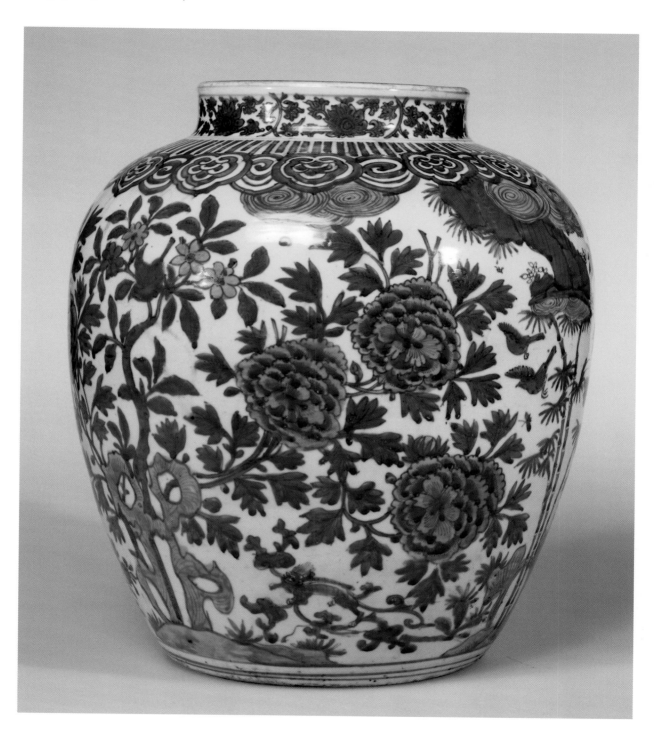

87. *Huqqa* (Water Pipe) Bases
Qing dynasty, Kangxi period (1662–1722)

88. Jar
Qing dynasty, Kangxi period, circa 1690–1710

89. Arrow Vase
Qing dynasty, Kangxi period, circa 1683–1710

90. Vase
Qing dynasty, Kangxi period, circa 1690–1720

91. Vase (*side a*)
Qing dynasty, Kangxi period,
circa 1700

92. Vase (*side a*)
Qing dynasty, Kangxi period,
circa 1700

91. Vase (*side b*)

92. Vase (*side b*)

93. Reticulated Double Vase in Imitation of Guan ware
Qing dynasty, Qianlong period, circa 1736–1756

94. Pair of bowls
Qing dynasty, Qianlong period (1736–1795)

95. Double-gourd vase with "Tea-dust" Glaze
Qing dynasty, Jiaqing period (1796–1820)

96. Vase with "Tea-dust" glaze
Qing dynasty, late 18th or early 19th century

97. Vase with "Robin's Egg" glaze
Qing dynasty, 18th or 19th century

98. Incense Burner

Late Ming or early Qing dynasty, 17th century. Cloisonné enamel and gilt copper. H. 72.4 cm.
Gift of Mrs. Benjamin Moore, 1955.543

The censer is composed of three separate parts: a tripod brazier that rests on elephant-head supports, a straight-sided openwork screen that fits between the brazier and lid, and a domed lid with gilt knob. The sides of the brazier are decorated in cloisonné with dragons; the hexagonal, foliate, flat rim has gilt edges and cloisonné decoration of fantastic animals among clouds and waves alternating with mountain and wave motifs. The hexagonal screen is formed of cloisonné panels with decoration of chrysanthemum surrounding openwork gilt inserts in the form of archaic dragon and clouds. The domed lid is constructed of openwork cloisonné panels of alternating upward- and downward-gazing dragons among clouds; projecting from the panel joins are gilt flanges in the form of archaic dragons. The top surface of the dome displays scrolling lotus blossoms in cloisonné and is surmounted by a gilt knob shaped like a coiled dragon among clouds and supported by a lotus-petal base. Wax infilling appears throughout. A four-character mark of Jingtai was cast into the base.

By the fourteenth century, cloisonné, a technique of decorating metal vessels with colored glass paste and metal wires, had been introduced to China from the Near East through the Islamic presence in Yunnan Province. Cloisonné was first described by Cao Zhao in the 1388 *Gegu Yaolun* [Essential Criteria of Antiques] as Dashi (Muslim) ware not befitting of the literati aesthetic. In Wang Zuo's expanded edition of Cao's treatise, published in 1462, Wang adds that Yunnanese artisans working in Beijing produced cloisonné for the imperial court.[1]

By the reign of the emperor Xuande (1426–1435), fine cloisonné vessels were being produced for ritual use in temples and for the imperial court. Technical innovations of the seventeenth century, such as drawing the wires through a die rather than hammering them, and attaching the wires to the vessel with vegetable glue rather than solder, made possible larger and more elaborate vessels such as those produced in the imperial workshops under the Qing emperors Kangxi, Yongzheng and Qianlong.[2] Many cloisonné vessels were produced in the Qing dynasty for use in temples and in the imperial palaces.

The short reign of the Ming emperor Jingtai (1450–1456) became associated with the finest cloisonné production. False marks of this emperor were added to many vessels during the Qing dynasty; the Museum's censer has such a four-character mark of Jingtai. This practice seems to have been followed primarily to show an admiration for tradition and to emulate the high artistic achievements in cloisonné reputed to have occured under that emperor's reign.

The process of production involved the application of bronze or copper wires, called cloisons, which first were bent into the desired shapes, to the surface of a bronze or copper vessel. The spaces between the wires then were filled in with various colored glass pastes, and the vessel was fired to melt the enamels and fix them into place. Because the enamel would shrink during firing, this process had to be repeated several times, until the cloisons were filled to overflowing. A final grinding and polishing of both the enamels and cloisons created a smooth, even surface. In addition to using brilliant solid colors such as turquoise, cobalt blue, red, yellow, white, black, and green, Qing dynasty cloisonné artists increased their palette by mixing two or more enamel colors together within the cloisons, as seen on this censer.

The shape and style of the Museum's censer suggest that it was made in the second half of the seventeenth century. Hexagonal basins and censers appear among the cloisonné of the Wanli reign (1573–1620) and throughout the seventeenth century. A smaller censer in the National Palace Museum, Taipei assigned to the Wanli period shows certain stylistic affinities with the Museum's censer in its hexagonal basin with wide rim, elephant feet, and screen with gilt openwork panels of archaic dragon scrolls.[3] But the Museum's censer betrays evidence of late seventeenth century in the rendering of motifs, such as the lotus scrolls with elongated, pointed petals and extended central petal.[4] And the depiction of eternal mountain and sea of bliss echoes the treatment of those motifs in Qing dynasty imperial textiles.

The decoration on this censer includes numerous mythical animals that represent aspects of ruling, suggesting that it was made for the imperial household. Dragons, symbolic of the emperor and eternal power, are the predominant motif, forming the openwork panels of the domed lid, the gilt top knob, and the flanges on the lid, and appearing in panels on the exterior sides of the brazier bowl. Each of the six panels that form the brazier's wide rim contains a mythical animal. These include the *luduan*, a stubby-horned mythical creature able to speak and understand all languages of the world and to travel extraordinary distances in a single day, which symbolizes the emperor's wise and compassionate rulership; lions, signifying power and energy; the *qilin*, representing benevolence and rectitude; and the horse, referring to quick-wittedness and military prowess. The waves and stylized mountains in which the animals appear illustrate *shou shan fu hai*, or "eternal mountain and sea of happiness." The lotus symbolizes Buddhist purity and the gilt supports in the form of elephant heads are emblems of strength, sagacity, and prudence. This dense and elaborate iconography blends to convey a universe of perfect order and harmony that results from the benevolence and wisdom of its ruler.

Provenance:
Alexandra Emery Moore

Notes:
1. David, *Chinese Connoisseurship*, p. 143–44. For discussions of the early history of cloisonné in China, see Brinker and Lutz, *Chinese Cloisonné*, pp. 46–51, and Watt, "Official Art and Commercial Art," pp. 452–54.
2. Brown, *Chinese Cloisonné*, p. 10.
3. Fong and Watt, *Possessing the Past*, plate 256.
4. Brinker and Lutz, *Chinese Cloisonné*, fig. 34i, identified as a late seventeenth century type, shows the same style of lotus blossom as on the CAM's censer.

99. Box

Ming dynasty, 16th century. Carved lacquer.
H.7.2, L.12.6, W.10 cm.
Gift of Mr. and Mrs. John J. Emery, 1964.713

The exterior of the rectangular box is covered with a thick coat of red lacquer carved in relief. The top surface of the lid has carved decoration of a scene of four scholars and their servants in a garden, all against a fine diaper pattern. The sides of the lid and box have carved decoration of blossoming sprays of flowers. The base and interior of both lid and box are coated with glossy black lacquer.

A variety of decorative techniques were employed by the Chinese to create works of art in lacquer. Carved lacquer, invented during the Song dynasty, required laborious preparation before surface designs could be executed. First a layer of hemp cloth soaked with lacquer and ash was applied to a wooden core. Then approximately forty coatings of lacquer were applied one by one, to build up a thickness sufficient for relief carving. The first layers were mixed with ground antler; subsequent layers consisted of pure lacquer to which mineral colorants were added. Cinnabar produced a rich red. The whole process was time-consuming and required great skill in manipulating a medium difficult to control. A careful combination of thinly applied coatings, and warm, moist conditions were required for the lacquer to set properly.

The Museum's exquisitely carved box depicts four scholars gathered in a garden to enjoy antiques. Under a large pawlonia tree beside a fantastic rock, three of the men sit at a table; one holds an open scroll. A *gu* and other antiques are placed on the table. A fourth scholar approaches with his walking stick, followed by a servant carrying a wrapped *qin*. In front of the table are a bell, an arrow vase, a handled vessel, and a vessel with a surface pattern known as "cracked ice." A table in the background holds a potted bamboo tree and an orchid plant. One servant prepares tea while another brings a large container.

The decoration of the sides of the box reflect the Ming dynasty taste for botanical motifs. The elegant sprays of various flowers of the four seasons include hibiscus, rose mallow, camellia, peony, magnolia, prunus, quince, crabapple, gardenia, and begonia.

100. Box Depicting the Gathering at the Orchid Pavilion (*Lanting Xiuqi*)

Ming dynasty, late 16th or early 17th century. Carved lacquer.
H.10.8, L.58.7 cm.
Lent by Dr. W. W. Seely, 4.1887

The rectangular box has curved sides and round corners. The exterior of the lid and the sides of the box are covered in red lacquer carved in relief. The lid is decorated with a landscape scene of sixteen scholars in a garden, surrounded by a border containing various auspicious symbols against a diaper-pattern background. Similar decoration with additional symbols against the same diaper-pattern background continues on the sides of the box. The interior of the lid and the box is painted in black lacquer.

This box probably served as a container for writing brushes and, appropriate to that function, it bears many literary and auspicious symbols. The central panel of the lid depicts the famous poetry party known as the Gathering at the Orchid Pavilion (*Lanting xiuqi*), an event held in the garden of master calligrapher Wang Xizhi (circa 303–circa 361) on the occasion of the Spring Purification Festival in A.D 353. The site of Wang's famous residence, located just outside Shaoxing in Shanyin, Zhejiang province, can still be visited today.

Wang Xizhi's most famous calligraphic work, widely considered one of the finest examples of *xingshu* (running script), is his written record of this occasion; it consists of a preface describing the gathering along with the poems composed that day by his guests. Although Wang's original is lost, a number of versions were preserved as stone engravings and were disseminated in the form of ink rubbings for later calligraphers to study and copy. In illustrations of the gathering, Wang typically is shown observing the party from his pavilion overlooking a small stream that meanders through the garden. Along both sides of the stream, small groups of scholars are engaged in a poetry-writing contest. They await the arrival of wine, which Wang's servants pour into small cups and set afloat on lotus leaves. Whenever a cup of wine reached the bank, the nearest guest was obliged to drink and compose a poem. The text relates the outcome of the contest: Eleven men succeeded in composing two poems each; fifteen guests each completed one; but each of the sixteen who failed to complete any poems had to drink three additional cups of wine.

Famous literary gatherings, notably those at Wang Shen's Western Garden or Wang Xizhi's Lanting, were popular subjects for late Ming- and early Qing-dynasty painters in Suzhou and Nanjing. A handscroll of the Lanting Gathering dated 1671, in the Cleveland Museum of Art (CMA 77.47), by the Nanjing painter Fan I (active 1658–1671), bears stylistic similarities to the depiction on this box, especially in the treatment of landscape elements.[1]

The border surrounding the pictorial scene contains numerous auspicious emblems against a diaper pattern of twelve-pointed stars in double squares. One of the most prominent motifs is the Eight Auspicious Symbols (*bajixiang*). The origin of this group was Buddhist, but its meaning was amplified according to the unique Chinese commingling of Confucianism, Daoism and Buddhism known as the "Three Doctrines" (*sanjiao*). The eight symbols and their significance include (clockwise from top left) the Wheel of the Law, representing Buddhist doctrine; the conch shell, equated with the Buddha's voice; the furled umbrella, signifying spiritual authority; the canopy, emblem of royal dignity and enlightenment; the lotus, for purity; water jars, representing harmony; paired fish, symbolizing fertility, protection from evil, conjugal bliss, and spiritual freedom; and the endless knot, or entrails of the Buddha, emblem of longevity and an unbroken link between wisdom and compassion.[2]

Interspersed throughout the border are depictions of numerous treasures of the Confucian scholar. These include pearls, symbol of purity and preciousness; a stone chime, representing celebration and joy; a coin, for wealth; a rhombus, talisman against evil and symbol of sound government; books and paintings, representing learning; rhinoceros-horn cups, emblem of righteous character; and the artemisia leaf, a symbol of happiness. Also appearing are auspicious motifs representing wishes for offspring, such as lichees, pomegranates, and the mouth organ *sheng*, a musical instrument whose name is a rebus for birth. Musical motifs in general symbolize the harmony of earth and heaven; others depicted here include a pair of castanets and the lute *pipa*, a symbol of conjugal harmony. A *ruyi*, or wish-granting scepter, conveys the hope that all one's wishes will come true.

Notes:
1. See *Eight Dynasties of Chinese Painting*, no. 218.
2. See Stuart, "Layers of Meaning," pp. 35–37 and 41–43.

101. Small Dish and Bowl

Fujian province, Qing dynasty, late 17th or early 18th century. Black lacquer with polychrome and white brass. Dish: diam. 9.8 cm., bowl: H. 5.7 cm.
Gift of Clifford Thies in honor of the Cincinnati Art Museum Security Department and Mr. and Mrs. Victor Raabe, by exchange, 1992.32, 33

The shallow, round dish is coated overall with black lacquer. It has an everted rim encased in white brass; its curved sides taper to a low foot. The exterior is plain; the interior has painted polychrome decoration of flowering sprays surrounding a central scene of flowers, butterflies, grasses, and rocks, enclosed in a gold keyfret band. The matching bowl has an everted rim and curved sides tapering to a straight, high footring. The interior is lined with white brass; the exterior is coated with black lacquer bearing a polychrome painted decoration of flowers, bees, and rocks. Just below the rim and around the footring are decorative borders consisting of single keyfret bands in gold.

Painted lacquerware is known in China as early as the fifth century B.C., the products of craftsmen from the southern state of Chu, who excelled in this art. It remained in favor for about a thousand years; then evidence of it disappears, except as recorded in paintings of the Song and Yuan dynasties.[1] Carved lacquer dominates lacquer decorative techniques in the Yuan and Ming dynasties because that type was preferred by the imperial court (see entries 99 and 100). In the Ming and Qing dynasties, there are numerous examples of painted lacquer, though they are less common than carved or inlaid lacquer.[2] Beginning in the sixteenth century, Fujian Province and the Ryukyu Islands excelled as centers for painted and inlaid lacquer production.

Painters employed either colored lacquer or oil-based paints to decorate lacquer. According to Yang Ming's 1625 preface to the *Xiushi Lu* [*Record of Decorations*], certain colors did not mix well with lacquer; these pigments were blended instead with vegetable or nut oils. Litharge (lead monoxide powder) was added as an agent to speed the drying process.[3] Mixed-media vessels and boxes combining metals, especially white brass, with lacquer appear frequently in the late Ming and early Qing dynasties. Seventeenth-century industrial growth in southern China, particularly in Fujian province, made such metals readily available to artisans.[4]

The present dish and bowl are exquisite examples of early Qing dynasty painted lacquer. The design of flowering plants and butterflies among rocks follows the style of imperial Kangxi (r. 1662–1722) porcelain decorated in overglaze enamels.[5]

Bowls and cups with metal linings were produced in other lacquer techniques as well, as exemplified by a Qianlong-period carved, covered lacquer bowl with metal lining in the collection of the Victoria and Albert Museum.[6]

Provenance:
Clifford Thies, inherited from his grandfather, who acquired the dish and bowl in China.
Exhibited:
Exhibited on loan to the Cincinnati Art Museum, 1982–92.
Notes:
1. Garner, *Chinese Lacquer*, p. 251.
2. Garner, *Chinese Lacquer*, pp. 251–58. For examples of painted lacquer with basketry panels, see Watt, *Sumptuous Basket*.
3. Summarized in Watt, *Sumptuous Basket*, p. 23.
4. Watt, *Sumptuous Basket*, p. 24. Lacquer boxes with basketry panels and white brass inlay, fittings and frames are illustrated in nos. 16–20.
5. Compare with a set of porcelain cups with decoration of the flowers of the twelve months, in the Hong Kong Museum of Art, illustrated in *Wonders of the Potter's Palette*, no. 15, pp. 48–49.
6. Garner, *Chinese Lacquer*, pl. 92.

102. Pendant

Han dynasty (206 B.C.–A.D. 220). Glass. Diam. 10.2 cm.
Gift of Drs. Martin and Carol Macht, 1992.241

The translucent deep-blue glass pendant is in the form of a flattened ring, elliptical in cross-section. The surface has remnants of burial incrustation.

Although faience beads and ornaments have been excavated from Western Zhou (1100–771 B.C.) sites, the earliest glass manufactured in China originated in the Spring and Autumn period (770–476 B.C.).[1] Archaeological excavations have yielded numerous Chinese-produced glass burial ornaments of light, opaque colors that imitated jade. Glass beads, ear spools, and vessels were also made in more intense colors such as blue, green, black, and purple-brown.

Though this pendant is difficult to date, assignment to the Han dynasty is suggested here. The thinness and delicacy of the Museum's piece would have made it impractical as a bracelet; most likely it functioned as a burial pendant, strung with other pendants to adorn the deceased. The colorant for blue glass produced in China was not cobalt but a copper barium tetrasilicate identified as Chinese blue. This substance is an analogue of Egyptian blue, a synthetic pigment known throughout the Near East from 1500 B.C. until Roman times (and possibly as late as medieval times). Depending on the temperature reached during heating of the glass batch, Chinese blue has a purple phase (1035–1080°C) and a blue phase (at 1080–1160°C).[2] The brilliant blue of this ring argues for its having been produced in the higher temperature range.[3]

Provenance:
Marshal Plumer; Sotheby's, New York; Drs. Martin and Carol Macht
Published:
Cincinnati Collects Oriental Art, no.157.
Exhibited:
"Cincinnati Collects Oriental Art," Cincinnati Art Museum, March 7–April 28, 1985.
Notes:
1. Gan, "Introduction to the Symposium," p. 2.
2. Brill, Tong, and Dohrenwend, "Chemical Analyses," p. 36; Brill, Barnes, and Joel, "Lead Isotope," p. 71.
3. For comparison see a Han-dynasty bronze mirror with blue glass inlay, *Grenville L. Winthrop*, no. 55.

103a. Vase in Imitation of Jade

Qing dynasty, 18th or 19th century. Glass. H. 22.2 cm.
Gift of Drs. Martin and Carol Macht, 1991.455

The translucent light grey-green glass vase has a short straight neck, wide shoulders tapering to the narrow base, and a shallow footring.

Exhibited:
"Glass in China: Utilitarian and Decorative Wares of the 18th and 19th Centuries," China Trade Museum, Milton, Massachusetts, 1983, no.16.
Exhibited on loan to the Cincinnati Art Museum, 1982–1991.

103b. Libation Cup with Longevity Design

Qing dynasty, 17th century. Glass. H. 5.7 cm.
Gift of Drs. Martin and Carol Macht, 1992.239

The tapered square cup is formed of translucent greenish white glass; it has two handles and four corner-feet. Relief-carved decoration on front and back consists of pairs of confronted dragons in profile chasing a pearl, below a longevity motif. The handles are in the form of dragon heads in profile.

103c. Bowl in Imitation of "Mutton-Fat" Jade

Qing dynasty, early 19th century. Glass. H.7.6, diam 16 cm.
Gift of Drs. Martin and Carol Macht, 1992.245

The translucent white bowl has a slightly everted rim and curved sides tapering to a recessed, wheel-cut, shallow foot. The exterior has a matte appearance, but the interior is polished.

Provenance:
P. H. Plesch; Sotheby's, London; Drs. Martin and Carol Macht
Exhibited:
"Glass in China: Utilitarian and Decorative Wares of the 18th and 19th Centuries," China Trade Museum, Milton, Massachusetts, 1983, no.19.

The patronage of the emperor Kangxi (r. 1662–1722) spurred the growth of glass manufacturing during the Qing dynasty; his fascination with European glass moved him to hire Jesuit craftsmen to establish an imperial glassworks in 1696. The Jesuits, under the supervision of a German priest, Kilian Stumpf, worked in collaboration with local Chinese artisans. They produced glass to be used at the imperial court and to supply gifts to reciprocate those presented to the emperor by foreign governments. Kangxi's intent, it seems, was not to imitate European glass, but to adopt the technology so as to produce uniquely Chinese glass that would impress the Europeans with its superior quality. Glassblowing, although known in China as early as the Northern Wei period (386–534), was employed more extensively under Jesuit encouragement than ever before.[1]

Potters and artisans throughout Chinese history have relished the challenge of finding ways to manipulate their materials to imitate other venerated substances. The earliest archaeological finds of Chinese glass include ornaments imitating jade.[2] Glass ornaments and vessels imitating jade were also produced during the Qing dynasty. The Museum's square cup (b), which was made in a mold, is related to jade libation cups of the period, whose handles are in the form of confronted dragons biting the rims.[3] Glass libation cups identical to the Museum's are in the collections of the Royal Ontario Museum[4] and Robert Clague.[5]

The bowl (c), imitating white nephrite called "mutton-fat," was blown into a mold and then cold-worked to refine the shape, smooth the surface, and polish the interior. The large vase was blown into a mold, then polished.

Although excavated examples exist from the Shang through the Han dynasties, jade vessels were extremely rare until the sixteenth and seventeenth centuries, when increased quantities of jade were imported from Xinjiang. Ming and Qing sumptuary laws, however, attempted to restrict the use of jade vessels to high ranking officials and members of the imperial court.[6] To collectors whose social status prevented their acquisition of jade vessels, fine glass imitations would have provided an appealing substitute, symbolizing the aspirations to wealth and rank associated with the possession of jade.

Notes:
1. Rabiner, "Chinese Glass and the West," pp.17–21; Brown and Rabiner, *Clear as Crystal*, pp.21–23.
2. Glass *bi* from the Warring States period (475–221 B.C.) produced in imitation of jade have been excavated in Hunan province.
3. A related example in jade is illustrated in Watt, *Chinese Jades*, no.141.
4. Dohrenwend, "Glass in China," fig. 31.

5. Brown and Rabiner, *Robert H. Clague Collection*, no. 74.
6. Rawson, *Chinese Jade*, pp. 385–90.

104. Bowl

Qing dynasty, mark and reign of Qianlong (1736–1795). Glass. H. 7.2, diam. 16.4 cm.
Gift of Drs. Martin and Carol Macht, 1991.456

The translucent rose-colored bowl has a polished interior. Its exterior surface is decorated in high relief with a scene of a pavilion, a man holding a fly whisk, and a bearded man carrying buckets and climbing a rocky slope. The base has a shallow footring and a four-character mark of Qianlong.

Glass vessels with relief carving were first blown into a mold and then cold-worked with abrasives, using the same techniques employed for carving jade. Much of the appearance of Qing dynasty glass draws its inspiration from contemporary ceramics. The color of the present bowl reflects the popularity of the rose-pink color in Yongzheng and Qianlong period porcelain. It is likely that the color was produced by the presence of colloidal gold in the glassbatch, just as it was in the composition of overglaze enamels.[1]

The decoration probably illustrates a story of the Daoist immortal Lu Dongbin, who is shown running and carrying his magical fly whisk.

Provenance:
    Mrs. Joseph Andrews, Sr.; Louis Aronoff; Drs. Martin and Carol Macht
Exhibited:
    "Glass in China: Utilitarian and Decorative Wares of the 18th and 19th Centuries," China Trade Museum, Milton, Massachusetts, 1983, no. 52.
    Exhibited on loan to the Cincinnati Art Museum, 1988–91.
Notes:
    1. Brown and Rabiner, *Robert H. Clague Collection*, p. 10. This cannot be confirmed until chemical analyses have been carried out. Also see Brown and Rabiner, *Clear as Crystal*, p. 29. Gold as a colorant in Qing dynasty glass is discussed in Rabiner, "Chinese Glass and the West," p. 25, with regard to a possible connection between the use of a precipitate of stannic acid with gold, used to achieve the rich ruby color of seventeenth and eighteenth century European glass, and the appearance of ruby glass in China during this period.

105. Lidded Vessel in Imitation of Aventurine

Qing dynasty, 18th century. Glass with copper filings. H. 23.2 cm.
Gift of Drs. Martin and Carol Macht, 1992.240

The flattened square vessel has a domed lid and a straight neck that flares to wide shoulders; from the shoulders the vessel tapers to the ring base. The vessel is made of opaque brown glass with suspended "gold" sparkles. Surface decoration in high relief includes a flying bird, a phoenix, a fruiting peach branch, and two handles in the form of longevity mush-rooms, each with a ring. The knob of the lid is in the form of a seated bird holding a fruiting peach branch in its mouth.

Aventurine glass, which was invented in Europe, imitated the sparkle of the semi-precious mineral through the suspension of copper filings in a blue or brown glass batch. The technique was introduced to the Chinese imperial glassworks by Jesuit craftsmen. Although the first examples of aventurine glass in China apparently were made from imported European glass batch,[1] palace records show that in 1741 Pierre d'Incarville and Gabriel-Leonard de Broussard created aventurine glass batch at the imperial glassworks in Beijing.[2]

Aventurine glass appealed to Daoists because its "gold" flecks were associated with gold, an important ingredient in elixirs of immortality. The Museum's vessel displays other connections to Daoist beliefs: its surface decoration includes peaches and *lingzhi* mushrooms, Daoist symbols of longevity and immortality, and the handsome lidded vessel is a typical archaizing form based on ancient ritual vessels. Such shapes were popular for later Chinese carvings in jade or other semiprecious minerals such as quartz, malachite, and lapis lazuli.

Provenance:
    Sotheby's London; Drs. Martin and Carol Macht
Exhibited:
    "Glass in China: Utilitarian and Decorative Wares of the 18th and 19th Centuries," China Trade Museum, Milton, Massachusetts, 1983, no. 94.
    "The Art of the Vessel: Decorative Arts from the Macht Collection," The Taft Museum, 1993–94.
Notes:
    1. Brown and Rabiner, *Robert H. Clague Collection*, p. 10.
    2. Yang, "A Brief Account of Qing Dynasty Glass," p. 79.

106. Square Bowl

Qing dynasty, 18th or 19th century. Glass. H. 6.8 cm.
Gift of Drs. Martin and Carol Macht, 1992.242

The opaque yellow glass square bowl has flaring sides, everted rim, square recessed foot, and relief decoration of flowering sprays of lotus, peony, narcissus, and plum.

The colors of monochrome glazed porcelain used within formal contexts had various ritual and rank associations prescribed in detailed regulations. Beginning in the Ming dynasty yellow vessels were used in the cyclical rituals at the Temple of the Earth. For formal table wares used within the imperial household, color denoted rank; those with golden yellow glaze known as "imperial yellow" on both the exterior and interior were designated for use only by those of the highest rank, namely the emperor, empress dowager, and empress.

While this square glass cup is of the imperial yellow color, its surface decoration of floral motifs suggests that it was made for informal usage or simply for display. The flowers depicted include lotus, symbol of Buddhist purity; peony, emblem of wealth and rank; narcissus, denoting good luck; and plum, signifying perseverance.

Exhibited:
    "Glass in China: Utilitarian and Decorative Wares of the 18th and 19th Centuries," China Trade Museum, Milton, Massachusetts, 1983, no. 56.
        Exhibited on loan to the Cincinnati Art Museum, 1982–88.

107. Vase

Qing dynasty, 18th century. Glass. H. 19 cm.
Gift of Drs. Martin and Carol Macht, 1992.243

The opaque olive-green vase has a long, straight neck, a bulbous body, a flaring foot, and a four-character incised mark of Qianlong.

This vase is another example of the close connection between glass and porcelain during the Qing dynasty. Both its shape and color imitate monochrome glazed porcelain vessels. The olive-green color is reminiscent of versions of "tea-dust" glazes (see entries 98 and 99).

Provenance:
    Sotheby's, London; Drs. Martin and Carol Macht

108. Plate

Qing dynasty, 19th century. Glass. Diam. 18.7 cm.
Gift of Drs. Martin and Carol Macht, 1992.244

The transparent light blue glass plate has an everted rim and a wheel-polished joined-rope foot. Decorations of fruiting sprays of pomegranates, Buddha-hand citron, peaches, and lichees surround a central five-petaled blossom, all carved in relief.

This transparent light-blue plate, adorned with elegant fruiting sprays of pomegranates, Buddha-hand citron, peaches, and lichees surrounding a wind-blown hibiscus blossom, draws its aesthetic inspiration from early Ming-dynasty porcelains with botanical designs (see entry 83). The botanical motifs signify wishes for fame and riches (hibiscus), happiness (Buddha-hand citron), longevity (peaches), and numerous progeny (lichees).
The present dish has an unusual wheel-polished joined-rope foot.

Exhibited:
    "Glass in China: Utilitarian and Decorative Wares of the 18th and 19th Centuries," China Trade Museum, Milton, Massachusetts, 1983, no. 44.
        Exhibited on loan to the Cincinnati Art Museum, 1982–88.

109. Vase

Qing dynasty, 19th or early 20th century. Glass, acid washed and incised. H. 22.1 cm.
Gift of Drs. Martin and Carol Macht, 1991.454

The semi-opaque green glass vase is of meiping shape with a straight rim, slightly curved neck, and narrow shoulders tapering to a curved flange and flat base. Decoration consists of a narrow band of incised lotus on the shoulder and, below the polished flange, a wide band of incised lotus plants, all against a frosted background. The plants in the lower band emerge from a pattern of overlapping partial rings, suggestive of waves, along the base. Flow lines are visible on the base. There is no mark.

The shape and decoration of this mold-blown vase were inspired by Cizhou ceramics (see entries 68–71). The surface decoration, depicting lithe lotus plants in a pond, was achieved through acid-etching. In this process, the polished surface was covered with a protective coating of wax in the form of the design elements. The surrounding area was then treated with hydrofluoric acid, to produce the matte background. Outlines and details were subsequently added with an engraving tool.

Published:
    Cincinnati Collects Oriental Art, no. 158.
Exhibited:
    "Glass in China: Utilitarian and Decorative Wares of the 18th and 19th Centuries," China Trade Museum, Milton, Massachusetts, 1983, no. 59.
        "Cincinnati Collects Oriental Art," *Cincinnati Art Museum*, 1985, no. 158.
        Exhibited on loan to the Cincinnati Art Museum, 1988–91.

110. Snuff Bottles

a. Qing dynasty, 1780–1840. Nephrite. H. 7.4, 1997.41 cm.
b. Qing dynasty, 1780–1880. Jadeite. H. 5.9, 1997.45 cm.
c. Qing dynasty, 1740–1850. Banded agate. H. 6.4, 1997.42 cm.
d. Qing dynasty, 1740–1860. Agate. H. 6.6, 1997.48 cm.
e. Qing dynasty, 1740–1830. Glass. H. 6.0, 1997.38 cm.
f. Qing dynasty, 1740–1820. Glass. H. 8.5, 1997.47 cm.
g. Qing dynasty, 1770–1880. Glass. H. 6.8 cm., 1997.37 cm.
h. Qing dynasty, 1740–1830. Amber. H. 5.6, 1997.46 cm.
i. Qing dynasty, 1850–1920. Coral. H. 6.0, 1997.43 cm.
j. Qing dynasty, 1800–80. Porcelain with overglaze enamel. H. 7.5, 1997.39 cm.
k. Qing dynasty, 1820–60. Porcelain with underglaze blue. H. 7.2, 1997.44 cm.
l. Qing dynasty, 1780–1880. Porcelain with underglaze blue and underglaze copper red. H. 8, 1997.40 cm.
m. Qing dynasty, 1780–1880. Porcelain with overglaze enamel. L. 7.3, 1997.49 cm.
Gifts of Sylvan and Faith Golder

The habit of taking snuff, a fine powder of dried tobacco mixed with herbs, spices, and aromatics, was first introduced to China by the Portuguese in the late Ming dynasty. Jesuit missionaries influenced the adoption of the habit at the Qing imperial court, which led to its wider popularity throughout China. In addition to its stimulative effects, snuff was valued by the Chinese as a curative for headaches, lockjaw, stomach disorders, respiratory ailments and other maladies. Medicine bottles and jars were the prototypes for specially designed snuff bottles in China.[1]

With the establishment in the 1680s of imperial workshops under the administration of the Zaobanchu, (Office of Manufacture and Procurement), snuff bottles were made in the Forbidden City. Drawing upon the considerable technical skills of imperial artisans and a fascination with miniaturization and the manipulation of one material to imitate another, exquisite snuff bottles were made from a wide variety of precious and semi-precious materials. These included jade, quartz, and other hard and soft stones; organic materials such as bamboo, coconut shell, ivory, hornbill, coral, and amber; as well as lacquer, cloisonné, painted enamels, glass and porcelain. Snuff bottles soon became prized more as works of art than as functional items; many were not intended to be used at all.[2] Large numbers of snuff bottles were made in the eighteenth and nineteenth centuries at workshops in Beijing, Suzhou, Yangzhou, Guangzhou, Jingdezhen, and other localities; many were collected by Westerners.

The nephrite bottle (a) was made from a natural pebble of so-called 'han' jade, distinguished by its yellowish olive-green color with a russet "skin." The artist, who possibly worked in Suzhou, a city noted for its 'han' jade carving,[3] cleverly utilized the skin of the pebble to create a two-color relief design of a scholar under a pine tree. This classic literati motif certainly would have appealed to collectors in the Jiangnan area.

Jadeite, the type of jade that comes from Burma, became popular in China in the latter part of the eighteenth century with the opening up of regular trade between China and Burma in 1784 following a period of protracted hostilities between the two countries. This bottle (b) appears to come from a pebble due to the brownish area among the more brilliant apple-green and white mottling. Most jadeite came from pebbles until the end of the nineteenth century, when jadeite began to be mined.[4]

Stones within the quartz group were rarely used by Chinese artists before the Qing dynasty. The wide variety of quartzes such as rock crystal, amethyst, agate and chalcedony, whose natural inclusions were treasured in their own right or incorporated into pictorial designs, became popular for the creation of snuff bottles. Classic Chinese aesthetics involve an admiration for naturalness that is exemplified by works such as the bottle of banded agate (c). The artist has carefully chosen and used the material to allow the multi-colored ribbons inherent in the stone to display their own simple elegance.

Chalcedony, a form of agate, was favored as a snuff bottle material because of the inclusions of dark brown or brown/black that either occurred naturally in forms that appeared pictorial, or that could be manipulated through carving to create relief designs in a contrasting color. A sub-group of the chaldedony carvings are those in the Suzhou style, of which the Museum's is a fine example (d). Characterized by masterful carving and astute use of color for tiny details such as eyes, the Suzhou artists created works to appeal to connoisseurs of the literati class. There are designs of a dragon and tiger on one side; on the other a bat emerges from clouds and a monkey sits beneath a peach tree. These motifs convey auspicious wishes for longevity, power, rank, and happiness.

Glass was a favorite material for snuff bottles. On one bottle (e), the decoration was carved in relief from an overlay of deep red transparent glass on a colorless, bubble-suffused ground, described by the Chinese as "little pearls." It may have been made at the Zaobanchu using glass batch from Boshan, Shandong Province.[5] The design consists of a carp leaping over waves to catch a pearl; on each side are jujube plants. The motif is a reference to passing the difficult civil service examinations at the highest level. The carp who could successfully jump the rapids was believed to turn into a dragon, a metaphor for the transformation of an examination candidate into a government official. The jujube, called *zaozi*, is a rebus for "quick sons."[6] The entire design expresses wishes for the birth of sons who will grow up to be government officials, thereby bringing wealth and status to the family.

Considered one of the five basic elements, realgar was an important ingredient in Daoist elixirs of immortality. As a compound of arsenic, the toxicity of realgar and the mineral's tendency to break down upon exposure to sunlight made it an impractical material for carving. A variety of glasses were made, however, that imitate the brightly colored mineral and these became popular for snuff bottles (f). In addition to its Daoist associations with longevity, the mixture of red and yellow also may have represented the duality of *yin* and *yang* in the form of the female and male essences.[7]

On another glass bottle (g), the decoration was carved in relief from an overlay of transparent blue glass on a transparent, colorless ground. The design consists of two dragons whose heads and bodies dissolve into a geometric pattern resembling a key fret border. Such a design refers to the dragon's ability to be visible or invisible as it chooses, especially during its ascent to heaven.[8]

Amber, the fossilized resin of coniferous trees, was imported from Europe but sources were also known in Burma, which was noted for its amber of deep red color. This bottle (h) is flawless in its clarity and displays a rich color. The decoration consists of finely executed relief designs of phoenix and peony repeated on both sides of the bottle. In addition, on one side a magpie sits on a peony branch. The motif conveys auspicious wishes for beauty, riches, and happiness.

Coral, though available throughout the Qing dynasty, was generally made into small items such as jewelry and stoppers but was rarely used for larger items such as bottles until larger quantities became available in the latter half of the nineteenth century.[9] This bottle (i) is finely carved overall in a vase shape with relief designs of phoenix and floral scrolls, tentatively identified as hibiscus. Both hibiscus and phoenix are symbolic of female beauty. In addition, the hibiscus is an emblem of fame and riches, while the phoenix represents the five human qualities of duty, virtue, ritually correct behavior, humanity, and reliability.[10]

Snuff bottles do not seem to have been made at Jingdezhen, the center of porcelain production, until the latter part of the Qian-long period (r. 1736–95).[11] Many were mold-made, as was this example (j), which has handsome relief design of peony and butterflies, symbolic of wealth and rank. It has been covered with white and green overglaze enamels, the green applied in scattered splashes, such that it emulates the brilliant apple-green blushes that some-times appear in jadeite from Burma. The design of the bottle painted in underglaze blue (k), consists of a family of Buddhistic lions (the so-called "Foo lions," which resemble the Pekingese dog more than they do an actual lion). Male and female lions often serve as guardians to temple or palace gates. The male adult rolls an embroidered ball, a symbol of fertility, since it contains a cub; the ball was thought to be formed with the hairs torn out during love-play.[12] The whole design expresses a wish for a happy marriage with numerous offspring. The cylindrical-shaped bottle (l) was es-pecially popular in the nineteenth century.[13] Jingdezhen potters and decorators employed their considerable skills in making bot-tles that combine both underglaze blue and underglaze copper red on a single piece. The decoration on this bottle consists of an exquisitely executed design of a large five-clawed dragon with four smaller five-clawed dragons, all against a wave pattern. The sub-ject of large and small dragons together expresses the wish "May your children have illustrious careers."[14]

Many of the earliest porcelain snuff bottles were mold-made and those in the form of animals were especially popular. The squirrel on grapevine motif is one of the most common types (m).

Exhibited:

"Cincinnati Collects 5000 Years of Chinese Art." Taft Museum, 1997 (f)

Exhibited on loan to the Cincinnati Art Museum 1982–97 (a, c, h, i, k, m); 1995–97 (b, d)

Notes:

1. See Friedman, *Chinese Snuff Bottles*, pp. 7–8.
2. Watt, "The Antique-Elegant," pp. 520–21.
3. Moss, Graham and Tsang, *Art of the Chinese Snuff Bottle*, vol. 1, p. 81.
4. Moss, Graham and Tsang, *Art of the Chinese Snuff Bottle*, vol. 1, pp. 122–23.
5. Watt, "The Antique Elegant," pp. 520–21.
6. Bartholomew, *The Hundred Flowers*, n.p.
7. Moss, Graham and Tsang, *Art of the Chinese Snuff Bottle*, vol. 2, pp. 578–79.
8. Eberhard, *Dictionary of Chinese Symbols*, p. 84.
9. Moss, Graham and Tsang, *Art of the Chinese Snuff Bottle*, vol. 1, p. 163.
10. Eberhard, *Dictionary of Chinese Symbols*, pp. 146–47, 234–36.
11. Moss, Graham and Tsang, *Art of the Chinese Snuff Bottle*, vol. 1, pp. 360–61.
12. Eberhard, *Dictionary of Chinese Symbols*, pp. 164–65.
13. Moss, Graham and Tsang, *Art of the Chinese Snuff Bottle*, vol. 1, p. 387.
14. Eberhard, *Dictionary of Chinese Symbols*, p. 84.

99. Box
Ming dynasty, 16th century

Right
101. Small Dish and Bowl
Qing dynasty, late 17th or early 18th century

100. Box Depicting the Gathering at the Orchid Pavilion
Ming dynasty, late 16th or early 17th century

102. Pendant
Han dynasty, 206 B.C.–A.D. 220

193

103a. Vase in Imitation of Jade
Qing dynasty, 18th or 19th century

103b. Libation cup with Longevity Design 103c. Bowl in Imitation of "Mutton-Fat" Jade
Qing dynasty, 17th century   Qing dynasty, early 19th century

104. Bowl
Qing dynasty, Qianlong period, 1736–1795

105. Lidded Vessel in imitation of aventurine
Qing dynasty, 18th century

106. Square bowl
Qing dynasty, 18th or 19th century

107. Vase
Qing dynasty, 18th century

108. Plate
Qing dynasty, 19th century

109. Vase
Qing dynasty, 19th or early 20th century

110a   110b   110c   110d

110e   110f   110g   110h

110i   110j   110k   110l

110m

Chronology

Xia dynasty	circa 2100–circa 1600 B.C.
Shang (Yin) dynasty	circa 1600–circa 1100 B.C.
Zhou dynasty	circa 1100–256 B.C.
Western Zhou	circa 1100–771 B.C.
Eastern Zhou	770–256 B.C.
Spring and Autumn period	770–481 B.C.
Warring States period	481–221 B.C.
Qin dynasty	221–206 B.C.
Han dynasty	206 B.C.–A.D. 220
Western Han	206 B.C.–A.D. 9
Eastern Han	25–220
Six dynasties period	220–589
Three Kingdoms	220–265
Western Jin	265–317
Southern Dynasties	317–589
Northern Dynasties	
Northern Wei	386–534
Northern Qi	550–577
Northern Zhou	557–581
Sui dynasty	581–618
Tang dynasty	618–907
Five dynasties	907–60
Liao dynasty	916–1125
Song dynasty	960–1279
Northern Song	960–1127
Southern Song	1127–1279
Jin dynasty	1115–1234
Yuan dynasty	1272–1368
Ming dynasty	1368–1644
Qing dynasty	1644–1911

110 a–m. Snuff bottles
Qing dynasty, 18th to 20th centuries

Emperors

Northern Song *dynasty*	Taizu	960–76
	Taizong	976–97
	Zhenzong	998–1022
	Renzong	1023–63
	Yingzong	1064–67
	Shenzong	1068–85
	Zhezong	1086–1100
	Huizong	1101–25
	Qinzong	1126–27
Southern Song *dynasty*	Gaozong	1127–62
	Xiaozong	1163–89
	Guangzong	1190–94
	Ningzong	1195–1224
	Lizong	1225–64
	Duzong	1265–74
	Gongdi	1275–78
	Duanzong	1276–78
	Di Bing	1278–79
Yuan *dynasty*	Shizu (Khubilai Khan)	1260–94
	Chengzong	1295–1307
	Wuzong	1308–11
	Renzong	1312–20
	Yingzong	1321–23
	Taidingdi	1324–28
	Wenzong	1328–29
	Mingzong	1329
	Wenzong (restored)	1330–32
	Ningzong	
	Shundi	1333–68
Ming *dynasty*	Hongwu	1368–98
	Jianwen	1399–1402
	Yongle	1403–24
	Hongxi	1425
	Xuande	1426–35
	Zhengtong	1436–49
	Jingtai	1450–56
	Tianshun	1457–64
	Chenghua	1465–87
	Hongzhi	1488–1505
	Zhengde	1506–21
	Jiajing	1522–66
	Longqing	1567–72
	Wanli	1573–1620
	Taichang	1620
	Tianqi	1621–27
	Chongzheng	1628–44
Qing *dynasty*	Shunzhi	1644–61
	Kangxi	1662–1722
	Yongzheng	1723–35
	Qianlong	1736–95
	Jiaqing	1796–1820
	Daoguang	1821–50
	Xianfeng	1851–61
	Tongzhi	1862–74
	Guangxu	1875–1908
	Xuantong	1909–11

Technical Appendix

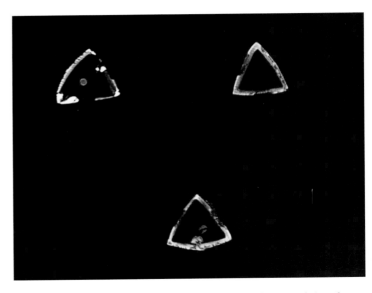

Fig. 3, Latitudinal cross-section through legs of *jia* showing location of pin and screw

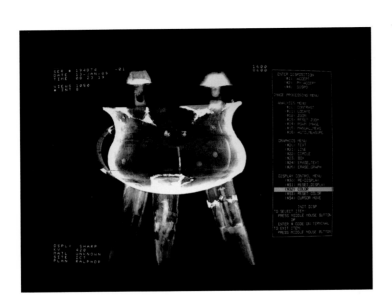

Fig. 1, Digital radiograph of *jia*, 1948.74

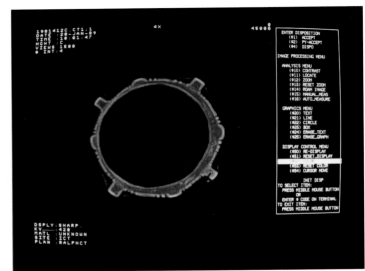

Fig. 4, Latitudinal cross-section through *gu*, 1981.412

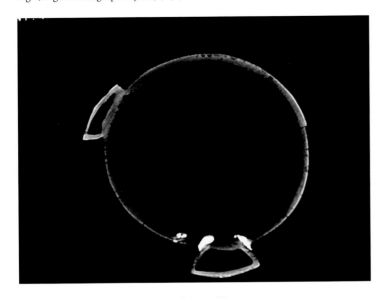

Fig. 2, Latitudinal cross-section through legs of *jia*

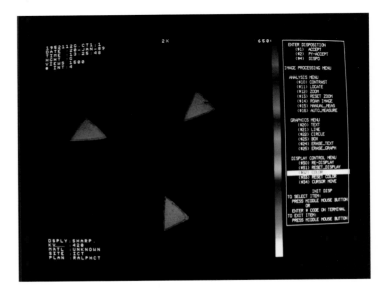

Fig. 5, Latitudinal cross-section through legs of *jue*, 1952.112

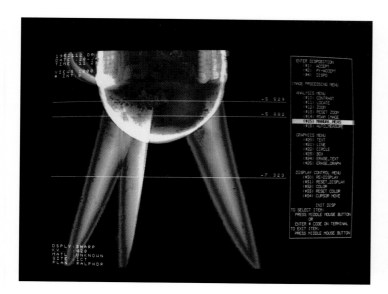

Fig. 6, Digital radiograph of *jue*

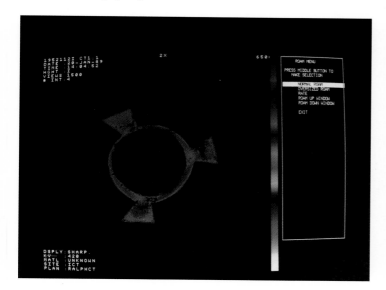

Fig. 7, Latitudinal cross-section through *jue* vessel bottom

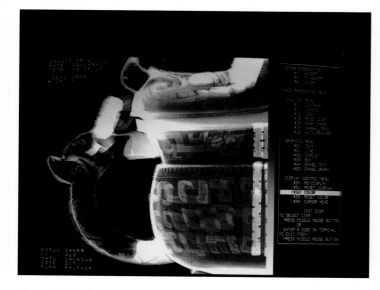

Fig. 8, Digital radiograph of *guang*, 1948.78

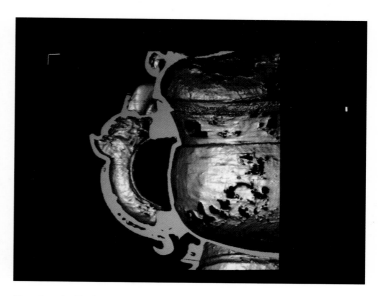

Fig. 9, Longitudinal cross-section through *guang* handle

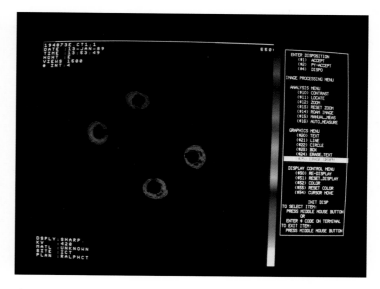

Fig. 10, Latitudinal cross-section through legs of *you*, 1948.73

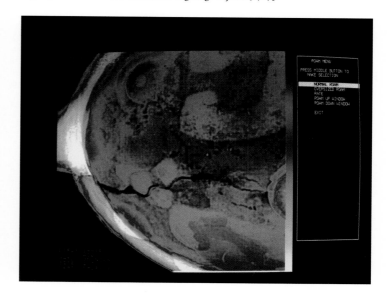

Fig. 11, Digital radiograph (detail) of *you* lid

Inscriptions

Transcribed by Nora Ling-yün Shih

Mirror, Tang dynasty, late 7th
or early 8th century A.D. (entry 11)

靈谿銅鏡[?],
神爐煉成.
臨臺月上,
屬物斯應,
皎潔逾明.
對日菱生.
鑒形惣(整)餝(餙),
方心表貞.

Seated Buddha, Northern Wei dynasty,
dated A.D. 474 (entry 13)

大魏治延興四年,
二月壬辰朔十七日
戊午.
定州
中山魏
昌坊上
村,牟聰妻劉令造
无量受佛一軀,願
生佛國故記之

Stele, Northern Wei dynasty,
dated A.D. 521 (entry 14)

Rear

正光二年歲
在辛丑,七月一
十三日己亥.
嚴小洛[發]
慈心感恩,
造石像一區.
屬所願從,
復為七世子生
龍華會.
本初者.

Front

清信士
嚴小洛
息男
阿俊(傷)
清信女
杜阿堯

Side

亡父嚴向男
亡母孫小陵

Stele, Northern Wei dynasty, dated A.D. 522 (entry 15)
Inscription on back, upper left

大魏正光三年，歲次壬寅，八月辛申，朔十一日
庚午，標□舉善，先聖□□，彰宣古?積，古今同
稱，所?乃乾川，覆載万物，蠢□仰尊，夫姓由王者?
之統，?先民尚天賜等七十人，汲郡汲人也，籍胄
祖陰，舊居此土，可謂殷王之墟，同文舊統，東業西洛，
□俠山河，夫?□殊也。賜等庆由人□□烯榮次
而千載特愚，生長昌?辰，運遭□□，聖母德配，二
儀俠才，万邦慈澤，宇宇?內知屈，电之興滞力?去神
龜(517 A.D.)元年，臺遣伏波將軍，司馬屬?大邑子顯賜先
職。賜等各菜?□宰，?不勝攑悦，身輕膀?重，万殞難
尹，自相師□，上□□帝?，聖母造像一區，指持精甘?

Wenshu, Bodhisativa of Wisdom, at a Writing Table, Yuan dynasty, dated 1354 (entry 32)

南?另壁
□上張村
世□□
□□□
□□□
王偲齊
李亨甫?
李通□
小□貴法師
高祐德
各保自身願門 速
靜長幼咸安□
□□□四?年歲次甲午秊?□月

Bibliography

Ackerman, Phyllis. *Ritual Bronzes of China.* New York: Dryden, 1945.

Adams, Philip Rhys. "Random Notes on Chinese Painting." *Cincinnati Art Museum Bulletin* (March 1953).

——. "Sculpture of the Far East." *The Cincinnati Art Museum Bulletin* (summer 1951).

Allee, Stephen D. "The Qiantang Tidal Bore." *Asian Art and Culture* 8, no. 2 (spring/summer 1995): 61–71.

An Jiayao. *Early Chinese Glassware.* The Oriental Ceramic Society Translations no. 12, translated by Matthew Henderson. London: Oriental Ceramic Society, 1987.

Ancient Chinese Tea Wares. Hong Kong: Urban Council, 1994.

Anthology of Chinese Art: Min Chiu Society Silver Jubilee Exhibition. Hong Kong: Urban Council, 1985.

Arlington, L. C. and William Lewisohn. *In Search of Old Peking.* Hong Kong, Oxford and New York: Oxford University Press, 1987.

Art on the Market: Selections of Antiquities and Oriental Art. Cincinnati: Cincinnati Art Museum, 1987.

The Arts of the Tang Dynasty: A Loan Exhibition Organized by the Los Angeles County Museum from Collections in America, the Orient and Europe. Los Angeles: Los Angeles County Museum, 1957.

Avril, Ellen B. "Highlights of Chinese Art." *Arts of Asia* 23, no. 2 (March/April 1993): 66–77.

Avril, Ellen B. and Stephen D. Bonadies. "Non-Destructive Analysis of Ancient Chinese Bronzes Utilizing Industrial Computed Tomography." In *Materials Issues in Art and Archaeology II*, Proceedings of the Materials Research Society, 1990 spring meeting, 49–63. Pittsburgh: Materials Research Society, 1990.

Ayers, John. *Far Eastern Ceramics in the Victoria and Albert Museum.* London: Sotheby Parke Bernet, 1980.

Bagley, Robert W. *Shang Ritual Bronzes in the Arthur M. Sackler Collections.* Washington, D.C.: Arthur M. Sackler Foundation, 1987.

Baker, Janet. *Seeking Immortality: Chinese Tomb Sculpture from the Schloss Collection.* Santa Ana: Bowers Museum of Cultural Art, 1996.

Baldwin, Michelle. "Monumental Wall Paintings of the Assembly of the Buddha from Shanxi Province: Historiography, Iconography, Three Styles, and a New Chronology." *Artibus Asiae* 54, nos. 3/4 (1994): 241–67.

Barnhart, Richard M. *Along the Border of Heaven: Sung and Yuan Paintings from the C. C. Wang Family Collection.* New York: Metropolitan Museum of Art, 1983.

——. *Painters of the Great Ming: The Imperial Court and the Zhe School.* Dallas: Dallas Museum of Art, 1993.

——. *Peach Blossom Spring: Gardens and Flowers in Chinese Paintings.* New York: Metropolitan Museum of Art, 1983.

——. "Reading the Paintings and Calligraphy of Bada Shanren." In *Master of the Lotus Garden: The Life and Art of Bada Shanren (1626–1705),* by Wang Fangyu and Richard Barnhart, 83–218. New Haven: Yale University Art Gallery, 1990.

——. "Tung Ch'i-ch'ang's Connoisseurship of Sung Painting and the Validity of His Historical Theories: A Preliminary Study." In *Proceedings of the Tung Ch'i-ch'ang International Symposium,* edited by Wai-ching Ho, 11–1 – 11–20. Kansas City: Nelson-Atkins Museum of Art, 1992.

——. "The 'Wild and Heterodox School' of Ming Painting." In *Theories of the Arts in China,* edited by Susan Bush and Christian Murck, 365–96. Princeton: Princeton University Press, 1983.

Bartholomew, Terese Tse. *The Hundred Flowers: Botanical Motifs in Chinese Art.* San Francisco: Asian Art Museum, 1985.

——. *Myths and Rebuses in Chinese Art.* San Francisco: Asian Art Museum, 1988.

Bechert, Heinz and Richard Gombrich, eds. *The World of Buddhism: Buddhist Nuns and Monks in Society and Culture.* London: Thames and Hudson, 1984.

Berger, Patricia. "Preserving the Nation: The Political Uses of Tantric Art in China." In *Latter Days of the Law: Images of Chinese Buddhism 850–1850,* edited by Marsha Weidner, 89–123. Lawrence, Kansas: Spencer Museum of Art and University of Hawaii Press, 1994.

Bian Yongyu. *Shigutang shuhua huikao* [Compilation of Writings on Calligraphy and Painting from the Shigu Hall], preface dated 1682. Reprint of the 1921 facsimile, Taipei: Cheng-chung Shu-chü, 1958.

Birrell, Anne. *Chinese Mythology: An Introduction.* Baltimore: Johns Hopkins University Press, 1993.

——, trans. *New Songs from a Jade Terrace: An Anthology of Early Chinese Love Poetry.* Harmondsworth: Penguin, 1986.

Bivar, A. D. H. "Trade between China and the Near East in the Sasanian and early Muslim periods." In *Pottery and Metalwork in T'ang China,* Colloquies on Art and Archaeology in Asia No. 1, edited by William Watson, 1–11. London: Percival David Foundation of Chinese Art, 1976.

Bonadies, Stephen and Ellen B. Avril. "Technical Examination of Chinese Bronzes." *Arts of Asia* 23, no. 2 (March/April 1993): 103–107.

Brill, Robert H., I. Lynus Barnes, and Emile C. Joel. "Lead Isotope Studies of Early Chinese Glasses." In *Scientific Research in Early Chinese Glass: Proceedings of The Archaeometry of Glass Sessions of the 1984 International Symposium on Glass, Beijing, September 7, 1984 with Supplementary Papers,* edited by Robert H. Brill and John H. Martin, 65–83. Corning, N.Y.: Corning Museum of Glass, 1991.

Brill, Robert H., Stephen S. C. Tong, and Doris Dohrenwend. "Chemical Analyses of Some Early Chinese Glasses." In *Scientific Research in Early Chinese Glass: Proceedings of The Archaeometry of Glass Sessions of the 1984 International Symposium on Glass Beijing, September 7, 1984 with Supplementary Papers,* edited by Robert H. Brill and John H. Martin, 31–58. Corning, N.Y.: Corning Museum of Glass, 1991.

Brinker, Helmut and Albert Lutz. *Chinese Cloisonné: The Pierre Uldry Collection.* Trans. Susanna Swoboda. New York: Asia Society, 1989.

Brown, Claudia. *Chinese Cloisonné: The Clague Collection.* Phoenix: Phoenix Art Museum, 1980.

Brown, Claudia and Donald Rabiner. *The Robert H. Clague Collection, Chinese Glass of the Qing Dynasty 1644–1911.* Phoenix: Phoenix Art Museum, 1987.

——. *Clear as Crystal, Red as Flame: Later Chinese Glass.* New York: China Institute in America, 1990.

Bunjinga suihen [Selected Masterpieces of Literati Painting]. 20 vols. Tokyo: Chūōkōron-sha, 1974–79.

Bush, Susan. "Five Paintings of Animal Subjects or Narrative Themes and Their Relevance to Chin Culture." In *China under Jurchen Rule: Essays on Chin Intellectual and Cultural History,* edited by Hoyt Cleveland Tillman and Stephen H. West, 183–215. Albany: State University of New York Press, 1995.

——. "Literati Culture under the Chin (1122–1234)." *Oriental Art* n.s. 15, no. 2 (summer 1969): 103–12.

Bush, Susan and Christian Murck, eds. *Theories of the Arts in China.* Princeton: Princeton University Press, 1983.

Bush, Susan and Hsio-yen Shih. *Early Chinese Texts on Painting.* Cambridge, Mass.: Harvard University Press, 1985.

Bushell, Stephen. *Oriental Ceramic Art.* New York, 1896. 2nd edition. London: 1981.

Butler, Sir Michael, Margaret Medley, and Stephen Little. *Seventeenth Century Chinese Porcelain from the Butler Family Collection.* Alexandria, Va.: Art Services International, 1990.

Cahill, James. "Ch'ien Hsüan and His Figure Paintings." *Archives of the Chinese Art Society of America* 12 (1958): 10–29.

——. *The Compelling Image: Nature and Style in Seventeenth-Century Chinese Painting.* Cambridge, Mass. and London: Harvard University Press, 1982.

——. *Hills Beyond a River: Chinese Painting of the Yuan Dynasty, 1279–1368.* New York and Tokyo: Weatherhill, 1976.

——. "The Imperial Painting Academy." In *Possessing the Past: Treasures from the National Palace Museum, Taipei,* by Wen C. Fong and James C. Y. Watt, 159–200. New York and Taipei: Metropolitan Museum of Art and National Palace Museum, 1996.

——. *An Index of Early Chinese Painters and Paintings.* Berkeley: University of California Press, 1980.

——. *The Painter's Practice: How Artists Lived and Worked in Traditional China.* New York: Columbia University Press, 1994.

——. *Parting at the Shore: Chinese Painting of the Early and Middle Ming Dynasty, 1368–1580.* New York and Tokyo: Weatherhill, 1978.

——. "The Three Zhangs, Yangzhou Beauties, and the Manchu Court." *Orientations* 27, no. 9 (October 1996): 59–68.

Cahill, Suzanne. *Transcendence and Divine Passion: The Queen Mother of the West in Medieval China.* Stanford: Stanford University Press, 1993.

Carswell, John. *Blue and White: Chinese Porcelain and Its Impact on the Western World.* Chicago: David and Alfred Smart Gallery, 1985.

——. "China and the Near East: The Recent Discovery of Chinese Porcelain in Syria." In *The Westward Influence of the Chinese Arts from the 14th to the 18th Century,* Percival David Foundation Colloquies on Art and Archaeology in Asia No. 3, edited by William Watson, 20–25. London: University of London, 1972.

——. "An Early Ming Porcelain Stand from Damascus," *Oriental Art* n.s. 12, no. 3 (autumn, 1966): 176–82.

Caswell, James O. "New Ways from Old Ways: The Testimony of a Chinese Painting." *Ars Orientalis* 25 (1995): 97–107.

——. *Written and Unwritten: A New History of the Buddhist Caves at Yungang.* Vancouver: University of British Columbia Press, 1988.

Chan, Hok-lam. "Chinese Official Historiography at the Yüan Court: The Composition of the Liao, Chin, and Sung Histories." In *China Under Mongol Rule,* edited by John D. Langlois, Jr., 56–106. Princeton: Princeton University Press, 1981.

Chang Kuang-yüan. "Ku kung Shang-dai chin-wen t'e-chan." *National Palace Museum Monthly of Chinese Art* 118 (January 1993): 35–45.

Chang Kuang-pin. *Yüan ssu-ta-chia* [Four great masters of the Yuan]. Taipei: National Palace Museum, 1975.

Chang Kwang-chih. *The Archaeology of Ancient China.* 4th ed. New Haven: Yale University Press, 1986.

——. *Art, Myth and Ritual: The Path to Political Authority in Ancient China.* Cambridge, Mass. and London: Harvard University Press, 1983.

——, ed. *Food in Chinese Culture: Anthropological and Historical Perspectives.* New Haven: Yale University Press, 1977.

——. *Shang Civilization.* New Haven: Yale University Press, 1980.

——, ed. *Studies of Shang Archaeology.* New Haven: Yale University Press, 1986.

Chang Wanli and Hu Jen-Mou. *The Selected Painting and Calligraphy of Pa-Ta-Shan-Jen.* 2 vols. Hong Kong: Cafa, 1969.

Chaves, Jonathan, trans. and ed. *The Columbia Book of Later Chinese Poetry.* New York: Columbia University Press, 1986.

Ch'en, Kenneth K. S. *Buddhism in China: A Historical Survey.* Princeton: Princeton University Press, 1964.

Chen Mengjia. *Yin Zhou qingtongqi fenlei tulu* [A corpus of Chinese bronzes in American collections]. 2 vols. Tokyo: Kyuko Shoin, 1977.

Cheng Chen-to, ed. *Wei-ta-ti i-shu-ch'uan-t'ung t'u-lu* [The great heritage of Chinese art]. 2 vols. Shanghai: Lampl and Poland, 1956.

——. *Yun-hui-chai-ts'ang T'ang Sung i-lai ming-hua-chi* [Paintings of the Tang, Song and later periods in the collection of Chang Ts'ung-yu]. Shanghai: 1947.

Cheng Mingshi. "The Calligraphy Art of Yang Weizhen." *Shufa congkan* 5 (December 1982): 59.

Ch'ien Yung, *Lu Yuan Tsung Hua,* 1825.

Chinese Antiquities from the Brian S. McElney Collection. Hong Kong: Urban Council, 1987.

The Chinese Exhibition: A Pictorial Record of the Exhibition of Archaeological Finds of the People's Republic of China. Kansas City: Nelson Gallery Foundation, 1975.

A Chorus of Colors: Chinese Glass from Three American Collections. San Francisco: Asian Art Museum, 1995.

Chou, Ju-hsi and Claudia Brown. *The Elegant Brush: Chinese Painting Under the Qianlong Emperor 1735–1795.* Phoenix: Phoenix Art Museum, 1985.

Christy, Anita. "Alice Boney: The Doyenne of Oriental Art Dealers," *Orientations* 19, no. 2 (December 1988): 54–59.

Chu I-tsun. *Pao Shu T'ing Shu Hua Pu,* 1693–1709.

Cincinnati Art Museum Handbook. Cincinnati: Cincinnati Art Museum, 1975.

Cincinnati Collects Oriental Art. Cincinnati: Cincinnati Art Museum, 1985.

Cohen, Warren I. *East Asian Art and American Culture: A Study in International Relations.* New York and Oxford: Columbia University Press, 1992.

Cort, Louise Allison, and Jan Stuart. *Joined Colors: Decoration and Meaning in Chinese Porcelain.* Washington, D.C.: Arthur M. Sackler Gallery, Smithsonian Institution, 1993.

Curtis, Julia B. *Chinese Porcelains of the Seventeenth Century: Landscapes, Scholars' Motifs and Narratives.* New York: China Institute in America, 1995.

Dardess, John. "Shun-ti and the End of Yüan Rule in China." In *The Cambridge History of China Volume 6: Alien Regimes and Border States 907–1368,* edited by Herbert Franke and Denis Twitchett, 561–86. Cambridge: Cambridge University Press, 1994.

David, Sir Percival, ed. and trans. *Chinese Connoisseurship: The Ko Ku Yao Lun, The Essential Criteria of Antiquities.* London: Faber and Faber, 1971.

Davidson, Martha. "Great Chinese Sculptures in America." *Art News Annual* (1939): 71–94.

Department of Archaeology at Peking University, ed. *Treasures from a Swallow Garden: Inaugural Exhibit of the Arthur M. Sackler Museum of Art and Archaeology at Peking University.* Beijing: Wenwu, 1992.

Derham, Anthony and David Johnson. *Chinese Ceramics and Works of Art.* Ed. Anthony du Boulay. Vol. 4 of *The Taft Museum: Its History and Collections.* Ed. Edward J. Sullivan. New York: Hudson Hills Press, 1995.

Deydier, Christian. *Les bronzes archaiques chinois [Archaic Chinese bronzes].* Paris: Editions d'Art et d'Histoire, 1995.

Dien, Albert. "A Study of Early Chinese Armor." *Artibus Asiae* 43, nos. 1 and 2 (1981–1982): 5–66.

Dohrenwend, Doris. "Glass in China: A Review Based on the Collection of the Royal Ontario Museum." *Oriental Art* 26 (1980–1981): 426–46.

Durrell, Jane A. *A Selection of New Acquisitions 1990–1992.* Cincinnati: Cincinnati Art Museum, 1992.

Eberhard, Wolfram. *A Dictionary of Chinese Symbols: Hidden Symbols in Chinese Life and Thought.* London and New York: Routledge, 1986.

Ebrey, Patricia Buckley, ed. *Chinese Civilization: A Sourcebook.* 2nd ed. New York: The Free Press, 1993.

———. *The Inner Quarters: Marriage and the Lives of Chinese Women in the Sung Period.* Berkeley: University of California Press, 1993.

Ebrey, Patricia Buckley, and Peter N. Gregory, eds. *Religion and Society in T'ang and Sung China.* Honolulu: University of Hawaii Press, 1993.

Ecke, Tseng Yu-ho. *Chinese Calligraphy.* Philadelphia: Philadelphia Museum of Art, 1971.

Edgren, Soren. *Chinese Rare Books in American Collections.* New York: China Institute, 1984.

Edwards, Richard. *The Art of Wen Cheng-ming (1470–1559).* Ann Arbor: University of Michigan Museum of Art, 1976.

———. "Ch'ien Hsüan and 'Early Autumn.'" *Archives of the Chinese Art Society* 7 (1953): 316–23.

———. "Sophistications of Chinese Art." *Apollo* 93 (April 1971): 82–89.

Eight Dynasties of Chinese Painting: The Collections of the Nelson-Atkins Museum, Kansas City, and the Cleveland Museum of Art. Cleveland: Cleveland Museum of Art, 1980.

Endicott-West, Elizabeth. "The Yüan Government and Society." In *The Cambridge History of China Volume 6: Alien Regimes and Border States 907–1368,* edited by Herbert Franke and Denis Twitchett, 587–615. Cambridge: Cambridge University Press, 1994.

Erickson, Susan N. "'Twirling their Long Sleeves, They Dance Again and Again....' Jade Plaque Sleeve Dancers of the Western Han Dynasty." *Ars Orientalis* 24 (1994): 39–64.

Fang, Achilles. "Some Observations [on Ma Yuan's *Four Sages of Shang-shan*]." Unpublished notes in Cincinnati Art Museum curatorial files.

Feng Xianming. "Chinese Celadons." *Orientations* 18, no. 6 (June 1987): 38–43.

Figgess, Sir John. "Chinese Ceramics in the Matsuoka Museum." *Transactions of the Oriental Ceramic Society* (1986–87): 9–12.

Fong, Wen C. *Beyond Representation: Chinese Painting and Calligraphy 8th–14th Century.* New York: Metropolitan Museum of Art, 1992.

———, ed. *The Great Bronze Age of China, An Exhibition from the People's Republic of China.* New York: Metropolitan Museum of Art, 1980.

———. "The Problem of Ch'ien Hsüan," *The Art Bulletin* 42 (September 1960): 173–89.

———. "The Problem of Forgeries in Chinese Paintings." *Artibus Asiae* 25 (1962): 95–140.

———. "Tung Ch'i-ch'ang and Artistic Revival." In *The Century of Tung Ch'i-ch'ang 1555–1636,* vol. 1, edited by Wai-kam Ho, 43–54. Kansas City: The Nelson-Atkins Museum of Art, 1992.

Fong, Wen C., Alfred Murck, Shou-chien Shih, Pao-chen Ch'en, and Jan Stuart. *Images of the Mind: Selections from the Edward L. Elliott Family and John B. Elliott Collections of Chinese Calligraphy and Painting at The Art Museum, Princeton University.* Princeton: The Art Museum, 1984.

Fong, Wen C. and James C.Y. Watt. *Possessing the Past: Treasures from the National Palace Museum, Taipei.* New York and Taipei: Metropolitan Museum of Art and National Palace Museum, 1996.

Fontein, Jan and Tung Wu. *Unearthing China's Past.* Boston: Museum of Fine Arts, 1973.

Foulk, T. Griffith. "Myth, Ritual, and Monastic Practice in Sung Ch'an Buddhism." In *Religion and Society in T'ang and Sung China,* edited by Patricia Buckley Ebrey and Peter N. Gregory, 147–208. Honolulu: University of Hawaii Press, 1993.

Franke, Herbert. "Two Yüan Treatises on the Technique of Portrait Painting." *Oriental Art* 3, no. 1 (1950): 27–32.

———. "The Chin Dynasty." In *The Cambridge History of China Vol. 6: Alien Regimes and Border States, 970–1368,* edited by Herbert Franke and Denis Twitchett, 215–320. Cambridge: Cambridge University Press, 1994.

Franke, Herbert and Denis Twitchett, eds. *The Cambridge History of China Vol. 6: Alien Regimes and Border States, 970–1368.* Cambridge: Cambridge University Press, 1994.

Frédéric, Louis. *Buddhism.* Paris and New York: Flammarion, 1995.

Freer Gallery of Art. *Masterpieces of Chinese and Japanese Art: Freer Gallery of Art Handbook.* Washington, D.C.: Smithsonian Institution, 1976.

Friedman, Pamela R. Lessing. *Chinese Snuff Bottles.* Denver: P. R. Lessing Friedman, 1990.

Fu, Marilyn and Shen C.Y. Fu. *Studies in Connoisseurship: Chinese Paintings from the Arthur M. Sackler Collections in New York, Princeton and Washington, D.C.* 3rd ed. Princeton: The Art Museum, Princeton University, 1987.

Fu, Shen C.Y. *Traces of the Brush: Studies in Chinese Calligraphy.* New Haven: Yale University Art Gallery, 1977.

———. *Yuan dai huangshi shuhua shoucang shilue [A brief history of the Yuan imperial collections of calligraphy and painting].* Taipei: National Palace Museum, 1981.

Fundaçao Oriente, Department for Culture, Macao and Macanese Communities. *A Cidade Proibida: The Forbidden City.* Lisbon, Fundaçao Oriente, 1992.

Gan Fuxi. "Introduction to the Symposium Papers." In *Scientific Research in Early Chinese Glass: Proceedings of The Archaeometry of Glass Sessions of the 1984 International Symposium on Glass, Beijing, September 7, 1984 with Supplementary Papers,* edited by Robert H. Brill and John H. Martin, 1–4. Corning: Corning Museum of Glass, 1991.

Gansu Provincial Museum. *Gansu Caitao [The Pottery of Gansu Province].* Beijing: Wenwu, 1984.

Gao Guopei, ed. *A Chinese-English Glossary and Illustrations of Antique.* Trans. Meng Jun. Hong Kong: The Woods, 1991.

Garner, Sir Harry. *Chinese and Japanese Cloisonné and Enamels.* London: Faber and Faber, 1962.

———. *Chinese Lacquer.* London and Boston: Faber and Faber, 1979.

Gedalecia, David. "Wu Ch'eng and the Perpetuation of the Classical Heritage in the Yüan." In *China Under Mongol Rule,* edited by John D. Langlois Jr., 186–211. Princeton: Princeton University, 1981.

Gong Jianyi. "The Ten Scenic Spots in Yushan." *Wenwu* no. 3, (1985): 29–31.

Goodrich, L. Carrington and Chaoying Fang, eds. *Dictionary of Ming Biography, 1368–1644.* 2 vols. New York: Columbia University Press, 1976.

Graham, A.C., trans. *Poems of the Late Tang.* London: Penguin, 1977.

Greensted, Mary and Peter Hardie. *Chinese Ceramics: The Indian Connection.* Bristol: City of Bristol Museum and Art Gallery, 1982.

Grenville L. Winthrop: Retrospective for a Collector. Cambridge, Mass.: Harvard University Press, 1969.

Guide to the Collections of the Cincinnati Art Museum. Cincinnati: Cincinnati Art Museum, 1952.

Guide to the Collections of the Cincinnati Art Museum. Cincinnati: Cincinnati Art Museum, 1956.

Gyllensvärd, Bo. *Chinese Gold, Silver and Porcelain: The Kempe Collection.* New York: Asia Society, 1971.

Gyllensvärd, Bo, and John Pope. *Chinese Art from the Collection of H. M. King Gustav VI Adolph of Sweden.* New York: Asia Society, 1966.

Hardie, Peter. "China's Ceramic Trade with India." *Transactions of the Oriental Ceramic Society* 48 (1983–1984): 15–31.

Harrist, Robert E. "Ch'ien Hsüan's *Pear Blossoms*: The Tradition of Flower Painting and Poetry from Sung to Yuan." *Metropolitan Museum Journal* 22 (1987): 53–70.

Hai-Wai Yi-Chen T'ung-Ch'i Chinese Art in Overseas Collections: Bronze. Taipei: National Palace Museum, 1985.

Hai-Wai Yi-Chen Chinese Art in Overseas Collections: Buddhist Sculpture 2. Taipei: National Palace Museum, 1990.

Hai-Wai Yi-Chen Chinese Art in Overseas Collections: Painting. Taipei: National Palace Museum, 1985.

Hai-Wai Yi-Chen Chinese Art in Overseas Collections: Painting 2. Taipei: National Palace Museum, 1988.

Hai-Wai Yi-Chen Chinese Art in Overseas Collections: Pottery and Porcelain 2. Taipei: National Palace Museum, 1989.

Hai-Wai Yi-Chen Chinese Art in Overseas Collections: Pottery and Porcelain 3. Taipei: National Palace Museum, 1992.

Handler, Sarah. "A Yokeback Chair for Sitting Tall." *Journal of the Classical Chinese Furniture Society* 3, no. 2 (Spring 1993): 4–23.

Hayashi Minao. "Go-Kan Jidai no Shaba Gyōretsu [Horse and chariot processions of the later Han]." *Tōhōgakuhō* 37 (1964): 183–226.

Heritage of the Brush: The Roy and Marilyn Papp Collection of Chinese Painting. Phoenix: Phoenix Art Museum, 1989.

Hetherington, A. L. *Chinese Ceramic Glazes.* London: Cambridge, 1937.

Ho, Judy Chungwa. "The Twelve Calendrical Animals in Tang Tombs." In *Ancient Mortuary Traditions of China*, edited by George Kuwayama, 60–83. Los Angeles: Far Eastern Art Council, Los Angeles County Museum of Art, 1991.

Ho, Wai-kam, ed. *The Century of Tung Ch'i-ch'ang 1555–1636.* 2 vols. Kansas City: Nelson-Atkins Museum of Art, 1992.

Ho, Wai-kam and Hironobu Kohara. *Bunjinga Suihen.* vols 3 and 6. Tokyo: Chūōkōron-sha, 1977–79.

Huber, Louisa G. "Indianapolis Museum of Art, The Oriental Collection: Ancient Chinese Bronzes." *Arts of Asia* 11, no. 2 (March-April, 1981): 74–87.

Hucker, Charles O. *A Dictionary of Official Titles in Imperial China.* Stanford: Stanford University Press, 1985.

Hummel, Arthur W., ed. *Eminent Chinese of the Ch'ing Period (1644–1912).* 2 vols. Washington, D.C.: Library of Congress, 1944.

Imperial Taste: Chinese Ceramics from the Percival David Foundation. Los Angeles: Los Angeles County Museum of Art and Chronicle Books, 1989.

The Indian Heritage: Court Life and Arts under Mughal Rule. London: Victoria and Albert Museum, 1982.

Indiana University Museum of Art. *One Thousand Years of Chinese Painting T'ang to Ch'ing 800–1800.* Bloomington: Indiana University, 1968.

James, Jean M. "An Iconographic Study of Two Late Han Funerary Monuments: The Offering Shrines of the Wu Family and the Multichamber Tomb at Holingor." Ph.D. dissertation, University of Iowa, 1983.

——. "An Iconographic Study of Xiwangmu during the Han Dynasty." *Artibus Asiae* 54, nos. 1/2 (1995): 17–41.

——. Review of *Art and Political Expression in Early China*, by Martin J. Powers. *China Review International* 2, no. 1 (spring 1995): 1–18.

——. "Some Iconographic Problems in Early Daoist-Buddhist Sculptures in China." *Archives of Asian Art* 42 (1989): 71–76.

Jing, Anning. "The Yuan Buddhist Mural of the Paradise of Bhaiṣajyaguru." *Metropolitan Museum Journal* 26 (1991): 147–66.

In Pursuit of the Dragon: Traditions and Transitions in Ming Ceramics. Seattle: Seattle Art Museum, 1988.

Iron in the Fire: The Chinese Potter's Exploration of Iron Oxide Glazes. London: Oriental Ceramic Society, 1988.

Keppel, Sheila. *China in 1700: Kangxi Porcelains at the Taft Museum.* Cincinnati: Taft Museum, 1988.

Kerr, Rose, ed., *Chinese Art and Design: The T. T. Tsui Gallery of Chinese Art.* London: Victoria and Albert Museum, 1991.

——. *Chinese Ceramics: Porcelain of the Qing Dynasty 1644–1911.* London: Victoria and Albert Museum, 1986.

Ko, Dorothy. *Teachers of the Inner Chambers: Women and Culture in Seventeenth-Century China.* Stanford: Stanford University Press, 1994.

Kohn, Livia. *The Taoist Experience, An Anthology.* Albany: State University of New York Press, 1993.

Kokubo Kazuhiro. *Kaiju budōkyō* [A Study of Tang Lion and Grape Mirrors]. Tokyo: Tōken Shunju Shinbunsha, 1985.

Krahl, Regina. *Chinese Ceramics from the Meiyintang Collection.* 2 vols. London: Azimuth, 1994.

——. *Chinese Ceramics in the Topkapi Saray Museum, Istanbul.* 3 vols. Ed. John Ayers. London: Sotheby's, 1986.

——. "Plant Motifs of Chinese Porcelain: Examples from the Topkapi Saray Identified through the *Bencao Gangmu*, Part I." *Orientations* 18, no. 5 (May, 1987): 52–65.

——. "Plant Motifs of Chinese Porcelain: Examples from the Topkapi Saray Identified through the *Bencao Gangmu*, Part II." *Orientations* 18, no. 6 (June, 1987): 24–37.

Kuwayama, George, ed. *Ancient Mortuary Traditions of China.* Los Angeles: Far Eastern Art Council, Los Angeles County Museum of Art, 1991.

——, ed. *New Perspectives on the Art of Ceramics in China.* Los Angeles: Far Eastern Art Council, Los Angeles County Museum of Art, 1992.

La Farge, Henry A. "Mr. Loo and the China Trade." *Art News* 49 (June 1950): 42–43ff.

Langlois, John D., Jr., ed. *China Under Mongol Rule.* Princeton: Princeton University Press, 1981.

Larson, John and Rose Kerr, *Guanyin: A Masterpiece Revealed.* London: Victoria and Albert Museum, 1985.

Lawton, Thomas, Shen Fu, Glenn D. Lowry, Ann Yonemura, and Milo C. Beach. *Asian Art in the Arthur M. Sackler Gallery-The Inaugural Gift.* Washington, D.C.: Smithsonian Institution, 1987.

Lee, Jung May and Michael Weisbrod. *Chinese Ceramic Art: Innovation and Imitation.* New York: Weisbrod, 1988.

Lee, Sherman E. "Asian Art at the Ackland Art Museum." *Orientations* 24, no. 4 (April 1993): 38–49.

——. *A History of Far Eastern Art.* 4th ed. New York: Abrams, 1982.

——. "Literati and Professionals: Four Ming Painters." *Bulletin of the Cleveland Museum of Art* (January 1966): 1–25.

———. "To See Big within Small." *The Burlington Magazine* 114 (May 1972): 314–22.

Lee, Sherman E. and Wai-kam Ho. *Chinese Art Under the Mongols: The Yuan Dynasty (1279–1368).* Cleveland: Cleveland Museum of Art, 1968.

Lewis, Candace J. *Into the Afterlife: Han and Six Dynasties Chinese Tomb Sculpture from the Schloss Collection.* Poughkeepsie: Vassar College Art Gallery, 1990.

Li Chi. *Anyang: A Chronicle of the Discovery, Excavation, and Reconstruction of the Ancient Capital of the Shang Dynasty.* Seattle: University of Washington Press, 1977.

Li, Chu-tsing, ed. *Artists and Patrons: Some Social and Economic Aspects of Chinese Painting.* Seattle: University of Washington Press, 1989.

———. *The Autumn Colors on the Ch'iao and Hua Mountains: A Landscape by Chao Meng-fu.* Ascona: Artibus Asiae, 1965.

———. "The Role of Wu-hsing in Early Yuan Artistic Development under Mongol Rule." In *China Under Mongol Rule*, edited by John D. Langlois Jr., 331–70. Princeton: Princeton University Press, 1981.

Li, Chu-tsing and James C.Y. Watt, eds. *The Chinese Scholar's Studio: Artistic Life in the Late Ming Period.* New York: Thames and Hudson, 1987.

Li Huibing. "Song Guan Wares. Song Official Wares." *Transactions of the Oriental Ceramics Society* 57 (1992–1993): 27–34.

Li, Wai-yee. "Dream Visions of Transcendence in Chinese Literature and Painting." *Asian Art* 3, no. 4 (Fall 1990): 53–78.

Liang Ssu-Ch'eng. *A Pictorial History of Chinese Architecture.* Cambridge, Mass. and London: MIT Press, 1984.

Liao Ping, ed. *The Yongle Palace Murals.* Beijing: Foreign Languages Press, 1985.

Lin Huiyin and Liang Sicheng. "Jinfen gu jianzhu yucha jiluo." *Zhongguo yingzao xuoche huikan* [Bulletin of the Society for Research in Chinese Architecture] 5, no. 3 (March 1935): 41–54.

Lion-Goldschmidt, Daisy. *Ming Porcelain.* Trans. Katherine Watson. London: Thames and Hudson, 1978.

Lippe, Aschwin. "Buddha and the Holy Multitude." *The Metropolitan Museum of Art Bulletin* (May 1965): 325–36.

Liu Liang-yu. *Chinese Enamel Ware: Its History, Authentication and Conservation.* Taipei: Cygnus, 1978.

Liu Xinyuan. "Imperial Porcelain of the Yongle and Xuande Periods Excavated from the Site of the Ming Imperial Factory at Jingdezhen." In *Imperial Porcelain of the Yongle and Xuande Periods Excavated from the Site of the Ming Imperial Factory at Jingdezhen,* 12–83. Hong Kong: Urban Council, 1989.

Loehr, Max. "Bronze Styles of the Anyang Period." *Archives of the Chinese Art Society in America* 7 (1953): 42–53.

———. *Chinese Bronze Age Weapons: The Werner Jannings Collection in the Chinese National Palace Museum, Peking.* Ann Arbor: University of Michigan Press, 1956.

———. *Ritual Vessels of Bronze Age China.* New York: Asia Society, 1968.

Loewe, Michael. *Chinese Ideas of Life and Death: Faith, Myth and Reason in the Han Period 202 BC–AD 220.* London and Boston: Allen & Unwin, ca. 1982.

Loo, C.T. *An Exhibition of Ancient Chinese Ritual Bronzes Loaned by C.T. Loo and Co.* New York: C.T. Loo, 1940.

———. *An Exhibition of Chinese Stone Sculpture.* New York: C.T. Loo, 1940.

Longmen Cultural Relics Preservation Agency. *Longmen Shiku.* Beijing: Wenwu, 1983.

Lu Shihua. *Wu Yue sojian shuhualu* [Calligraphy and paintings seen in the Jiangsu/Zhejiang area]. Shanghai: [1776], 1910 reprint.

Luo Zhenyu. *Sandai jijin wen cun.* 1937.

Ma Tsung-ho, ed. *Shu-lin tsao-chien* [Calligraphy Seen in an Elegant Mirror]. Preface dated 1936. Reprint, Taipei: Shang-wu Yin-shu-kuan, 1965; 1982.

Masterpieces from the Cincinnati Art Museum. Cincinnati: Cincinnati Art Museum, 1984.

Mathes, Charles. *Treasures of American Museums.* New York: Mallard, 1991.

Medley, Margaret. *The Chinese Potter: A Practical History of Chinese Ceramics.* 2nd ed. Oxford: Phaidon, 1980.

———. "Patterns of Chinese Taste in Porcelain." *Transactions of the Oriental Ceramic Society* (1987–88): 63–82.

———. *T'ang Pottery and Porcelain.* London and Boston: Faber and Faber, 1981.

———. *Yuan Porcelain and Stoneware.* London: Faber and Faber, 1974.

Mino, Yutaka. *Freedom of Clay and Brush through Seven Centuries in Northern China: Tz'u-chou Type Wares 960–1600 A.D.* Indianapolis: Indianapolis Museum of Art, 1980.

———. *Pre-Sung Dynasty Chinese Stonewares in the Royal Ontario Museum.* Toronto: Royal Ontario Museum, 1974.

Mino, Yutaka and James Robinson. *Beauty and Tranquility: The Eli Lilly Collection of Chinese Art.* Indianapolis: Indianapolis Museum of Art, 1983.

Mino, Yutaka and Katherine Tsiang. *Ice and Green Clouds: Traditions of Chinese Celadon.* Indianapolis: Indianapolis Museum of Art, 1986.

Mizuno, Seiichi and Nagahiro Toshio. *Yun-kang: The Buddhist Cave Temples of the Fifth Century AD in North China.* 16 vols. Kyoto: Kyoto University, Jimbun kagaku kenkyusho, 1952–56.

Monroe, Betty Iverson. *Chinese Ceramics from Chicago Collections.* Evanston, Il: Mary and Leigh Block Gallery, 1982.

Moore, Janet Gaylord. *The Eastern Gate: An Invitation to the Arts of China and Japan.* Cleveland: Collins, 1979.

Moss, Hugh, Victor Graham and Ka Bo Tsang. *The Art of the Chinese Snuff Bottle: The J & J Collection.* 2 vols. New York and Tokyo: Weatherhill, 1993.

Moss, Paul. *Scrolling Images.* London: Sydney L. Moss, 1991.

Mowry, Robert D. *Hare's Fur, Tortoiseshell, and Partridge Feathers: Chinese Brown- and Black-Glazed Ceramics, 400–1400.* Cambridge, Mass.: Harvard University Press, 1996.

———. "Koryo Celadons." *Orientations,* 17, no. 5 (May, 1986): 24–39.

Munakata, Kiyohiko. *Sacred Mountains in Chinese Art.* Urbana-Champaign: University of Illinois Press, 1991.

Munsterberg, Hugo. *The Arts of China.* Rutland, Vt. and Tokyo: Tuttle, 1972.

———. *Chinese Buddhist Bronzes.* Rutland, Vt. and Tokyo: Tuttle, 1967.

———. "The Collection of Chinese Paintings in the Cincinnati Art Museum," *The Art Quarterly* (Winter, 1952), 307–21.

———. *The Crown of Life: Artistic Creativity in Old Age.* San Diego: Harcourt Brace Jovanovich, 1983.

Murck, Alfreda. "Eight Views of the Hsiao and Hsiang Rivers by Wang Hung." In *Images of the Mind: Selections from the Edward L. Elliott Family and John B. Elliott Collections of Chinese Calligraphy and Painting at The Art Museum, Princeton University,* edited by Wen C. Fong, 214–35. Princeton: The Art Museum, 1984.

Murck, Alfreda and Wen Fong, eds. *Words and Images: Chinese Poetry, Calligraphy, and Painting.* New York: Metropolitan Museum of Art, 1991.

The Museum of East Asian Art, Bath, England. *Inaugural Exhibition.* 2 vols. Bath, England: The Museum of East Asian Art, 1993.

Museum of the Western Han Tomb of the Nanyue King, Guangzhou.

Chinese Ceramic Pillows: The Mr. and Mrs. Yeung Wing Tak Gift. Hong Kong: Perfekta, 1993.

Nagel's Encyclopedia Guide: China. Geneva: Nagel, 1982.

Nakano, Toru. *Bronze Mirrors from Ancient China — Donald H. Graham Jr. Collection.* Hong Kong: Donald H. Graham, Jr., 1994.

Nakata, Yujiro and Shen Fu. *Masterpieces of Chinese Calligraphy in American and European Collections* [Ōbei shozō chūgoku hōsho meiseki shū, vol. 4.] Tokyo: Chuokoron-sha, 1982.

National Palace Museum. *Special Exhibition of Ch'ing Dynasty Enamelled Porcelains of the Imperial Ateliers.* Taipei: National Palace Museum, 1992.

National Palace Museum. *Special Exhibition of Sung Dynasty Kuan Ware.* Taipei: National Palace Museum, 1989.

Neill, Mary Gardner. "The Flowering Plum in the Decorative Arts." In *Bones of Jade, Soul of Ice: The Flowering Plum in Chinese Art,* by Maggie Bickford, 193–244. New Haven: Yale University Press, 1985.

Oriental Ceramics: The World's Great Collections. 12 vols. Tokyo, New York and San Francisco: Kodansha, 1982.

Osaka Municipal Museum of Art. *Masterpieces from the Osaka Municipal Museum of Art.* Osaka: Osaka Municipal Museum of Art, 1986.

Pal, Pratapaditya. *Light of Asia: Buddha Sakyamuni in Asian Art.* Los Angeles: Los Angeles County Museum of Art, 1984.

Pal, Pratapaditya and Hsien-ch'i Tseng. *Lamaist Art: The Aesthetics of Harmony.* Boston: Museum of Fine Arts, 1969.

Pearlstein, Elinor. "Pictorial Stones from Chinese Tombs." *The Bulletin of the Cleveland Museum of Art For November 1984.*

Poor, Robert J. "The Master of the 'Metropolis'-Emblem Ku." *Archives of Asian Art* 41 (1988): 70–89.

Pope, John Alexander. *Chinese Porcelains from the Ardebil Shrine.* Washington D.C.: Freer Gallery of Art, 1956.

Pope, John Alexander, Rutherford John Gettens, James Cahill, and Noel Barnard. *The Freer Chinese Bronzes.* 2 vols. Freer Gallery of Art Oriental Studies, no. 7. Washington, D.C.: Smithsonian Institution, 1967.

Powers, Martin J. *Art and Political Expression in Early China.* New Haven and London: Yale University Press, 1991.

Priest, Alan. *Chinese Sculpture in the Metropolitan Museum of Art.* New York: Metropolitan Museum of Art, 1944.

Qi Yingtao and others. "Liangnian lai Shanxi sheng xin faxian de gu jianzhu [The ancient architecture in Shanxi Province newly discovered in the last two years]." *Wenwu cankao ziliao* 11 (1954): 61–66.

The Quest for Eternity: Chinese Ceramic Sculptures from the People's Republic of China. Los Angeles and San Francisco: Los Angeles County Museum of Art and Chronicle Books, 1987.

Rabiner, Donald. "Chinese Glass and the West." In *A Chorus of Colors: Chinese Glass from Three American Collections,* 17–27. San Francisco: Asian Art Museum, 1995.

Rawson, Jessica. *Chinese Bronzes: Art and Ritual.* London: British Museum, 1987.

——. *Chinese Jade from the Neolithic to the Qing.* London: British Museum Press, 1995.

——. *Chinese Ornament: The Lotus and the Dragon.* London: British Museum, 1984.

——. "Late Shang Bronze Design: Meaning and Purpose." In *The Problem of Meaning in Early Chinese Ritual Bronzes.* Colloquies on Art & Archaeology in Asia No. 15, edited by Roderick Whitfield, 67–95. London: School of Oriental and African Studies, University of London, 1993.

——, ed. *Mysteries of Ancient China: New Discoveries from the Early Dynasties.* London: British Museum, 1996.

Rawson, Jessica, M. Tite and M. J. Hughes, "The Export of Tang *Sancai* Wares: Some Recent Research." *Transactions of the Oriental Ceramic Society* 52 (1987–88): 39–61.

Records of the Grand Historian of China. Translated from the *Shih chi* of Ssu-Ma Ch'ien by Burton Watson. 2 vols. London: Columbia University Press, 1961.

"Recent Acquisitions at the Cincinnati Art Museum." *The Burlington Magazine,* 135 (January, 1993): 60–64.

Relics Salvaged from the Seabed off Sinan. Materials I. Compiled by the Bureau of Cultural Properties, Ministry of Culture and Information. Seoul: Dong Hwa, 1985.

Ren Daobin. "Ch'en Chi-ju as Critic and Connoisseur." In *Proceedings of the Tung Ch'i-ch'ang International Symposium,* edited by Wai-ching Ho, 9–1 – 9–26. Kansas City: Nelson-Atkins Museum of Art, 1992.

Rexroth, Kenneth, and Ling Chung. *Women Poets of China.* New York: New Directions, 1982.

Rhie, Marilyn M. "Aspects of Sui K'ai-huang and T'ang T'ien-pao Buddhist Images." *East and West* n.s. 17, nos. 1–2 (March-June 1967): 96–114.

——. "Late Sui Buddhist Sculpture: A Chronology and Regional Analysis." *Archives of Asian Art* 35 (1982): 27–54.

Rhie, Marilyn M. and Robert A. F. Thurman. *Wisdom and Compassion: The Sacred Art of Tibet.* New York: Abrams, 1991.

Ridley, Michael. "When is a Fake not a Fake?" *Arts of Asia* 1, no. 6 (November/December 1971): 42–45.

Robinson, James Jay. "The Vitality of Style: Aspects of Flower and Bird Painting during the Yuan Dynasty (1279–1368)." Ph.D. dissertation, University of Michigan, 1984.

Rogers, Howard. "Court Painting under the Qianlong Emperor." In *The Elegant Brush: Chinese Painting under the Qianlong Emperor 1735–1795,* edited by Ju-hsi Chou and Claudia Brown, 303–17. Phoenix Art Museum, 1985.

Rogers, Howard and Sherman E. Lee. *Masterworks of Ming and Qing Painting from the Forbidden City.* Lansdale, Pa.: International Arts Council, 1988.

Rogers, Mary Ann. "The Mechanics of Change: The Creation of a Song Imperial Ceramic Style." In *New Perspectives on the Art of Ceramics in China,* edited by George Kuwayama, 64–79. Los Angeles: Far Eastern Art Council, Los Angeles County Museum of Art, 1992.

Rogers, Millard F., Jr. "Quest for Quality: Selected Masterwork Purchases 1974–1994." *The Cincinnati Art Museum Bulletin* n.s. 14, no. 2 (1994): 5–52.

Rowland, Benjamin. "Notes on the Dated Statues of the Northern Wei Dynasty and the Beginnings of Buddhist Sculpture in China." *The Art Bulletin* 19, no. 1 (March, 1937): 92–107.

Rudova, Maria. *Chinese Popular Prints.* Translated by Viacheslav Sobolev. Leningrad: Aurora, 1988.

Ruyao di Faxian [The Discovery of Ru Kiln]. Shanghai: People's Publishing, 1987.

Salmon, Vanessa Clewes. "Report from London." *Orientations* 17, no. 10 (October 1986): 71–74.

Schafer, Edward H. *The Golden Peaches of Samarkand: A Study of T'ang Exotics.* Berkeley: University of California Press, 1963.

Schloss, Ezekiel. *Art of the Han.* New York: China Institute in America, 1979.

Scott, Rosemary. "Archaism and Invention: Sources of Ceramic Design in the Ming and Qing Dynasties." In *New Perspectives on the Art of Ceramics in China,* edited by George Kuwayama, 80–96. Los Angeles: Far Eastern Council, 1992.

——. "Guan or Ge Ware? A re-examination of some pieces in the Percival David Foundation." *Oriental Art* 39, no. 2 (summer, 1993): 13–23.

——. *Percival David Foundation of Chinese Art: A Guide to the Collection.* London: University of London Press, 1989.

Sculpture Collection of the Cincinnati Art Museum. Cincinnati: Cincinnati Art Museum, 1970.

Shan, Guoqiang. "Gentlewoman Paintings of the Qing Palace Ateliers." *Orientations* 26, no. 7 (July/August, 1995): 56–59.

——. "The Tendency Toward Mergence of the Two Great Traditions in Late Ming Painting." In *Proceedings of the Tung Ch'i-ch'ang International Symposium,* edited by Wai-ching Ho, 3-1 — 3-28. Kansas City: Nelson-Atkins Museum of Art, 1992.

Shanghai bowuguan cang bao lu. Shanghai: Wenxue Chubanshe, 1989.

Shangraw, Clarence. *Origins of Chinese Ceramics.* New York: China Institute in America, 1978.

Shanxi sheng chutu tongjing [Bronze mirrors unearthed in Shanxi province]. Beijing: Wenwu, 1958.

She Ch'eng. "The Painting Academy of the Qianlong Period: A Study in Relation to the Taipei National Palace Museum Collection." In *The Elegant Brush: Chinese Painting Under the Qianlong Emperor 1735–1795,* by Ju-hsi Chou and Claudia Brown, 318–342. Phoenix: Phoenix Art Museum, 1985.

Shih, Chung-wen. *The Golden Age of Chinese Drama: Yüan Tsa-chü.* Princeton: Princeton University Press, 1976.

Shih, Hsio-yen. "Early Chinese Pictorial Style: From the Later Han to the Six Dynasties." Ph.D. dissertation, Bryn Mawr College, 1961.

Shimada, Shujiro. "So Teki to Shosho hakkei [Song Di and the Eight Views of the Xiao and Xiang Rivers]." *Nanga Kansho* 104 (1941): 6–13.

Shiqu Baoji [Treasured Boxes of the Stony Moat]. Catalog of Painting and Calligraphy in the Qianlong Imperial Collection, 1745. Comp. Chang Chao and others. Facsimile reprint. Taipei: National Palace Museum, 1971.

Sickman, Laurence. "Notes on Later Chinese Buddhist Art." *Parnassus* 11, no. 4 (April 1939): 13–17.

——. "Wall Paintings of the Yuan Period in Kuang-sheng-ssu, Shansi." *Revue des arts asiatiques* 2, no. 2 (June, 1937): 53–67.

Sickman, Laurence and Alexander Soper. *The Art and Architecture of China.* Reprint. New York: Penguin, 1978.

Sirén, Osvald. "Chinese Marble Sculptures of the Transition Period." *Bulletin of the Museum of Far Eastern Antiquities, Stockholm,* no. 12 (1940): 473–495.

——. *Chinese Painting: Leading Masters and Principles.* 7 vols. New York: Ronald Press, 1956–58.

——. *Chinese Sculpture from the fifth to the fourteenth century.* 4 vols. London: E. Benn, 1925.

——. *Chinese Sculptures in the von der Heyt Collection.* Zurich: Museum Rietberg, 1959.

So, Jenny F. "New Departures in Eastern Zhou Bronze Designs: The Spring and Autumn Period." In *The Great Bronze Age of China: An Exhibition from the People's Republic of China,* edited by Wen Fong, 251–301. New York: Metropolitan Museum of Art, 1980.

Soper, Alexander. *Literary Evidence for Early Buddhist Art in China.* Ascona, Switzerland: Artibus Asiae, 1959.

Spiro, Audrey. "Max Loehr's Periodization of Shang Vessels." *Journal of Asian Culture* 5 (1981): 107–35.

Steinhardt, Nancy Shatzman. "Zhu Haogu Reconsidered: A New Date for the ROM Painting and the Southern Shanxi Buddhist-Daoist Style." *Artibus Asiae* 48, nos. 1/2 (1987): 5–20.

Stephen Solovy Fine Art. *Splendors of Chinese Art.* Chicago: Stephen Solovy Fine Art, 1996.

Stronge, Susan. "Huqqa." In *The Indian Heritage: Court Life and Arts under Mughal Rule,* 124. London: Victoria and Albert Museum, 1982.

Stuart, Jan. "Layers of Meaning." In *Joined Colors: Decoration and Meaning in Chinese Porcelain,* by Louise Allison Cort and Jan Stuart, 33–61. Washington, D.C.: Arthur M. Sackler Gallery, Smithsonian Institution, 1993.

Sullivan, Michael. *The Arts of China.* 3rd. ed. Berkeley: University of California Press, 1987.

Sun, K'o-k'uan. "Yu Chi and Southern Taoism during the Yüan period." In *China Under Mongol Rule,* edited by John D. Langlois Jr., 212–54. Princeton: Princeton University Press, 1981.

Sun-Bailey, Suning. "What is the 'Hill Jar'?" *Oriental Art* n.s. 34, no. 2 (Summer, 1988): 88–90.

Suzuki, Kei. *Chugoku kaigashi* [History of Chinese Painting]. Tokyo: Yoshikawa Kobunkan, 1988.

——. *Comprehensive Illustrated Catalog of Chinese Paintings.* 5 vols. Tokyo: University of Tokyo Press, 1982.

Tanabe, Willa J. *Paintings of the Lotus Sutra.* New York and Tokyo: Weatherhill, 1988.

Tausend Jahre Chinesische Malerei. Munich: Haus der Kunst, 1959.

Thompson, Nancy. "The Evolution of the Tang Lion and Grapevine Mirror." *Artibus Asiae* 29 (1967): 25–54.

Thorp, Robert L. "The Archaeology of Style at Anyang: Tomb 5 in Context." *Archives of Asian Art* 42 (1988): 47–69.

——. *Son of Heaven: Imperial Arts of China.* Seattle: Son of Heaven Press, 1988.

——. "The Sui Xian Tomb: Re-Thinking the Fifth Century." *Artibus Asiae* 43 (1982–1983): 67–92.

Thote, Alain. "Paul Pelliot: A Bridge Between Western Sinology and Chinese Scholarship." *Orientations* 26, no. 6 (June, 1995): 38–45.

Thurman, Robert A. F. "Tibet, Its Buddhism and Its Art." In *Wisdom and Compassion: The Sacred Art of Tibet* by Marilyn Rhie and Robert A. F. Thurman, 20–38. New York: Abrams, 1991.

Tillman, Hoyt Cleveland and Stephen H. West, eds. *China under Jurchen Rule: Essays on Chin Intellectual and Cultural History.* Albany: State University of New York Press, 1995.

Tregear, Mary. *Song Ceramics.* London: Thames and Hudson, 1982.

Ts'ai Ho-pi. *Catalogue of the Special Exhibition of Sung Dynasty Kuan Ware.* Taipei: National Palace Museum, 1989.

——. "Song Dynasty Guan Ware and Its Influence on Later Wares." *Transactions of the Oriental Ceramic Society* 57 (1992–93): 35–43.

Tsang, Ka Bo. "Further Observations on the Yuan Wall Painter Zhu Haogu and the Relationship of the Chunyang Hall Wall Paintings to 'The Maitreya Paradise' at the ROM." *Artibus Asiae* 52, nos. 1/2 (1992): 94–118.

Tsao Hsing-yüan. "From Hair to Ear: Head Ornaments Represented in Chinese Art as Signs of Cultural Identity." *Orientations* 28, no. 3 (March 1997): 79–89.

T'Serstevens, Michele. *L'Art Chinois.* Paris: Editions Charles Massin, 1962.

The Tsui Museum of Art. Hong Kong: Tsui Museum of Art, 1991.

Vainker, S. J. *Chinese Pottery and Porcelain From Prehistory to the Present.* New York: Braziller, 1991.

——. "Ge Ware Conference Report." *Oriental Art* 39, no. 2 (Summer, 1993): 5–11.

Valenstein, Suzanne G. *A Handbook of Chinese Ceramics.* New York: Metropolitan Museum of Art, 1989.

Vandiver, Pamela B. "Technical Studies of Ancient Chinese Ceramics." In *New Perspectives on the Art of Ceramics in China*, edited by George Kuwayama, 116–141. Los Angeles: Far Eastern Art Council, Los Angeles County Museum of Art, 1992.

Vandiver, Pamela B. and W. David Kingery. "Celadons: The Technological Basis of Their Visual Appearance." In *Ice and Green Clouds: Traditions of Chinese Celadon*, by Yutaka Mino and Katherine Tsiang, 217–24. Indianapolis: Indianapolis Museum of Art and Indiana University, 1986.

Vervoorn, Aat. *Men of the Cliffs and Caves: The Development of the Eremitic Tradition to the End of the Han Dynasty*. Hong Kong: The Chinese University Press, 1990.

Vinograd, Richard. *Boundaries of the Self: Chinese Portraits 1600–1900*. Cambridge: Cambridge University Press, 1992.

Vollmer, John E., E.J. Keall, and E. Nagai-Berthrong. *Silk Roads, China Ships*. Toronto: Royal Ontario Museum, 1983.

von der Heyt, Edward. "Cheng-Tsai Loo." *Artibus Asiae* 20, no. 2/3 (1957): 186.

von Falkenhausen, Lothar. *Suspended Music: Chime-Bells in the Culture of Bronze Age China*. Berkeley: University of California Press, 1993.

Wang Chi-ch'uan. *An Exhibition of Authenticated Chinese Paintings*. New York: C.T. Loo, 1947.

Wang Fangyu and Richard M. Barnhart. *Master of the Lotus Garden: The Life and Art of Bada Shanren (1626–1705)*. New Haven: Yale University Art Gallery, 1990.

Wang K'o-yü. *Shan-hu-wang hua-lu* [The coral net; a record of calligraphy and paintings]. Preface dated 1643. *Kuo hsüeh chi-pen ts'ung-shu* ed. Taipei, 1958.

Wang Qingzheng. "Ru Ware." *Transactions of the Oriental Ceramic Society* 54 (1989–90): 25–29.

——. "Some Questions Concerning Ge Ware." *Transactions of the Oriental Ceramic Society* 54 (1989–90): 31–34.

——. "Yongzheng Imitations of Guan, Ge, Ru and Jun Wares." *Orientations* 22, no. 2 (February, 1991): 54–59.

Wang Qing-zheng, Fan Dong-qing and Zhou Li-li. *The Discovery of Ru Kiln: A Famous Song-ware Kiln of China*. Trans. Lillian Chin, Xu Jie. Hong Kong: The Woods, 1991.

Wang Renbo. "General Comments on Chinese Funerary Sculpture," trans. Julia F. Andrews. In *The Quest for Eternity: Chinese Ceramic Sculptures from The People's Republic of China*, 39–62. Los Angeles and San Francisco: Los Angeles County Museum of Art and Chronicle Books, 1987.

Wang Shih-hsiang. "Chinese Ink Bamboo Paintings." *Archives of the Chinese Art Society* 3 (1948–1949): 49–58.

Wang Tao. "A Textual Investigation of the Taotie." In *The Problem of Meaning in Early Chinese Ritual Bronzes*, Colloquies on Art and Archaeology in Asia No. 15, edited by Roderick Whitfield, 102–118. London: School of Oriental and African Studies, 1993.

Wang, Zhongshu. *Han Civilization*. Trans. K.C. Chang and collaborators. New Haven and London: Yale University Press, 1982.

Watson, William. *T'ang and Liao Ceramics*. London: Thames and Hudson, 1984.

Watt, James C.Y. *Chinese Jades from the Collection of the Seattle Art Museum*. Seattle: Seattle Art Museum, 1989.

——. *Chinese Jades from Han to Ch'ing*. New York: Asia Society, 1980.

——. "Antiquarianism and Naturalism." In *Possessing the Past: Treasures from the National Palace Museum, Taipei*, edited by Wen C. Fong and James C.Y. Watt, 219–256. New York and Taipei: Metropolitan Museum of Art and National Palace Museum, Taipei, 1996.

——. "The Antique-Elegant." In *Possessing the Past: Treasures from the National Palace Museum, Taipei*, edited by Wen C. Fong and James C.Y. Watt, 503–553. New York and Taipei: Metropolitan Museum of Art and National Palace Museum, Taipei, 1996.

——. *The Sumptuous Basket: Chinese Lacquer with Basketry Panels*. New York: China Institute, 1985.

Wei Shuzhou, ed. *Fa Hai si bi hua* [The wall paintings of the Fa Hai temple]. Beijing: China Travel and Tourism, 1993.

Weidner, Marsha, ed. *Latter Days of the Law: Images of Chinese Buddhism 850–1850*. Lawrence, Kans.: Spencer Museum of Art and University of Hawaii Press, 1994.

Werner, A.E., and Mavis Bimson. "Some Opacifying Agents in Oriental Glass." In *Advances in Glass Technology: Part 2*, edited by Frederick R. Matson and Guy E. Rindome, 303–05. New York: Plenum, 1963.

White, Julia M. and Ronald Y. Otsuka. *Pathways to the Afterlife: Early Chinese Art from the Sze Hong Collection*. Denver and Honolulu: Denver Art Museum and University of Hawaii, 1993.

White, William Charles. *Bronze Culture of Ancient China: An Archaeological Study of Bronze Objects from Northern Honan, dating from about 1400 B.C.–771 B.C.* Museum Studies, no. 5. Toronto: University of Toronto, 1956.

Whitfield, Roderick. *The Art of Central Asia: The Stein Collection in the British Museum*. 3 vols. Tokyo: Kodansha, 1983.

——. "Exhibition Review: London, Victoria and Albert Museum: The T.T. Tsui Gallery of Chinese Art." *Burlington Magazine* (November 1991): 788–791.

——, ed. *The Problem of Meaning in Early Chinese Ritual Bronzes*. Colloquies on Art & Archaeology in Asia No. 15. London: School of Oriental and African Studies, University of London, 1993.

——. "Tz'u-Chou Pillows with Painted Decoration." In *Chinese Painting and the Decorative Style*, Colloquies on Art and Archaeology in Asia No. 5, edited by Margaret Medley, 74–94. London: Percival David Foundation of Chinese Art, 1975.

Whitfield, Roderick and Anne Farrer. *Caves of the Thousand Buddhas: Chinese art from the Silk Route*. New York: Braziller, 1990.

Wirgin, Jan. *Sung Ceramic Designs*. London: Han Shan Tang, 1979.

The Wonders of the Potter's Palette: Qing Ceramics from the Collection of the Hong Kong Museum of Art. Hong Kong: Urban Council, 1984.

Wong, Kwan S. "Hsiang Yuan-pien and Suchou Artists." In *Artists and Patrons: Some Social and Economic Aspects of Chinese Painting*, edited by Chu-tsing Li, 155–60. Seattle: University of Washington Press, 1989.

Wood, Frances. *Chinese Illustration*. London: The British Library, 1985.

Wood, Nigel. "Ceramic Puzzles from China's Bronze Age." *New Scientist* 18 (February 1989): 50–53.

——. "Recent Researches into the Technology of Chinese Ceramics." In *New Perspectives on the Art of Ceramics in China*, edited by George Kuwayama, 142–156. Los Angeles: Far Eastern Art Council, 1992.

Wood, Nigel, Julian Henderson and Mary Tregear. "An Examination of Chinese Fahua Glazes." In *Proceedings of 1989 International Symposium on Ancient Ceramics*, edited by Li Jiazhi and Chen Xianqiu, 172–182. Shanghai: Institute of Ceramics, Academia Sinica, 1989.

Wu Hung. "Buddhist Elements in Early Chinese Art." *Artibus Asiae* 47, nos. 3/4 (1986): 263–352.

——. *Monumentality in Early Chinese Art and Architecture*. Stanford: Stanford University, 1995.

——. "A Sanpan Shan Chariot Ornament and the Xiangrui Design in Western Han Art." *Archives of Asian Art* 37 (1984): 38–59.

——. *The Wu Liang Shrine: The Ideology of Early Chinese Pictorial Art.* Stanford: Stanford University, 1989.

——. "Xiwangmu, the Queen Mother of the West." *Orientations* 18, no. 4 (April 1987): 24–33.

Wu, Tung and Denise Patry Leidy. "Recent Archaeological Contributions to the Study of Chinese Ceramics." In *Imperial Taste: Chinese Ceramics from the Percival David Foundation*, 93–104. San Francisco: Los Angeles County Museum of Art and Chronicle Books, 1989.

——. "The Ch'ien-lung Painting Academy." In *Words and Images: Chinese Poetry, Calligraphy, and Painting*, edited by Alfreda Murck and Wen C. Fong, 333–56. New York: Metropolitan Museum of Art, 1991.

——. "Leng Mei ji qi *Bishu Shanzhuang Tu.*" In *Gugong Bowuyuan Cang Bao Lu*, 172–77. Hong Kong and Shanghai: 1985.

Yang Hsi-chang. "The Shang Dynasty Cemetery System." In *Studies of Shang Archaeology*, edited by K. C. Chang, 49–63. New Haven: Yale University, 1986.

Yang Xiaoneng. *Sculpture of Xia and Shang China.* Hong Kong: Tai Dao, 1988.

Yang Hsüan-chih. *A Record of Buddhist Monasteries in Lo-Yang.* Trans. Yi-t'ung Wang. Princeton: Princeton University, 1984.

Yinxu Fu Hao mu [Tomb of Lady Hao at Yinxu in Anyang]. Beijing: Wenwu, 1980.

Yinxu qingtongqi [Bronzes of Yinxu]. Beijing: Wenwu, 1985.

Yü, Chün-fang. "Guanyin: The Chinese Transformation of Avalokiteshvara." In *Latter Days of the Law: Images of Chinese Buddhism 850–1850*, edited by Marsha Weidner, 151–182. Lawrence, Kans.: Spencer Museum of Art, 1994.

Yu Fengqing. *Yu Shi shuhua tibaji* [Mr. Yu's Record of Colophons on Calligraphy and Painting]. In *Yishu zhangjian xuanzhen.* Facsimile reprint of manuscript copy in the National Central Library. Taipei, 1970.

Yu Xingwu. *Shang Zhou jinwen luyi.* Beijing: Xinhua Shudian, 1957.

Zhao Qingyun. "Jinshi nianlai Henan taoci kaogu de xin shouhua." *Huaxia kaogu*, no. 3 (1989): 84–86.

Zhongguo Taoci [Chinese Ceramics]. Beijing: Wenwu, 1985.

Index

Note: italic page numbers indicate illustrations